MATHEMATICS
FOR SECONDARY SCHOOL
TEACHERS

MATHEMATICS FOR SECONDARY SCHOOL TEACHERS

BRUCE E. MESERVE

*Professor of Mathematics and
Chairman of the Mathematics Department,
Montclair State College*

MAX A. SOBEL

*Associate Professor of Mathematics,
Montclair State College*

Englewood Cliffs, N. J.
PRENTICE-HALL, INC.

First printing .... March , 1962
Second printing... September , 1962

PREFACE

This book is based upon materials selected from lectures given by the authors to groups of in-service secondary school mathematics teachers. These teachers were seeking an interpretation of contemporary recommendations for the mathematics curricula and an understanding of modern concepts of mathematics as an aid to improving their classroom teaching. The authors have emphasized the relationships between some of the basic concepts contained in contemporary recommendations for secondary school mathematics and their counterparts in the traditional curricula.

Teachers will find this book an effective aid to individual study. To this end the authors have included numerous exercises, with answers in the book, so that practical experience with applications of the concepts may be obtained. The book will be equally effective for teachers who wish to study together in small, informal groups. It may also be used as a text for formal courses, especially in-service programs designed to provide an understanding of recent developments in secondary school mathematics curricula.

The authors wish to express their appreciation of the assistance of numerous teachers who have participated actively in in-service programs using the materials that provided a basis for this book. Special recognition is given to Mrs. Dorothy T. Meserve for her careful analysis of the manuscript and her detailed work in preparing the answers for many of the exercises.

B. E. M.
M. A. S.

v

CONTENTS

PART TWO / ALGEBRA

PART THREE / GEOMETRY

Contents

MATHEMATICS
FOR SECONDARY SCHOOL
TEACHERS

CHAPTER

ONE

MODERN TRENDS IN
MATHEMATICS
CURRICULA

There is a very healthy public interest in the secondary school mathematics program. This is most evident through the use of federal tax funds to support numerous National Science Foundation institutes for teachers and extensive experimentation such as that of the School Mathematics Study Group. There are also similar groups in physics, chemistry, and other areas.

The national experiments reflect and are, indeed, based upon numerous state and local experiments. Many teachers find the great variety confusing, since they do not recognize the common characteristics. The primary purpose of this book is to help teachers understand and interpret the content of the various contemporary curricula so that they may utilize in their classrooms any portions that appeal to them. In the process of pursuing this goal, teachers should gain insight into, and an over-all grasp of, the principles underlying nearly all of the mathematics taught in secondary schools.

During the past decade there have been several major curriculum studies whose influences are now appearing in secondary school mathematics. We shall consider five of them briefly in their chronological order.

1–1 The New York State Mathematics Syllabus Committee

The New York Board of Regents appointed a Mathematics Syllabus Committee in 1942. This committee published outlines for an integrated sequence of mathematics courses for the early secondary school grades [38]† in 1955 and for the last three secondary school grades [39] in 1954. As implied by the term "integrated sequence," the emphasis is upon minimizing the artificial and superficial subdivisions of mathematics into arithmetic, algebra, geometry, trigonometry, and so forth. This point of view permeates each grade level without changing the basic course content. For example, the tenth-year program has a primary emphasis upon geometry but includes the use of algebra in studying geometry. At each grade level the logical foundations and everyday applications of the reasoning used are stressed.

The direct influence of the New York program is in the schools using the Regents examinations. However, it has, and deserves, a much wider significance through its influence upon authors of textbooks and upon other groups developing materials for use in mathematics programs.

1–2 The University of Illinois Committee on School Mathematics

The University of Illinois Committee on School Mathematics (UICSM) is an outgrowth of an earlier committee at that university which studied the mathematical preparation needed for college. In October 1951 the work of this earlier committee was published as a University of Illinois Bulletin [47]. Ninety-seven mathematical competencies were listed as minimal needs for students planning to start their mathematical training in college with analytic geometry and calculus; 67 of these were also needed for students starting their college mathematics with a freshman program including algebra and trigonometry. Any list has serious disadvantages in that it is difficult to interpret what is implied by saying that a topic should be mastered. Thus, in order for the Illinois list of competencies to be meaningful for any high school teacher, interpretation was necessary. This was attempted by the staff of the University of Illinois High School in cooperation with staff members from the University's Department of Mathematics and College of Education. This work has significance because it applies

† Numbers in brackets refer to references at the end of the book.

to all students planning to go to college. Since 1956 the work of the UICSM has been supported primarily by the Carnegie Corporation of New York.

The outstanding features of the UICSM are the freedom to experiment and the courage to admit that further experimentation is needed. There has been a very capable staff under the leadership of Dr. Max Beberman. The freedom to experiment has been due in substantial measure to the support of the University's College of Engineering. For example, while the committee members were still outlining the eleventh- and twelfth-year programs, the Dean of the College of Engineering was assuring public school administrators that the College of Engineering would be delighted to accept students from this program. The courage to continue experimentation and to avoid the temptation to announce that a final solution of our educational problems has been found is evidenced by the course for the tenth year. In accord with the philosophy of teaching mathematics without any formal recognition of the subdivisions of algebra, geometry, and so forth, the tenth-year program has included some formal geometry and some continuation of the algebra and informal geometry studied in earlier years. At least four different organizations of this material have been developed with text materials. Each has been thoroughly tested and revised to obtain new and improved materials. Such objectivity and willingness to experiment are essential—and too often missing—parts of a scientifically developed mathematics program.

The major significance of the work of the UICSM will lie in its discoveries. Its philosophy of pupil discovery and precision of terminology, as well as some of its methods, are already being applied by other groups. Information regarding the availability of text materials may be obtained by writing to the UICSM at the address given at the end of this chapter. Its texts are very interesting and, for teachers who have the background and the time to develop new classroom techniques, can be used very effectively.

1–3 The Commission on Mathematics

The College Entrance Examination Board (CEEB), recognizing that the CEEB examinations exert a strong influence upon teachers, appointed a Commission on Mathematics to study the mathematics program that should be used as a basis for the examinations. The report of this Commission [13] was published in 1959. It is concerned with the mathematics for college preparatory students in grades 9 through 12. The ninth year program is primarily concerned with the properties of the set of rational numbers, that is, with the properties of a field. The tenth-year program is based upon geometry and is characterized by an emphasis upon the use of coordinates in the teaching of high school geometry. This requires that the Pythagorean Theorem, based upon similar triangles, must be available as early in the course as possible. The eleventh-grade program includes the usual topics from a second course in algebra with an emphasis upon properties of real numbers and of complex numbers. Trigonometry is studied in both the eleventh and the twelfth grades; solid geometry is introduced in the tenth grade and applied in eleventh and twelfth grades. The recommended twelfth-grade program consists of any two of the following three courses: elementary functions, introductory probability with statistical inference, and introduction to modern algebra. A textbook on probability and statistical inference was prepared [12]. Information on the availability of materials may be obtained by writing to the CEEB at the address given at the end of this chapter.

The influence of the CEEB Commission on Mathematics operates primarily through the CEEB examinations and their influence upon authors of textbooks and other experimental programs. Teachers do not need to panic or to undertake any crash programs. The report of the Commission is intended primarily to indicate the direction in which there will be a gradual transition of the content of the CEEB examinations. There will be ample time for teachers to acquaint themselves with the changes. *The changes are primarily in the point of view used in presenting the usual topics and only secondarily in the introduction of new topics.*

1–4 The University of Maryland Mathematics Project

The report of the Commission on Mathematics included a statement of prerequisites for the mathematics program in grades 9 through 12. Other professional groups, including the Secondary School Curriculum Committee of the National Council of Teachers of Mathematics [37], have indicated a deep concern for the mathematics program in grades 7 and 8. The University of Maryland Mathematics Project has developed text materials for grades 7 and 8. In these materials the emphases are on the development of a precise vocabulary, recognition of the structure of arithmetic using letters to represent numbers, extension of the concept of "number," comprehension of systems of numeration, an introduction to geometry, and applications in each of these areas. Information regarding the availability of text materials may be obtained by writing to the University of Maryland Mathematics Project at the address given at the end of this chapter.

This program is continuing and has provided a sound basis for other experiments in grades 7 and 8 on both local and national levels. The Carnegie Corporation of New York has provided funds for this project.

1–5 The School Mathematics Study Group

The School Mathematics Study Group (SMSG) is financed with federal funds administered by the National Science Foundation. Under the leadership of Professor E. G. Begle a group of 20 high school teachers and 20 college teachers spent several weeks at Yale University in the summer of 1958 seeking more detailed outlines for mathematics courses in grades 9 through 12. These outlines were based initially upon the recommendations of the CEEB Commission on Mathematics. The outline for each grade was polished by a committee during 1958–1959 and provided a basis for a writing group to prepare text materials during the summer of 1959. Another writing group used the work of the University of Maryland Mathematics Project as a basis and prepared units of text materials for use in grades 7 and 8. All of these materials were used experimentally in selected schools in 1959–1960, were revised in the summer of 1960, and became generally available in the fall of 1960.

The text materials of SMSG represent a crash program. They undoubtedly will help establish a pattern for the evolving mathematics curriculum, but they cannot be expected to provide a national program. Such an assertion is based upon the authors' firm conviction that there should not be a single national program in this country. The CEEB Commission's recommendations on trigonometry became a part of the national program in Russia within a year of their publication! However, we do not and should not proceed in this manner. Rather, we recognize several sincere and desirable goals requiring quite different text materials in our classes. We recognize the need for providing guidance for local groups while leaving them autonomous in deciding what their mathematics program should be.

The SMSG materials are presented as an algebra–geometry–intermediate mathematics–functions and matrix algebra sequence for the better students in grades 9 through 12. The algebra includes an emphasis upon its mathematical structure. In geometry the first SMSG group decided to emphasize a new set of postulates (quite different from those that most teachers have been using), to stress the study of both plane and solid geometry, and to restrict the considerations of coordinates to the final chapter. The conflict between this policy and the report of the Commission on Mathematics led to the appointment of a new group to prepare another geometry text which would follow more closely the work of the Commission. The intermediate mathematics course is concerned with the real and complex number systems, including most of the usual topics, trigonometry, vectors, logarithms, and mathematical induction. The twelfth-grade course is based upon functions—polynomial, exponential, logarithmic, and trigonometric. Students able to complete this course in half a year are encouraged to study either matrix algebra or probability and statistics during the second half year. No text has been prepared for the probability and statistics course, since a text covering this material has already been prepared by the Commission on Mathematics [12].

The scope of the SMSG is very broad. It is concerned with teacher training, as evidenced by the preparation of study guides and a series of "Studies in Mathematics." The SMSG has an interest in general students and has prepared materials for them. It has an interest in grades 7 and 8 and has materials for use in these grades, and it has an interest in the elementary school grades and has materials for use there. Briefly, the SMSG is the major avenue through which federal funds are available for the development of experimental materials for mathematics classes, and these funds are being used to study the most pressing problems of teachers and students in so far as these problems can be foreseen. Information regarding available materials may be obtained by writing to the SMSG at the address given at the end of this chapter.

In accord with the philosophy that a national program is incompatible with the American way of life, the SMSG should be expected to speed up the establishment of patterns which will gradually be implemented through commercially available series of textbooks as well as the SMSG experimental materials. Another valuable contribution of the SMSG materials is as reading matter for teachers to help them see the structure and better understand the overtones of the concepts that they teach.

1–6 Training of Teachers

There are many other local and state groups working on mathematics curricula. In nearly all cases there is an increased emphasis upon:

the underlying mathematical assumptions,

precise definitions and vocabulary,

the nature of proof in both algebra and geometry,

sets of elements as a unifying concept,

the study of both equations and inequalities, and

comparisons of algebraic and geometric representations.

These emphases require a new point of view for teachers, students, and textbooks. The general scope of courses may be expected to remain, but the development of concepts and the "classroom patter" used in discussing topics is expected to be modified. In order to implement these recommendations, most teachers will need to continue their professional training either in formal courses, in local informal groups, or by personal study.

This book has been used successfully in preliminary forms with many local groups of teachers. All persons seeking to improve their understanding of mathematics should realize that this is not a "spectator sport." In order to learn mathematics, one must *do* mathematics. Numerous exercises (with a few of the more difficult ones starred) are included periodically in this book to encourage readers to apply, and thus to establish, their knowledge. Complete answers for all of the exercises are given at the end of each chapter.

The division of the remaining chapters of the book into three parts:

I. Arithmetic

II. Algebra

III. Geometry

is intended to help teachers find materials appropriate to their immediate needs. At the same time, it is felt that all teachers of secondary school mathematics should understand the scope and the point of view of the mathematics courses which precede and follow their own. Thus, it is suggested that teachers at all levels consider all parts of this book.

Only in this way can teachers effectively implement contemporary recommendations:

to recognize arithmetic as providing the basis for algebra,

to use algebra in teaching geometry, and

to use geometry in teaching algebra.

Application and Additional Readings

This chapter is intended to provide orientation for all readers of this book as to the contemporary trends and the point of view of the authors. Additional information about materials produced by the curriculum study groups mentioned may be obtained by writing to the addresses given here:

The New York State Mathematics Syllabus Committee: Mr. Frank Hawthorne, Supervisor of Mathematics, State Education Department, Albany, New York.

The University of Illinois Committee on School Mathematics: Dr. Max Beberman, University of Illinois, 1208 West Springfield, Urbana, Illinois.

The Commission on Mathematics: College Entrance Examination Board, 475 Riverside Drive, New York 27, New York.

The University of Maryland Mathematics Project: College of Education, University of Maryland, College Park, Maryland.

The School Mathematics Study Group: Stanford University, Stanford, California.

PART
ONE

***

ARITHMETIC

The study of arithmetic has always been an important phase of the work of grades 7 and 8, and will probably always be the core of the program in these grades. There seems to be common agreement, however, that the arithmetic taught during these years should emphasize basic concepts and meanings and not dwell heavily on the consumer applications of arithmetic.

To this end, the various groups studying the junior high school curriculum suggest a strong emphasis on the nature and structure of the number system. It is claimed that this is best done by means of a study of other number systems including those with number bases other than ten.

A unit on probability and statistics, taught by means of an experimental laboratory approach, can do much to develop such concepts as ratio, proportion, "law of averages," and so forth. The chapters in Part I provide some of the necessary background subject matter needed by teachers of junior high school mathematics who wish to use some of the current curricula recommendations in their classrooms.

Chapter 2. Number Bases.
Chapter 3. Modular Arithmetic.
Chapter 4. Mathematical Systems.
Chapter 5. Empirical Probability.

CHAPTER

TWO

NUMBER BASES

Almost all of the emerging curricula for junior high school mathematics emphasize the importance of instruction in number bases other than ten. Such a unit has the advantage of presenting the student with something new and exciting, while providing the means for developing some of the basic concepts and understandings of our decimal system of notation. Thus the student is able to study the basic properties of a number system in a novel and challenging setting.

2–1 Decimal Notation

In ordinary arithmetic, numbers are expressed in a decimal system of notation. The numerals 0, 1, 2, 3, 4, 5, 6, 7, 8, and 9 serve as decimal digits. In the decimal notation for a number, the value of the digit depends upon the position which it occupies. Thus we have:

$$725 = 7 \times 10^2 + 2 \times 10^1 + 5 \times 10^0$$

$$3,876.5 = 3 \times 10^3 + 8 \times 10^2 + 7 \times 10^1 + 6 \times 10^0 + 5 \times 10^{-1}$$

The choice of ten as a base is arbitrary. We could just as well have used five. In such a system we would use only the digits 0, 1, 2, 3, and 4. The number 89, which is expressed as $8 \times 10^1 + 9 \times 10^0$ in the base

10 system, would be expressed as 324 when written in base 5 notation. This can be shown as follows:

$$324 \text{ (base 5)} = 3 \times 5^2 + 2 \times 5^1 + 4 \times 5^0$$
$$= 3 \times 25 + 2 \times 5 + 4 \times 1$$
$$= 75 + 10 + 4 = 89$$

We can write this as 324_{five}. However, for convenience we shall write 324 in the base 5 notation as 324_5 even though there is no digit 5 in base 5 notation. When no subscript is used, we assume that the number has been written in base 10 (that is, decimal) notation.

2–2 Counting by Fives

Counting on one's fingers can be done by fives as follows:

	Hands	Fingers
one		1
two		2
three		3
four		4
one hand	1	0
one hand one	1	1
one hand two	1	2
one hand three	1	3
one hand four	1	4
two hands	2	0
two hands one	2	1
(and so forth)	. . . .	

This method of counting on one's fingers becomes complicated when the numbers are large. However, when "hands" are considered as "5's" and the position of each digit is used to indicate whether it is a number of "1's," "5's," or "25's," and so forth, this method of counting by fives can be easily extended. The numbers 1 to 30 are written in the base 5 in the table on page 13.

Read each number in the base 5 as in these examples:

14_5 means one five and four, that is, 9;
23_5 means two fives and three, that is, 13;
102_5 means one twenty-five, no fives, and two, that is, 27.

Base 10	Base 5	Base 10	Base 5	Base 10	Base 5
1	1	11	21	21	41
2	2	12	22	22	42
3	3	13	23	23	43
4	4	14	24	24	44
5	10	15	30	25	100
6	11	16	31	26	101
7	12	17	32	27	102
8	13	18	33	28	103
9	14	19	34	29	104
10	20	20	40	30	110

Counting by fives is basically a matter of grouping. Now consider the following set of asterisks:

```
*****
*****
***
```

These can be grouped in many ways. In base 10, they would be grouped as:

 One group of 10 and 3 is 13.

In base 5 the grouping would be:

Two groups of 5 and 3 may be written as 23_5.

Exercises

Express each of the following numbers in terms of powers of ten:

1. 735   **2.** 42.8   **3.** 3,965   **4.** 827.25

Express each of the following numbers in terms of powers of five:

5. 324_5 **6.** $4,213_5$ **7.** $12,340_5$ **8.** 34.2_5

9. Write the numbers from 31 through 75 in base 5 notation.

10. Draw rings around groups of five in the following set of asterisks and write a numeral to represent the total number of asterisks in base 5 notation:

```
*****
*****
*****
****
```

†*11. Repeat Ex. 10 with groups of: (a) six; (b) eight; (c) twelve.

2–3 Computation in Base 5 Notation

We can form an addition table for the numbers in base 5 notation very easily. Consider, for example, the problem $4_5 + 3_5$. This may be written as $4_5 + 1_5 + 2_5$. Now, $(4_5 + 1_5)$ is one group of 5, or 10_5. We then add 2_5 to obtain 12_5. This is equivalent to $(1 \times 5) + (2 \times 5^0) = (1 \times 5) + (2 \times 1) = 5 + 2 = 7$.

In a similar manner, $4_5 + 4_5 = 4_5 + 1_5 + 3_5$. Now $(4_5 + 1_5) = 10_5$. We then add 3_5 to obtain the sum 13_5. This result could also have been obtained by grouping:

$4_5 + 4_5$ can be represented as (****) + (****), which can be re-grouped as (*****) + (***), that is, 13_5.

Here is a table of the number facts needed for addition problems in base 5. (You should verify each entry.)

+	0	1	2	3	4
0	0	1	2	3	4
1	1	2	3	4	10_5
2	2	3	4	10_5	11_5
3	3	4	10_5	11_5	12_5
4	4	10_5	11_5	12_5	13_5

The facts given in the preceding table may be used in finding sums of numbers as illustrated in the following example.

Example 1. Find the sum of 432_5 and 243_5. Then check in base 10 notation.

SOLUTION: *Check:*

$$
\begin{array}{rll}
432_5 & 432_5 = 4 \times 5^2 + 3 \times 5 + 2 & = 117 \\
+243_5 & +243_5 = 2 \times 5^2 + 4 \times 5 + 3 & = \ \ 73 \\
\hline
1{,}230_5 & 1{,}230_5 = 1 \times 5^3 + 2 \times 5^2 + 3 \times 5 + 0 & = \overline{190}
\end{array}
$$

† Whenever an exercise is preceded by a star, it shall indicate that it is more difficult or challenging than the others.

Here are the steps used in Example 1. In each case the familiar symbol 5 has been used in place of 10_five to help the reader recognize that powers of 5 are involved. This convention will be followed throughout this chapter.

(a) Add the column of 1's.

$$\begin{array}{r} 4 \times 5^2 + 3 \times 5 + 2 \\ 2 \times 5^2 + 4 \times 5 + 3 \\ \hline 10_5 \end{array}$$

(b) Write the sum 10_5 of the 1's as 1×5 in the 5's column, and add the column of 5's.

$$\begin{array}{r} 1 \times 5 \\ 4 \times 5^2 + 3 \times 5 + 2 \\ 2 \times 5^2 + 4 \times 5 + 3 \\ \hline 13_5 \times 5 + 0 \end{array}$$

(c) Write $10_5 \times 5$ from the previous sum in the 5^2 column and add the column of 5^2 entries.

$$\begin{array}{r} 1 \times 5^2 \\ 4 \times 5^2 + 3 \times 5 + 2 \\ 2 \times 5^2 + 4 \times 5 + 3 \\ \hline 12 \times 5^2 + 3 \times 5 + 0 = 1{,}230_5 \end{array}$$

Note that we "carry" groups of fives in base 5 computation, just as we "carry" groups of ten in decimal computation.

Subtraction is not difficult if it is thought of as the inverse operation of addition. The table of addition facts in base 5 may again be used.

Example 2. Subtract in base 5 and check in base 10: $211_5 - 142_5$.
SOLUTION: Think of 211_5 as $2 \times 5^2 + 1 \times 5 + 1$; then, as $1 \times 5^2 + 6 \times 5 + 1$; then, as $1 \times 5^2 + 5 \times 5 + 6$. Thus:

$$\begin{array}{rl} 211_5 = 1 \times 5^2 + 5 \times 5 + 6 \\ -142_5 = 1 \times 5^2 + 4 \times 5 + 2 \\ \hline 14_5 = \qquad\qquad 1 \times 5 + 4 \end{array} \qquad \begin{array}{rl} \textit{Check:} & 211_5 = 56 \\ & -142_5 = 47 \\ \hline & 14_5 = 9 \end{array}$$

This problem can be solved by borrowing and thinking in base 5 in the following steps:

$$\text{(a)} \quad \begin{array}{r} 211_5 \\ -142_5 \\ \hline \end{array} \qquad \text{(b)} \quad \begin{array}{r} 20^11_5 \\ -14\,2_5 \\ \hline 4_5 \end{array} \qquad \text{(c)} \quad \begin{array}{r} 1^10^11_5 \\ -1\,4\,2_5 \\ \hline 1\,4_5 \end{array}$$

Problems in multiplication can be performed either as repeated additions or in base 10 and converted to base 5.

Example 3. Find the product of 243_5 and 4_5.
SOLUTION: We need the following facts:

$$4 \times 3 = 12_{10} = 2 \times 5^1 + 2 \times 5^0 = 22_5$$
$$4 \times 4 = 16_{10} = 3 \times 5^1 + 1 \times 5^0 = 31_5$$
$$4 \times 2 = 8_{10} = 1 \times 5^1 + 3 \times 5^0 = 13_5$$

The pattern for the computation when multiplying and "carrying" in base 5 notation is then precisely the same as that used in base 10 computation. For example, partial products are indented to represent the powers of 5 involved. In the long form, no attempt is made to "carry" mentally from one place to the next.

$$\begin{array}{r} 243_5 \\ \times \quad 4_5 \\ \hline 22_5 \\ 31_5 \\ 13_5 \\ \hline 2{,}132_5 \end{array} \qquad \begin{array}{c} \text{In condensed form:} \\ 243_5 \\ \times \quad 4_5 \\ \hline 2{,}132_5 \end{array}$$

Division can be performed in base 5 by considering it as the inverse operation of multiplication.

Example 4. Divide 121_5 by 4_5; check by multiplication in base 5.
SOLUTION: We need the following facts:

$$12_5 = 1_5 \times 4_5 + 3_5; \quad 12_5 - 4_5 = 3_5; \quad 31_5 = 4_5 \times 4_5.$$

The pattern for the computation when dividing in base 5 notation is then precisely the same as that used in base 10 computation.

$$\begin{array}{r} 14_5 \\ 4_5 \overline{)121_5} \\ 4_5 \\ \hline 31_5 \\ 31_5 \end{array} \qquad \begin{array}{l} Check: \quad 14_5 \\ \quad \times 4_5 \\ \quad \overline{121_5} \end{array}$$

Exercises

Add in base 5 and check in base 10:

1. 31_5	2. 31_5	3. 324_5	4. $2{,}341_5$	5. 321_5
$\underline{12_5}$	$\underline{32_5}$	$\underline{233_5}$	$\underline{1{,}034_5}$	120_5
				$\underline{432_5}$

Subtract in base 5 and check in base 10:

6. 43_5 7. 43_5 8. 312_5 9. 421_5
     -21_5 -24_5 -121_5 -223_5

10. Complete the following table for the basic multiplication facts in base 5:

×	0	1	2	3	4
0					
1					
2					
3					
4					

Multiply in base 5 and check in base 10:

11. 342_5 12. 212_5 13. 413_5 14. 324_5 ★15. 24_5 ★16. 342_5
    $\times 1_5$ $\times 2_5$ $\times 2_5$ $\times 4_5$ $\times 32_5$ $\times 24_5$

Divide in base 5 and check in base 10:

17. $4_5\overline{)143_5}$ 18. $3_5\overline{)121_5}$ ★19. $11_5\overline{)143_5}$ ★20. $32_5\overline{)3,031_5}$

2–4 Change of Base

Translating from base 5 to base 10 or from base 10 to base 5 may be accomplished as follows:

To translate from base 5 to base 10, express the number in terms of powers of 5 and simplify.

Example 1. Write $3,214_5$ in base 10 notation.

SOLUTION: $3,214_5 = 3 \times 5^3 + 2 \times 5^2 + 1 \times 5^1 + 4 \times 5^0 = 434$

Example 2. Write 2.34_5 in base 10 notation.

SOLUTION: $2.34_5 = 2 \times 5^0 + 3 \times 5^{-1} + 4 \times 5^{-2}$
$= 2 \times 1 + 3 \times \frac{1}{5} + 4 \times \frac{1}{25}$
$= 2 \times 1 + 6 \times \frac{1}{10} + 16 \times \frac{1}{100}$
$= 2.76$

To translate from base 10 to base 5, any one of several procedures may be adopted. Consider the problem

$$339 = \underline{\hspace{3cm}}_5$$

When a number is expressed to the base 5, it is written in terms of powers of 5:

$$5^0 = 1,\ 5^1 = 5,\ 5^2 = 25,\ 5^3 = 125,\ 5^4 = 625,\ \dots$$

The highest power of 5 which is not greater than the given number is 5^3. This power of 5, namely, $5^3 = 125$, can be subtracted from 339 twice. Then the remainder 89 is positive and less than 125. Thus, we write 2×5^3 in the expansion of 339 to the base 5.

$$\begin{array}{r} 339 \\ -125 \\ \hline 214 \\ -125 \\ \hline 89 \end{array}$$

The next lower power of 5 is 5^2. This number can be subtracted from 89 three times to obtain a non-negative remainder less than 25. Thus, we write 3×5^2 in the expansion.

$$\begin{array}{r} 89 \\ -25 \\ \hline 64 \\ -25 \\ \hline 39 \\ -25 \\ \hline 14 \end{array}$$

Finally, we subtract 5 from 14 twice, write 2×5 in the expansion, and obtain 4 as a remainder.

$$\begin{array}{r} 14 \\ -\ 5 \\ \hline 9 \\ -\ 5 \\ \hline 4 \end{array}$$

$$329 = 2(125) + 3(25) + 2(5) + 4$$
$$= 2 \times 5^3 + 3 \times 5^2 + 2 \times 5^1 + 4 \times 5^0 = 2{,}324_5.$$

A group of 339 elements can be considered as 2 groups of 125 elements, 3 groups of 25 elements, 2 groups of 5 elements, and 4 elements.

Another procedure for changing 339 to the base 5 depends upon successive division by 5:

$$339 = 67 \times 5 + 4$$
$$67 = 13 \times 5 + 2$$
$$13 = 2 \times 5 + 3$$

Next, substitute from the third equation into the second; from the second to the first; and simplify as follows:

$$13 = 2 \times 5 + 3$$
$$67 = 13 \times 5 + 2 = (2 \times 5 + 3) \times 5 + 2$$
$$339 = 67 \times 5 + 4 = [(2 \times 5 + 3) \times 5 + 2] \times 5 + 4$$
$$= 2 \times 5^3 + 3 \times 5^2 + 2 \times 5^1 + 4 \times 5^0 = 2,324_5$$

The arithmetical steps involved in these computations can be performed as shown in the following array (often called an algorithm).

$$
\begin{array}{l}
5\,\underline{|339} \\
\quad 5\,\underline{|67}\text{—}4 \\
\qquad 5\,\underline{|13}\text{—}2 \\
\qquad\quad 5\,\underline{|2}\text{—}3 \\
\qquad\qquad 0\text{—}2
\end{array}
\qquad \text{Read up as } 2,324_5.
$$

Note that the remainder is written after each division by 5. Then the remainders are used in reverse order to obtain the expression for the number to the base 5.

Example 3. Write 423 in base 5 notation.

SOLUTION:

$$
\begin{array}{l}
5\,\underline{|423} \\
\quad 5\,\underline{|84}\text{—}3 \\
\qquad 5\,\underline{|16}\text{—}4 \\
\qquad\quad 5\,\underline{|3}\text{—}1 \\
\qquad\qquad 0\text{—}3
\end{array}
\qquad \textit{Answer: } 3,143_5.
$$

Check: $3,143_5 = 3 \times 5^3 + 1 \times 5^2 + 4 \times 5^1 + 3 \times 5^0$
$= 375 + 25 + 20 + 3 = 423.$

The method of successive division by the new base may be used in changing from any one base to another. Thus, we can use this procedure to change from base 5 to base 10, successively dividing by 20_5. The computation must be done in base 5 notation. This is illustrated in the following example.

Example 4. Change $2,114_5$ to base 10.

SOLUTION:

$$
\begin{array}{l}
20_5\,\underline{|2,114_5} \\
\quad 20_5\,\underline{|103_5}\text{—}4_5 \\
\qquad 20_5\,\underline{|2_5}\text{—}13_5 \\
\qquad\quad 0_5\text{—}2_5
\end{array}
$$

Answer:
$$2_5 \times 10^2 + 13_5 \times 10^1 + 4_5 \times 10^0$$
$$= 2 \times 100 + 8 \times 10 + 4$$
$$= 284$$

Exercises

Write each number in decimal notation:

1. 423_5 **2.** 120_5 **3.** 444_5 **4.** $1,230_5$ **5.** 131.42_5

Change to base 5 and check:

6. 382   **7.** 593   **8.** 782   **9.** 194   **10.** 625

2–5 Other Bases

The base 5 system has been used merely for illustrative purposes; any other positive integer greater than 1 would have served just as well as a base. For each base N, the digits used are 0, 1, 2, . . ., $N - 1$. For each base, powers of that base are used as place values for the digits.

Example 1. Change 324_8 to base 10.
SOLUTION: $324_8 = 3 \times 8^2 + 2 \times 8^1 + 4 \times 8^0 = 212$.

Example 2. Change $1,231_4$ to base 10.
SOLUTION: $1,231_4 = 1 \times 4^3 + 2 \times 4^2 + 3 \times 4^1 + 1 \times 4^0 = 109$.

Any number may be changed from base 10 to another base by dividing successively by the new base and using the remainders as in § 2–4. This procedure is always performed in the notation of the old base. It has already been used for the base 5 and may be adapted for other bases as well.

Example 3. Change 354 to base 8.
SOLUTION:

$$
\begin{array}{r}
8\,\lfloor 354 \\
\hline
8\,\lfloor 44\text{—}2 \\
\hline
8\,\lfloor 5\text{—}4 \\
\hline
0\text{—}5
\end{array}
$$

Answer: 542_8

$$
\begin{aligned}
\text{Check: } 542_8 &= 5 \times 8^2 + 4 \times 8^1 + 2 \times 8^0 \\
&= 320 + 32 + 2 \\
&= 354
\end{aligned}
$$

Exercises

1. Change to base 10:

   (a) 327_8 (b) $3,213_4$ (c) $5,440_6$

2. Change to the stated base:

(a) $724 =$ _____$_4$ (b) $396 =$ _____$_8$

(c) $472 =$ _____$_6$ (d) $25 =$ _____$_2$

⋆3. Change to the stated base without making use of base 10:

(a) $1{,}764_8 =$ _____$_4$ (b) $324_5 =$ _____$_2$

4. Complete the following tables of addition and multiplication facts for base 4:

+	0	1	2	3
0				
1				
2				
3				

×	0	1	2	3
0				
1				
2				
3				

5. Complete the following tables of addition and multiplication facts for base 8:

+	0	1	2	3	4	5	6	7
0								
1								
2								
3								
4								
5								
6								
7								

×	0	1	2	3	4	5	6	7
0								
1								
2								
3								
4								
5								
6								
7								

6. Using *t* for 10 and *e* for 11, complete the following tables of addition and multiplication facts for base 12:

+	0	1	2	3	4	5	6	7	8	9	*t*	*e*
0												
1												
2												
3												
4												
5												
6												
7												
8												
9												
t												
e												

×	0	1	2	3	4	5	6	7	8	9	t	e
0												
1												
2												
3												
4												
5												
6												
7												
8												
9												
t												
e												

7. Explain why two new symbols, t and e, were necessary for completing the tables in Ex. 6.

Perform the following computations in the bases stated:

8. 246_8
        $+375_8$

9. 524_6
        -235_6

*10. 469_{12}
          $\times 37_{12}$

*11. $32_4\overline{)1{,}220_4}$

12. $59t_{12}$
         $+\ 837_{12}$

13. 732_8
         -276_8

14. $3{,}213_4$
        $\times 23_4$

15. $23_8\overline{)1{,}436_8}$

2–6 Binary Notation

Numbers written to the base 2 are of special interest because of their application in computers. This system of notation is called **binary notation.** Only two digits are used, namely, 0 and 1.

Each number can be written as a sequence of 0's and 1's. Computers may use a hole in a card for 1 and no hole for 0, or a closed switch for 1 and an open switch for 0. Thus, numbers in binary notation can be easily utilized by machines. The operations performed by the machines are all based on two very simple operations—addition and multiplication. Tables for addition and multiplication are relatively simple.

Base 10	Base 2	Base 10	Base 2
1	1	9	1,001
2	10	10	1,010
3	11	11	1,011
4	100	12	1,100
5	101	13	1,101
6	110	14	1,110
7	111	15	1,111
8	1,000	16	10,000

+	0	1
0	0	1
1	1	10_2

×	0	1
0	0	0
1	0	1

Exercises

Write each number in binary notation:

1. 28   **2.** 32   **3.** 19   **4.** 64   **5.** 152

Change each number to decimal notation:

6. $110,111_2$ **7.** $101,010_2$ **8.** $100,001_2$ **9.** $11,011,011,011_2$

Perform the indicated operation in binary notation and check in base 10:

10. $1,101_2$
     $+1,011_2$

11. $10,011_2$
     $+10,101_2$

12. $11,011_2$
     $-10,110_2$

13. $110,101_2$
     $-10,111_2$

14. $1,101_2$
     $\times 11_2$

15. $10,110_2$
     $\times 101_2$

16. Write the number 214 in base 8 and then in base 2 notation. Can you discover a relationship between these two bases?

2–7 Just for Fun

Many recreational items are based on the binary system of notation. Consider, for example, the following boxes within which the numbers 1 to 15 are placed according to the following scheme:

In box A place all numbers which have a 1 in the units place when written in binary notation. In box B place those with a 1 in the second position from the right in binary notation. In C and D are those numbers with a 1 in the third and fourth positions, respectively.

A	B	C	D
1	2	4	8
3	3	5	9
5	6	6	10
7	7	7	11
9	10	12	12
11	11	13	13
13	14	14	14
15	15	15	15

Next, ask someone to think of a number and tell you in which box or boxes it appears. You then tell that person his number by finding the sum of the first number in each box he mentions. Thus, if his number is 11, he lists boxes A, B, and D. You then find the sum $1 + 2 + 8$ as the number under discussion.

Exercises

1. Explain why the method given in §2–7 for finding a number after knowing the boxes in which it appears works as it does.

2. Extend the boxes given in §2–7 to include all the numbers through 31. (A fifth column, E, will be necessary.)

3. Find a reference to the game of Nim and study its relationship to the binary system of notation.

Application and Additional Readings

All of the material in this chapter has been successfully used in grade 7 and higher grades. Currently some experimentation is taking place to determine which portions of the material can be taught to youngsters in the elementary grades; to date, the outcomes appear to be encouraging.

For teachers who do not wish to include such a unit in the classroom, we suggest the desirability of this topic as part of the program of a mathematics club. For such groups more difficult problems are to be encouraged. Thus, we might ask the student to change 324_5 to a number in base 8 notation without expressing the number in base 10.

Finally, it should be pointed out that a teaching unit on other systems of notation has proved to be successful with students of average and below-average ability. For this group, the material presented has the advantage of being novel, yet it serves as a means of reviewing the fundamentals of arithmetic as well as of developing an understanding of the decimal system of notation.

For an introduction to other number bases which can be adapted directly to the classroom, see the junior high school text produced by the School Mathematics Study Group [42]. An interesting discussion of number scales, especially the binary scale and its application to computers, is treated in the text by Freund [17]. Other elementary treatments are found in texts by Richardson [40] and Swain [45]. A more advanced-level exposition may be read in the text by Meserve [31].

Answers for Exercises

2–2 *Counting by Fives*

1. $7 \times 10^2 + 3 \times 10^1 + 5 \times 10^0$

2. $4 \times 10^1 + 2 \times 10^0 + 8 \times 10^{-1}$

3. $3 \times 10^3 + 9 \times 10^2 + 6 \times 10^1 + 5 \times 10^0$

4. $8 \times 10^2 + 2 \times 10^1 + 7 \times 10^0 + 2 \times 10^{-1} + 5 \times 10^{-2}$

5. $3 \times 5^2 + 2 \times 5^1 + 4 \times 5^0$

6. $4 \times 5^3 + 2 \times 5^2 + 1 \times 5^1 + 3 \times 5^0$

7. $1 \times 5^4 + 2 \times 5^3 + 3 \times 5^2 + 4 \times 5^1 + 0 \times 5^0$

8. $3 \times 5^1 + 4 \times 5^0 + 2 \times 5^{-1}$

9. 111, 112, 113, 114, 120, 121, 122, 123, 124, 130, 131, 132, 133, 134, 140, 141, 142, 143, 144, 200, 201, 202, 203, 204, 210, 211, 212, 213, 214, 220, 221, 222, 223, 224, 230, 231, 232, 233, 234, 240, 241, 242, 243, 244, 300; all in base 5 notation.

10. 34_5

11. (a) 31_6; (b) 23_8; (c) 17_{12}.

2–3 *Computation in Base 5 Notation*

1. 43_5 **2.** 113_5 **3.** $1,112_5$ **4.** $3,430_5$ **5.** $1,423_5$

6. 22_5 **7.** 14_5 **8.** 141_5 **9.** 143_5

10. All numbers are expressed in base 5 notation:

×	0	1	2	3	4
0	0	0	0	0	0
1	0	1	2	3	4
2	0	2	4	11	13
3	0	3	11	14	22
4	0	4	13	22	31

11. 342_5 **12.** 424_5 **13.** $1,331_5$ **14.** $2,411_5$

15.
$$\begin{array}{r} 24_5 \\ \times 32_5 \\ \hline 103_5 \\ 132_5 \\ \hline 1,423_5 \end{array}$$

16.
$$\begin{array}{r} 342_5 \\ \times 24_5 \\ \hline 3023_5 \\ 1234_5 \\ \hline 20,413_5 \end{array}$$

17. 22_5 **18.** 22_5

19.
$$\begin{array}{r} 13_5 \\ 11_5 \overline{)143_5} \\ 11_5 \\ \hline 33_5 \\ 33_5 \end{array}$$

20.
$$\begin{array}{r} 43_5 \\ 32_5 \overline{)3031_5} \\ 233_5 \\ \hline 201_5 \\ 201_5 \end{array}$$

2–4 *Change of Base*

1. 113 **2.** 35 **3.** 124 **4.** 190 **5.** 41.88

6. $3,012_5$ **7.** $4,333_5$ **8.** $11,112_5$ **9.** $1,234_5$ **10.** $10,000_5$

2-5 *Other Bases*

1. (a) 215; (b) 231; (c) 1,248.

2. (a) $23,110_4$; (b) 614_8; (c) $2,104_6$; (d) $11,001_2$.

3. (a) $33,310_4$; (b) $1,011,001_2$.

4. All numbers are expressed in base 4 notation:

+	0	1	2	3
0	0	1	2	3
1	1	2	3	10
2	2	3	10	11
3	3	10	11	12

×	0	1	2	3
0	0	0	0	0
1	0	1	2	3
2	0	2	10	12
3	0	3	12	21

5. All numbers are expressed in base 8 notation:

+	0	1	2	3	4	5	6	7
0	0	1	2	3	4	5	6	7
1	1	2	3	4	5	6	7	10
2	2	3	4	5	6	7	10	11
3	3	4	5	6	7	10	11	12
4	4	5	6	7	10	11	12	13
5	5	6	7	10	11	12	13	14
6	6	7	10	11	12	13	14	15
7	7	10	11	12	13	14	15	16

×	0	1	2	3	4	5	6	7
0	0	0	0	0	0	0	0	0
1	0	1	2	3	4	5	6	7
2	0	2	4	6	10	12	14	16
3	0	3	6	11	14	17	22	25
4	0	4	10	14	20	24	30	34
5	0	5	12	17	24	31	36	43
6	0	6	14	22	30	36	44	52
7	0	7	16	25	34	43	52	61

6. All numbers are expressed in base 12 notation:

+	0	1	2	3	4	5	6	7	8	9	t	e
0	0	1	2	3	4	5	6	7	8	9	t	e
1	1	2	3	4	5	6	7	8	9	t	e	10
2	2	3	4	5	6	7	8	9	t	e	10	11
3	3	4	5	6	7	8	9	t	e	10	11	12
4	4	5	6	7	8	9	t	e	10	11	12	13
5	5	6	7	8	9	t	e	10	11	12	13	14
6	6	7	8	9	t	e	10	11	12	13	14	15
7	7	8	9	t	e	10	11	12	13	14	15	16
8	8	9	t	e	10	11	12	13	14	15	16	17
9	9	t	e	10	11	12	13	14	15	16	17	18
t	t	e	10	11	12	13	14	15	16	17	18	19
e	e	10	11	12	13	14	15	16	17	18	19	$1t$

×	0	1	2	3	4	5	6	7	8	9	t	e
0	0	0	0	0	0	0	0	0	0	0	0	0
1	0	1	2	3	4	5	6	7	8	9	t	e
2	0	2	4	6	8	t	10	12	14	16	18	1t
3	0	3	6	9	10	13	16	19	20	23	26	29
4	0	4	8	10	14	18	20	24	28	30	34	38
5	0	5	t	13	18	21	26	2e	34	39	42	47
6	0	6	10	16	20	26	30	36	40	46	50	56
7	0	7	12	19	24	2e	36	41	48	53	5t	65
8	0	8	14	20	28	34	40	48	54	60	68	74
9	0	9	16	23	30	39	46	53	60	69	76	83
t	0	t	18	26	34	42	50	5t	68	76	84	92
e	0	e	1t	29	38	47	56	65	74	83	92	t1

7. There are no symbols in base 12 to represent groups of ten or eleven. Thus, 10 is needed to represent one group of twelve.

8. 643_8

9. 245_6

10.
$$
\begin{array}{r}
469_{12} \\
\times\,37_{12} \\
\hline
27e3_{12} \\
1183_{12} \\
\hline
14{,}423_{12}
\end{array}
$$

11.
$$
\begin{array}{r}
13_4 \\
32_4\,\overline{\smash{)}\,1220_4} \\
\underline{32_4} \\
300_4 \\
\underline{222_4} \\
12_4
\end{array}
$$

12. $1{,}215_{12}$

13. 434_8

14.
$$
\begin{array}{r}
3213_4 \\
\times\,23_4 \\
\hline
22311_4 \\
13032_4 \\
\hline
213{,}231_4
\end{array}
$$

15.
$$
\begin{array}{r}
52_8 \\
23_8\,\overline{\smash{)}\,1436_8} \\
\underline{137_8} \\
46_8 \\
\underline{46_8}
\end{array}
$$

2–6 *Binary Notation*

1. $11,100_2$ **2.** $100,000_2$ **3.** $10,011_2$ **4.** $1,000,000_2$

5. $10,011,000_2$ **6.** 55   **7.** 42   **8.** 33   **9.** 1,755   **10.** $11,000_2$

11. $101,000_2$ **12.** 101_2 **13.** $11,110_2$ **14.** $100,111_2$

15. $1,101,110_2$ **16.** $214 = 326_8 = 11,010,110_2$. When placed in groups of three, starting from the units digit, the binary representation can be translated directly into the octal system, and conversely. Thus:

$$\underbrace{11}_{3} \quad \underbrace{010}_{2} \quad \underbrace{110_2}_{6_8}$$

2–7 *Just for Fun*

1. For a discussion of this method, see the text by Meserve [31, p. 79].

2.

A	B	C	D	E
1	2	4	8	16
3	3	5	9	17
5	6	6	10	18
7	7	7	11	19
9	10	12	12	20
11	11	13	13	21
13	14	14	14	22
15	15	15	15	23
17	18	20	24	24
19	19	21	25	25
21	22	22	26	26
23	23	23	27	27
25	26	28	28	28
27	27	29	29	29
29	30	30	30	30
31	31	31	31	31

3. See [24].

MODULAR ARITHMETIC

In the preceding chapter we explored the possibility of using various number bases as a means of developing a clear understanding of our own decimal system of notation. In a similar vein, this section will examine a mathematical system called *modular arithmetic*, which is unique insofar as the typical secondary school curriculum is concerned. A study of modular arithmetic is interesting in that it can be developed quite early in the junior high school years, yet it is frequently found as a subject of instruction in graduate courses on the foundations of algebra, albeit from a different point of view.

3–1 Around the Clock

The clock can provide an excellent introduction for modular arithmetic. Suppose that it is now 10 o'clock. What time will it be:

3 hours from now? $10 + 3 = 1$ (on the clock)

This is read: "$10 + 3$ is equivalent to 1 on the clock."

4 hours from now? $10 + 4 = 2$ (on the clock)
10 hours from now? $10 + 10 = 8$ (on the clock)

Consider the same questions at 11 o'clock:

$$11 + 3 = 2 \text{ (on the clock)}$$
$$11 + 4 = 3 \text{ (on the clock)}$$
$$11 + 10 = 9 \text{ (on the clock)}$$

Around the clock we have another arithmetic. No matter where we start, 12 hours later we shall always be at the same place:

$$t + 12 = t \text{ (on the clock)}$$

In other words, the appearance of the clock is unchanged when it is set back, or ahead, 12 hours or any integral multiple of 12 hours. A similar statement can be made for 24-hour intervals. The 12-hour intervals are the smallest for which the statement can be made. We describe this situation by saying that the arithmetic around the clock is **modulo 12**.

Two times of day appear the same on the clock if and only if they differ by a multiple of 12. Two numbers are called **congruent modulo 12** if and only if they differ by a multiple of 12. We write:

$$a \equiv b \pmod{12}; \text{ read "}a \text{ is congruent to } b \text{ modulo 12";}$$

if and only if $a - b = (k)(12)$ for some integer k.

Only 12 numerals are needed on the face of a clock; only 12 numerals are needed in arithmetic modulo 12. We continue to use decimal notation, as may be seen in the following examples.

Example 1. Solve the equation $x + 5 = 3$ for x, where x may be replaced by any one of the numerals on a 12-hour clock.

SOLUTION: In the modulo 12 system, $10 + 5 = 3$; therefore, $x = 10$. Alternatively we may look directly at the numeral 5 on a clock and count the number of hours, in a clockwise direction, until we reach 3.

Example 2. Using the numerals on a 12-hour clock, find a replacement for x such that $3 - x = 10$.

SOLUTION: $x = 5$. Looking at the numeral 3 on a clock, we note that one must move five units in a counterclockwise direction to reach 10. Alternatively we may subtract by the additive method; that is, we wish to find a number which added to 10 gives 3. On a 12-hour clock, that is, in arithmetic modulo 12, the answer is 5.

Exercises

1. Complete this addition table as on a 12-hour clock:

+	1	2	3	4	5	6	7	8	9	10	11	12
1												
2												
3												
4												
5												
6												
7												
8												
9												
10												
11												
12												

Solve each equation where x *may be replaced by any one of the numerals on a 12-hour clock:*

2. $x + 3 = 7$ **3.** $x + 3 = 1$ **4.** $x + 5 = 2$

5. $11 + x = 3$ **6.** $10 + x = 5$ **7.** $x - 12 = 5$

8. $x - 12 = x$ **9.** $x - 10 = x$ **10.** $2 - x = 9$

11. $2 + x = 9$ **★12.** $2 + x = 2 - x$ **★13.** $3 - x = 5 + x$

3–2 Modulo 2

Two numerals, 0 and 1, are needed in arithmetic modulo 2. Each even integer may be represented by 0; each odd integer by 1. Two integers are represented by the same numeral if and only if they are both even or both odd; that is, if and only if the numbers differ by a multiple of 2.

Two numbers are called **congruent modulo 2** if and only if they differ by a multiple of 2. Thus, we may write:

$$a \equiv b \pmod 2; \text{ read "}a \text{ is congruent to } b \text{ modulo 2";}$$

if and only if $a - b = (k)(2)$ for some integer k.

The arithmetic modulo 2 may be summarized by means of the following tables:

Addition Table Modulo 2

+	0	1
0	0	1
1	1	0

Multiplication Table Modulo 2

×	0	1
0	0	0
1	0	1

Exercises

Restate each of the following, using the notation of arithmetic modulo 2:

1. The sum of any two even integers is even.

2. The sum of any two odd integers is even.

3. The product of two even integers is even.

4. The product of an even integer and an odd integer is even.

5. The sum of an even integer and an odd integer is odd.

3-3 Modulo 5

Think of a clock for five hours numbered 0, 1, 2, 3, 4 as in the accompanying figure. Consider addition on this five-hour clock in the same manner as on a regular clock, that is, by rotation in a clockwise direction. Thus, $2 + 1$ shall mean: rotate first two spaces from 0, then one more space. The result is 3.

To add 3 and 4, we rotate three spaces from 0, then four more spaces in the same direction. The result is 2. We interpret 0 to mean no rotation or an

integral number of complete rotations of five spaces each. Thus, we
have such facts as:

$$3 + 2 = 0 \text{ (on a five-hour clock)}$$
$$4 + 0 = 4 \text{ (on a five-hour clock)}$$
$$4 + 4 = 3 \text{ (on a five-hour clock)}$$

Regardless of where we start on this five-hour clock, we shall always
be at the same place five hours later. In other words, the appearance
of the clock is unchanged when it is set back, or ahead, five hours or
any integral multiple of five hours. We describe this situation by saying
that the arithmetic around this clock is **modulo 5**.

Two numbers are said to be **congruent modulo 5** if and only if they
differ by a multiple of 5. We write:

$$a \equiv b \text{ (mod 5)}; \text{ read "}a \text{ is congruent to } b \text{ modulo 5";}$$

if and only if $a - b = (k)(5)$ for some integer k. Thus, $12 \equiv 2 \pmod 5$
because $12 - 2$ is a multiple of 5.

Multiplication may be considered as repeated addition. Thus, 2×4
means $4 + 4$ or 3, modulo 5. We know this as an addition fact
modulo 5. We could also obtain this result by rotations on the five-
hour clock. Start at 0; rotate four spaces clockwise; then rotate four
more spaces clockwise to arrive at 3. Similarly, 3×4 means
$4 + 4 + 4$. By rotation on the five-hour clock, we find that three
rotations of four spaces each brings us to 2. Thus, $3 \times 4 \equiv 2 \pmod 5$.

Exercises

*Use the definitions of addition and multiplication given above and complete
the following tables of the basic facts modulo 5.*

+	0	1	2	3	4
0					
1					
2					
3					
4					

×	0	1	2	3	4
0					
1					
2					
3					
4					

3–4 Properties of Arithmetic Modulo 5

Any mathematical system is based upon a set of elements and one or more operations (such as addition and multiplication). As in §3–3, arithmetic modulo 5 is based upon a set of five elements: 0, 1, 2, 3, and 4. Now consider these properties of addition in any arithmetic and, in particular, of modulo 5 arithmetic:

1. There is exactly one entry in each place of the table of addition facts modulo 5. (See the exercises for §3–3.) In other words, for any pair of elements, there is a unique element which represents the sum of the two given elements in the order in which they are given. Furthermore, this element is one of the original set of five elements.

Accordingly, we say that the set of elements in arithmetic modulo 5 is **closed** with respect to addition. Note that the operation of addition is a **binary operation**; that is, it is a process of associating a number with two given numbers.

2. When three numbers are to be added in arithmetic modulo 5, two of these must be added first. Thus, to find the sum of 3, 1, and 2, we may proceed in either of the following ways:

$$(3 + 1) + 2 = 4 + 2, \text{ or } 1, \text{ modulo } 5$$
$$3 + (1 + 2) = 3 + 3, \text{ or } 1, \text{ modulo } 5$$

In general, we say that the set of elements in arithmetic modulo 5 satisfies the **associative law for addition**. That is, for all possible choices of three numbers a, b, and c from this set, the sum is independent of the way in which they are paired. Thus, we may summarize this law as follows:

$$(a + b) + c = a + (b + c)$$

3. Consider the following facts in arithmetic modulo 5:

$$0 + 0 = 0, \quad 1 + 0 = 1, \quad 2 + 0 = 2, \quad 3 + 0 = 3, \quad 4 + 0 = 4.$$

The set of elements in arithmetic modulo 5 includes an element, 0, such that the sum of any given element and 0 is the given element. That is, for any number a in this set, we have:

$$a + 0 = a.$$

We call 0 the **identity element** for addition.

4. Notice the following facts in arithmetic modulo 5:

$$0 + 0 = 0, \quad 1 + 4 = 0, \quad 2 + 3 = 0, \quad 3 + 2 = 0, \quad 4 + 1 = 0.$$

For each element x in arithmetic modulo 5, there exists another element, x', such that the sum of the two numbers is the identity element 0. That is $x + x' = 0$, where x and x' are elements in arithmetic modulo 5.

The element x' is called the **inverse** of x under addition, or the **negative** of x. Thus, in arithmetic modulo 5, the inverse of 3 (with respect to addition) is 2, since $3 + 2 = 0$. Similarly, the inverse of 4 is 1.

We may also consider the preceding four properties with respect to the binary operation of multiplication as follows:

1. **Closure.** The set of elements in arithmetic modulo 5 is closed with respect to multiplication. That is, for any pair of elements, there is a unique element which represents the product of the two given elements. (Notice that there is exactly one entry in each place of the table of multiplication facts in §3–3.)

2. **Associative Law.** Note that $(3 \cdot 2) \cdot 4 = 3 \cdot (2 \cdot 4)$ in the arithmetic modulo 5. In general, the product of any three numbers a, b, and c in arithmetic modulo 5 is independent of the way in which the factors are paired when they are multiplied. That is, for all possible choices of three numbers, we know that the associative law for multiplication is satisfied, namely: $(a \cdot b) \cdot c = a \cdot (b \cdot c)$.

3. **Identity Element.** We note such facts as $(4)(1) = 4$, $(3)(1) = 3$, and $(2)(1) = 2$ in arithmetic modulo 5. This system contains an element, 1, such that the identity $(a)(1) = a$ is satisfied for every number a in arithmetic modulo 5. Thus, 1 is the identity element in this system with respect to multiplication.

4. **Inverse Element.** In arithmetic modulo 5, the inverse of 3 (with respect to multiplication) is 2, since $3 \cdot 2 \equiv 1 \pmod 5$. Similarly, the inverse of 4 is 4, in that $4 \cdot 4 \equiv 1 \pmod 5$.

In arithmetic modulo 5 we find that for every element x, $x \neq 0$, there exists an element x' such that $x \cdot x' = 1$, the identity element for multiplication. The element x' is called the inverse of x. The inverse of any element under multiplication is called its **reciprocal**.

The preceding properties have been discussed in detail for arithmetic modulo 5, but they will be explored again in greater detail in subsequent chapters for other systems as well. There are also two other laws which are satisfied by the modulo 5 system and which are of importance in mathematics, namely, the **commutative law** and the **distributive law**.

Note that in arithmetic modulo 5 we have the following relationships:

$$2 + 3 = 3 + 2, \quad 4 + 3 = 3 + 4, \quad 2 \times 3 = 3 \times 2, \quad 4 \times 3 = 3 \times 4.$$

We see that the sum or product of two numbers is independent of the order in which they are added or multiplied. In general, we say that the elements of arithmetic modulo 5 satisfy the commutative laws for addition and for multiplication.

The distributive law for multiplication with respect to addition relates the two operations of multiplication and addition. It states that, for any three numbers a, b, and c in arithmetic modulo 5, we have the relationship: $a(b + c) = a \cdot b + a \cdot c$. As a specific example in this system:

$$3(4 + 2) = 3(1) = 3$$
$$3(4 + 2) = (3)(4) + (3)(2) = 2 + 1 = 3$$

Thus, $3(4 + 2) = (3)(4) + (3)(2).$

Exercises

Each of the following is based upon the set of elements in arithmetic modulo 5:

1. Find the inverse of each element with respect to addition.

2. Find the inverse of each element with respect to multiplication.

3. Verify that the associative law for addition holds for at least two specific instances.

4. Repeat Ex. 3 for the associative law for multiplication.

5. Verify that the distributive law for multiplication with respect to addition holds for at least two specific instances.

Define subtraction thus: $a - b = c$ *if and only if* $b + c = a$. *Then complete these exercises in arithmetic modulo 5:*

6. 1	**7.** 3	**8.** 2	**9.** 2	**10.** 1
-4	-4	-3	-4	-3

Define division thus: $a \div b = c$ *if and only if* $b \times c = a$. *Then complete these exercises in arithmetic modulo 5:*

11. $\frac{3}{2}$ **12.** $\frac{2}{3}$ **13.** $\frac{2}{4}$ **14.** $\frac{4}{3}$ **15.** $\frac{1}{2}$

16. Is the set of elements in arithmetic modulo 5 closed with respect to subtraction?

17. Answer Ex. 16 for division.

18. What is a necessary condition for the product of two elements in arithmetic modulo 5 to be zero?

3–5 Congruence

For any integer m, we say that two integers a and b are congruent modulo m if and only if there exists an integer k such that

$$a = b + km.$$

We write this as $a \equiv b$ (mod m) and read it as "a is congruent to b modulo m." The integer m is called the **modulus** of the congruence. The statement that two numbers are congruent modulo m is equivalent to the statement that the difference of the two numbers is divisible by m. For example: "$6 \equiv 1$ (mod 5)" and "$6 - 1$ is divisible by 5" are equivalent statements.

In each modular arithmetic only a finite set of numerals is required. In arithmetic modulo m we use the set of numerals $\{0, 1, 2, . . ., m - 1\}$. Each number in ordinary arithmetic is congruent modulo m to a number with one of these numerals.

In arithmetic modulo 2, each even integer is represented by 0 and each odd integer by 1 as in §3–2. Note that each even integer is congruent to 0 modulo 2 and each odd integer is congruent to 1 modulo 2.

In arithmetic modulo 5 the five-hour clock can now be replaced by congruences. For example, $3 \times 2 = 6 \equiv 1$ (mod 5). Each integer of ordinary arithmetic is congruent modulo 5 to exactly one of the numbers 0, 1, 2, 3, and 4. Thus, each integer of ordinary arithmetic may be represented modulo 5 by one of these five numerals.

In the arithmetic of numbers around an ordinary clock, 12 numerals were used; any number from ordinary arithmetic was represented by one of the 12 numerals used on the face of the clock. Thus,

$$10 + 5 = 15 \equiv 3 \text{ (mod 12)}; \qquad 11 + 2 = 13 \equiv 1 \text{ (mod 12)}.$$

We may develop a modular arithmetic for any positive integer m. Some of the arithmetics will have special properties. A few of these properties are developed in the exercises. Others may be considered in terms of elementary concepts of abstract algebra.

Exercises

1. Complete the multiplication table for integers modulo 12. (Note that 0 is used here to serve the same purpose as the numeral 12 used in Ex. 1 of §3–1.)

×	0	1	2	3	4	5	6	7	8	9	10	11
0												
1												
2												
3												
4												
5												
6												
7												
8												
9												
10												
11												

2. Make a list of the integers modulo 12 and their reciprocals, whenever such exist. Note that some integers, such as 3, do not have reciprocals modulo 12.

3. We describe the property illustrated by the equation $3 \times 4 = 0$ in arithmetic modulo 12, where the product is zero but neither number is zero, by saying that 3 and 4 are zero divisors. Are there other zero divisors in arithmetic modulo 12? List them.

4. Each integer greater than 1 is either prime or composite. Will there be zero divisors when the modulus is prime? When the modulus is composite?

Solve each equation in the specified modular arithmetic:

5. $x + 3 = 5$ (mod 7)   8. $2x = 7$ (mod 11)

6. $x + 5 = 3$ (mod 7)   9. $2x = 7$ (mod 12)

7. $x + 5 = 3$ (mod 6)

★10. Make addition and multiplication tables for arithmetic modulo 3, modulo 4, and modulo 7. Examine these tables to determine which of the properties described in §3–4 are satisfied by each of these systems.

Application and Additional Readings

Much of the material presented in this chapter has been successfully taught to youngsters in the seventh and eighth grades without recourse to the formal vocabulary herein developed. As with the preceding chapter on number bases, the work on modular arithmetic is well suited for students of almost all levels of ability. It serves to develop certain important concepts in a setting which is unique and thus serves to motivate learning.

Interesting and readable presentations of modular arithmetic appropriate for use in junior high school classes may be found in the materials produced by the University of Maryland Mathematics Project [49] and the School Mathematics Study Group [42]. Further readings for teachers are available in Richardson [40]. For more advanced treatments see the references by Andree [6], Courant and Robbins [15], and Meserve [31].

Answers for Exercises

3-1 *Around the Clock*

All answers are expressed as on a 12-hour clock.

1.

+	1	2	3	4	5	6	7	8	9	10	11	12
1	2	3	4	5	6	7	8	9	10	11	12	1
2	3	4	5	6	7	8	9	10	11	12	1	2
3	4	5	6	7	8	9	10	11	12	1	2	3
4	5	6	7	8	9	10	11	12	1	2	3	4
5	6	7	8	9	10	11	12	1	2	3	4	5
6	7	8	9	10	11	12	1	2	3	4	5	6
7	8	9	10	11	12	1	2	3	4	5	6	7
8	9	10	11	12	1	2	3	4	5	6	7	8
9	10	11	12	1	2	3	4	5	6	7	8	9
10	11	12	1	2	3	4	5	6	7	8	9	10
11	12	1	2	3	4	5	6	7	8	9	10	11
12	1	2	3	4	5	6	7	8	9	10	11	12

2. 4   **3.** 10   **4.** 9   **5.** 4   **6.** 7   **7.** 5   **8.** Any number.

9. No solution.   **10.** 5   **11.** 7   **12.** 6, 12   **13.** 5, 11

3–2 *Modulo 2*

All answers are in arithmetic modulo 2 notation.

1. $0 + 0 = 0$ **2.** $1 + 1 = 0$ **3.** $0 \times 0 = 0$ **4.** $0 \times 1 = 0$

5. $0 + 1 = 1$

3–3 *Modulo 5*

All entries are in arithmetic modulo 5 notation.

+	0	1	2	3	4
0	0	1	2	3	4
1	1	2	3	4	0
2	2	3	4	0	1
3	3	4	0	1	2
4	4	0	1	2	3

×	0	1	2	3	4
0	0	0	0	0	0
1	0	1	2	3	4
2	0	2	4	1	3
3	0	3	1	4	2
4	0	4	3	2	1

3–4 *Properties of Arithmetic Modulo 5*

All answers are in arithmetic modulo 5 notation.

1. The inverse under addition of 4 is 1, of 3 is 2, of 2 is 3, of 1 is 4, and of 0 is 0.

2. The inverse under multiplication of 4 is 4, of 3 is 2, of 2 is 3, and of 1 is 1. Note that 0 does not have an inverse with respect to multiplication.

There are many correct answers for Exercises 3, 4, and 5; those given here are samples.

3. $(2 + 3) + 4 = 2 + (3 + 4);$ $(3 + 4) + 1 = 3 + (4 + 1).$

4. $(2 \times 3) \times 4 = 2 \times (3 \times 4);$ $(1 \times 0) \times 3 = 1 \times (0 \times 3).$

5. $3 \times (4 + 2) = (3 \times 4) + (3 \times 2);$ $2 \times (3 + 1) = (2 \times 3) + (2 \times 1).$

6. 2   **7.** 4   **8.** 4   **9.** 3   **10.** 3   **11.** 4   **12.** 4   **13.** 3

14. 3   **15.** 3

16. Yes.

17. No, one may not divide by 0.

18. At least one of the elements must be 0.

3–5 *Congruence*

In Exercises 1, 2, and 3, all answers are in arithmetic modulo 12 notation.

1.

×	0	1	2	3	4	5	6	7	8	9	10	11
0	0	0	0	0	0	0	0	0	0	0	0	0
1	0	1	2	3	4	5	6	7	8	9	10	11
2	0	2	4	6	8	10	0	2	4	6	8	10
3	0	3	6	9	0	3	6	9	0	3	6	9
4	0	4	8	0	4	8	0	4	8	0	4	8
5	0	5	10	3	8	1	6	11	4	9	2	7
6	0	6	0	6	0	6	0	6	0	6	0	6
7	0	7	2	9	4	11	6	1	8	3	10	5
8	0	8	4	0	8	4	0	8	4	0	8	4
9	0	9	6	3	0	9	6	3	0	9	6	3
10	0	10	8	6	4	2	0	10	8	6	4	2
11	0	11	10	9	8	7	6	5	4	3	2	1

2. Only 1, 5, 7, and 11 have reciprocals. Each of these numbers is its own reciprocal.

3. $2 \times 6 = 0$, $3 \times 8 = 0$, $4 \times 6 = 0$, $4 \times 9 = 0$, $6 \times 6 = 0$, $6 \times 8 = 0$, $6 \times 10 = 0$, $8 \times 9 = 0$.

4. Zero divisors arise if and only if the product of two numbers is a multiple of the modulus where each number is a positive integer less than the modulus. Thus, there cannot be any zero divisors when the modulus is prime; there will be zero divisors when the modulus is composite.

5. 2 (mod 7) **6.** 5 (mod 7) **7.** 4 (mod 6) **8.** 9 (mod 11) **9.** No solution (mod 12).

10.

Modulo 3:

+	0	1	2
0	0	1	2
1	1	2	0
2	2	0	1

×	0	1	2
0	0	0	0
1	0	1	2
2	0	2	1

Modulo 4:

+	0	1	2	3
0	0	1	2	3
1	1	2	3	0
2	2	3	0	1
3	3	0	1	2

×	0	1	2	3
0	0	0	0	0
1	0	1	2	3
2	0	2	0	2
3	0	3	2	1

Modulo 7:

+	0	1	2	3	4	5	6
0	0	1	2	3	4	5	6
1	1	2	3	4	5	6	0
2	2	3	4	5	6	0	1
3	3	4	5	6	0	1	2
4	4	5	6	0	1	2	3
5	5	6	0	1	2	3	4
6	6	0	1	2	3	4	5

×	0	1	2	3	4	5	6
0	0	0	0	0	0	0	0
1	0	1	2	3	4	5	6
2	0	2	4	6	1	3	5
3	0	3	6	2	5	1	4
4	0	4	1	5	2	6	3
5	0	5	3	1	6	4	2
6	0	6	5	4	3	2	1

Each of the three systems is closed with respect to both addition and multiplication. In each one, the associative and commutative laws for both addition and multiplication are satisfied, as is the distributive law. Each system contains an identity element with respect to addition (0) and an identity element with respect to multiplication (1). Finally, we note that, in all three systems, each element has an inverse element with respect to addition. The same is true for each non-zero element with respect to multiplication in the modulo 3 and 7 systems. However, in the modulo 4 system, the element 2 does not have an inverse with respect to multiplication. That is, there is no element x such that $2x \equiv 1 \pmod 4$.

CHAPTER

FOUR

MATHEMATICAL
SYSTEMS

The work of the preceding chapter on modular arithmetic exhibited several examples of mathematical systems. In this chapter we shall consider additional systems, some of them abstract, and examine several of the important properties of these systems as they relate to concepts necessary for understanding the material to be considered later.

4-1 A Mathematical System

A **mathematical system** consists of a collection or set of elements together with one or more operations defined for this set. Thus, we may speak of the set of positive integers under the operation of addition, or the set of rational numbers under the operations of multiplication and division. Given the set of elements and the operation or operations, we then proceed to examine these for various properties. Thus, as one example, we note that the set of positive integers is closed under addition. That is, given any two positive integers, their sum is also a positive integer; closure is one of the properties enjoyed by this particular system under addition.

Let us *define* an abstract system composed of the set of elements $\{*, \#, \Sigma, [\,]\}$. Let us call this set Y; that is, $Y = \{*, \#, \Sigma, [\,]\}$.

Furthermore, we shall *define* an operation $\sim$, called "multition," by means of the following table:

(mod 4)

$\sim$	$*$	$\#$	Σ	$[\ ]$
$*$	$*$	$\#$	Σ	$[\ ]$
$\#$	$\#$	Σ	$[\ ]$	$*$
Σ	Σ	$[\ ]$	$*$	$\#$
$[\ ]$	$[\ ]$	$*$	$\#$	Σ

Thus, it is correct to write:

$$\# \sim [\ ] = * \quad \text{and} \quad \Sigma \sim * = \Sigma.$$

We read the first element in the vertical column and the second element in the horizontal column, and find the answer where these two columns intersect within the table.

As another example, we may say that $[\ ]$ "multified" by $\#$ is $*$; or, symbolically, $[\ ] \sim \# = *$.

Exercises

Find the answer to the following from the table given in §4–1:

1. $\# \sim *$

2. $* \sim \#$

3. $* \sim [\ ]$

4. $\Sigma \sim [\ ]$

5. $[\ ] \sim [\ ]$

4–2 Properties of a System

We now examine the system defined in the preceding section for certain properties, all of which have been introduced in §3–4.

1. *The set Y is closed with respect to the binary operation* $\sim$. That is, whenever any two of the elements of *Y* are combined by the process

of multition, the result is a unique member of the original collection of elements.

In general, a set is said to be closed with respect to a given operation if the process of performing that operation upon any two members of the set produces a unique result which is also a member of the original set.

In ordinary arithmetic, the set of positive integers is closed with respect to addition, since the sum of any two positive integers is a positive integer. The set of positive integers is *not* closed, however, with respect to subtraction. For example, there is no positive integer x such that $2 - 5 = x$.

2. *The elements of the set Y satisfy the associative law for multition.* In symbols we may write:

$$a \sim (b \sim c) = (a \sim b) \sim c,$$

where a, b, and c may be replaced by any element of set Y.

In ordinary arithmetic, we are primarily interested in the associative law as it applies to addition and multiplication. Thus, a set is said to satisfy the associative law for addition if, for all possible choices of three numbers a, b, and c of this set, we have the equality:

$$(a + b) + c = a + (b + c).$$

Similarly, a set is said to satisfy the associative law for multiplication if the equality $(a \cdot b) \cdot c = a \cdot (b \cdot c)$ holds for all possible choices of three elements from the set.

3. *The set Y contains an identity element, $*$, for multition.* In other words, for any element n of the set Y, we have the identity:

$$* \sim n = n \sim * = n.$$

In ordinary arithmetic, the identity element for addition is 0. That is, for any number a, we have the identity $a + 0 = a$. The identity element for multiplication is 1. Thus, for any number a, we have the identity $(a)(1) = a$.

4. *For each element of Y there exists an element of Y which is its inverse under multition.* That is, for each element n in Y, there is another element n' such that we have the equality:

$$n \sim n' = *.$$

In ordinary arithmetic, every number has an inverse under addition. For example, the inverse of 5 is -5 in that $(5) + (-5) = 0$. Similarly, every number except 0 has an inverse under multiplication. For example, the inverse of 3 is $\frac{1}{3}$ in that $(3)(\frac{1}{3}) = 1$.

We have seen that the set Y possesses four properties which have been described in detail; namely, it is closed with respect to multition, the elements of the set satisfy the associative law for multition, the set contains an identity element with respect to multition, and each element of the set possesses an inverse under multition. Any set of elements which satisfy these four conditions with respect to an operation is called a **group** with respect to that operation. *Thus, we see that the set* Y *forms a group under multition.*

5. *The elements of the set* Y *satisfy the commutative law for multition.* We write this symbolically as:

$$a \sim b = b \sim a,$$

where a and b may be replaced by any element of set Y. When a set of elements forms a group with respect to a given operation, and is also commutative under that operation; the group is called a **commutative** (or **Abelian**) **group** under the given operation. *Thus, the set* Y *is a commutative group under multition.*

In ordinary arithmetic, the positive integers satisfy the commutative laws for both addition and multiplication. (For example, $4 + 5 = 5 + 4$ and $4 \times 5 = 5 \times 4$.) However, the set of positive integers does not form a group with respect to addition; for example, the set does not contain an identity element under addition. The set of *all* integers (positive, negative, and zero) does form a group with respect to addition.

Exercises

1. Give a specific example of each of the five properties listed in this section for the set Y.

2. Does the set of elements of arithmetic modulo 5 form a group under addition? If so, is it a commutative group?

3. Does the set of elements in arithmetic modulo 5 form a group under multiplication? Explain your answer.

*4. Alter the definition of $\sim$ such that $\# \sim [\,] = \Sigma$. Does the set Y now form a group under multition? Explain your answer.

4–3 Other Examples of Mathematical Systems

The general mathematical system that we have just considered could be thought of as representing any one of an infinite number of possible systems. Here are some additional examples of mathematical systems:

1. Let R be the set of positive integers less than or equal to 20, with the binary operation $\#$ defined as "the larger of the two numbers." Thus, we have:

$$7 \# 9 = 9, \quad 4 \# 3 = 4, \quad 6 \# 6 = 6.$$

Although this system does not form a group with respect to $\#$ (why not?), it does have interesting properties. For example, the set is both closed and commutative under this defined operation. Verify this fact. Is the set associative under the operation?

2. Consider the set of positive integers less than or equal to 20, but let the operation $\ast$ be defined as "the first of the two numbers." As examples we have:

$$7 \ast 9 = 7, \quad 12 \ast 3 = 12, \quad 8 \ast 8 = 8.$$

The set is certainly closed with respect to the given operation, but it is not commutative. Thus, whereas $7 \ast 9 = 7$, we note that $9 \ast 7 = 9$. Is the set associative with respect to the operation of $\ast$? That is, as one possible example, does $8 \ast (5 \ast 9) = (8 \ast 5) \ast 9$? We find here an example of a set which is associative under a given operation but not commutative under the same operation. Examine the set for other properties.

3. Consider next the same set of integers less than or equal to 20, but with two binary operations, $\ast$ and $\#$, defined as follows:

$\ast$: take the first of the two numbers;
$\#$: take the larger of the two numbers.

We may now examine this set for one additional property, namely, the distributive law. Given any three members of the set, a, b, and c, we say that the operation $\ast$ is distributive with respect to the operation $\#$ if we have the following relationship established:

$$a \ast (b \# c) = (a \ast b) \# (a \ast c).$$

Show that the set under consideration enjoys this property and, furthermore, that $a \ast (b \# c) = (a \ast b) \# (a \ast c) = a$. Note that this follows immediately from the definitions of the given binary operations.

Exercises

Which of the following systems are closed under the operations stated:

1. The set of positive integers under subtraction.

2. The set of positive integers under multiplication.

3. The set of even integers under division.

4. The set of odd integers under addition.

Which of the following sets of elements form groups with respect to the operations given:

5. The set of positive integers under addition.

6. The set of all integers under addition.

7. The set of all integers under multiplication.

8. The set of even integers under addition.

9. Consider the set of even integers between 0 and 20. Let the binary operation † be defined as selecting the smaller number of the two. Is the set closed under †? Is it associative? Commutative? Does the set contain an identity element under †?

10. Consider a set of elements {0, 1, 2, 3}, together with two binary operations ( ) and ◇, defined as follows:

( )	0	1	2	3
0	0	1	2	3
1	1	3	2	0
2	2	0	1	3
3	3	1	2	0

◇	0	1	2	3
0	0	0	0	0
1	0	1	2	3
2	0	2	0	2
3	0	3	1	2

(a) Is the set closed with respect to ( )? With respect to ◇?

(b) Is the set commutative under either of these operations?

(c) Is the set associative under either of these operations?

(d) Does the set contain an identity element under either of these operations?

(e) Do the elements of the set include inverse elements with respect to either of the operations?

(f) Is the operation ( ) distributive with respect to the operation $\Diamond$?

Application and Additional Readings

Each of the sets of numbers that we ordinarily use is part of a mathematical system. The properties of such systems are important and should be brought to the attention of students. An abstract discussion of novel systems, as presented in this chapter, serves to arouse interest and focuses attention upon general properties, which may then be considered for other sets of numbers ordinarily used.

Experimental units have been prepared and successfully used with junior high school students. For two classroom presentations, both quite alike in their approach, see the materials prepared by the School Mathematics Study Group [42] and the University of Maryland Mathematics Project [49]. For a popular approach, see the book by Adler [2].

Answers for Exercises

4–1 *A Mathematical System*

1. #   **2.** #   **3.** [ ]   **4.** #   **5.** Σ

4–2 *Properties of a System*

1. There are many correct answers for this exercise. Those given here are samples: (1) $\Sigma \sim \# = [\,]$; (2) $(\# \sim [\,]) \sim \Sigma = \# \sim ([\,] \sim \Sigma)$; (3) $[\,] \sim * = * \sim [\,] = [\,]$; (4) $[\,] \sim \# = *$; (5) $\# \sim \Sigma = \Sigma \sim \#$.

2. Yes; yes, see § 3–3.

3. No; the element 0 does not possess an inverse under multiplication.

4. No; the element # does not have an inverse under this definition.

4–3 *Other Examples of Mathematical Systems*

1. Not closed; for example, $3 - 7$ is not a positive integer.

2. Closed.

3. Not closed; for example, $12 \div 4$ is not an even integer.

4. Not closed; for example, $3 + 5$ is not an odd integer.

5. Does not form a group; this set does not contain an identity element.

6. Forms a group.

7. Does not form a group; this set does not contain the inverses of the elements.

8. Forms a group.

9. The set is closed, associative, and commutative, but does not contain an identity element.

10. (a) Yes; yes.

(b) Not commutative under either operation; for example, $2 \, ( ) \, 1 = 0$, whereas $1 \, ( ) \, 2 = 2$; and $2 \diamond 3 = 2$, whereas $3 \diamond 2 = 1$.

(c) Not associative under either operation; for example, $\{1 \, ( ) \, 2\} \, ( ) \, 3 = 2 \, ( ) \, 3 = 3$, whereas $1 \, ( ) \, \{2 \, ( ) \, 3\} = 1 \, ( ) \, 3 = 0$; and $\{3 \diamond 3\} \diamond 2 = 2 \diamond 2 = 0$, whereas $3 \diamond \{3 \diamond 2\} = 3 \diamond 1 = 3$.

(d) Yes; 0 and 1, respectively.

(e) Each of the elements contains an inverse with respect to $( )$; for example: $3 \, ( ) \, 3 = 0; 2 \, ( ) \, \mathbf{1} = 0; 1 \, ( ) \, \mathbf{3} = 0; 0 \, ( ) \, \mathbf{0} = 0$. Not all of the elements contain inverses with respect to $\diamond$; note that 0 and 2 do not have inverses.

(f) No; one case will suffice to show that this does not hold:
$$2 \, ( ) \, [3 \diamond 1] = 2 \, ( ) \, 3 = 3$$
$$2 \, ( ) \, [3 \diamond 1] = [2 \, ( ) \, 3] \diamond [2 \, ( ) \, 1] = 3 \diamond 0 = 0.$$

CHAPTER

FIVE

EMPIRICAL
PROBABILITY

The topic of probability can be treated from a very rigorous point of view and is so treated in graduate courses. The approach presented in this chapter, however, is an empirical one which stresses laboratory experimental exercises which can easily be developed at an early stage of a student's mathematical training.

5–1 Definition of Probability

Some events are more likely to occur than others. We shall consider here sets of equally likely events, such as:

(a) The result (1, 2, 3, 4, 5, 6) obtained by rolling a die for which each event has an equal likelihood of appearing;

(b) The result (heads or tails) obtained by tossing a coin for which each event is equally likely.

When events appear to be about equally likely, we often assume that such is the case and proceed under this assumption.

By **probability of success** we mean the ratio of the number of ways an event can succeed to the total number of ways in which the event can occur. The ratio of the number of ways an event can fail to occur to the total number of ways in which the event can take place is called the **probability of failure**.

Example 1. Find the probability of obtaining a 3 on one toss of a single die.

SOLUTION: The total number of ways in which a 3 can be obtained on one toss of a single die is 1; the total number of ways in which the die can fall is 6. Therefore, the probability of obtaining a 3 on one toss of a single die is $\frac{1}{6}$. Similarly, the probability of failure to obtain a 3 on one toss of a die is $\frac{5}{6}$.

Example 2. Find the probability of obtaining a 3 *or* a 4 on a single toss of a die.

SOLUTION: There are two ways to succeed out of a total of six equally likely events; therefore, the probability is $\frac{2}{6}$ or $\frac{1}{3}$. Note that the probability of obtaining a 3 is $\frac{1}{6}$ and the probability of obtaining a 4 is $\frac{1}{6}$; then, the probability of a 3 or a 4 is the sum of these probabilities, $\frac{1}{6} + \frac{1}{6}$.

We generally assign a measure, p, to a probability. This measure is often called the "probability"; it satisfies the relation $0 \leq p \leq 1$. When success is inevitable, the probability is 1; when an event is impossible of success, the probability is 0. For example, the probability of getting a head *or* tail on a single toss of a coin is 1 (we assume that the coin does not land on an edge). The probability of tossing a sum of 13 with a single toss of a pair of normal dice is 0.

Note that the probability of the success of an event plus the probability of the failure of that event is always equal to 1; that is, an event will either occur or will fail to occur.

Exercises

What is the probability:

1. Of tossing an even number on one throw of a single die? (Here, and in all future exercises, assume that normal dice are used.)

2. Of tossing an even number or a number greater than 3 on a single toss of a die?

3. Of drawing an ace in a single draw from a deck of 52 bridge cards?

4. Of drawing a red card in a single draw from a deck of 52 bridge cards?

5. Of tossing a 10 on a single toss of a die?

6. The probability of obtaining all heads in a single toss of three coins is $\frac{1}{8}$. What is the probability that not all three coins are heads?

7. A single die is tossed. What is the probability that it is not a 5? that it is not a 7?

8. What is the probability that your neighbor was not born on a Sunday?

5–2 Probability in the Long Run

By "probability" we always mean "probability in the long run." That is, the fact that the probability of obtaining a head on one toss of a coin is $\frac{1}{2}$ does not imply that you will obtain exactly 4 heads in 8 tosses. Rather, it means that the longer you continue to toss a coin, the closer will you expect to come to having 50 per cent of the tosses produce a head. This can be demonstrated by actually tossing a coin and recording the results. For example, the results obtained from 10 tosses of a single coin are summarized in the following chart. Note that the first two tosses were heads, the third was a tail, the fourth was a head, and so forth.

Number of Throws	1	2	3	4	5	6	7	8	9	10
Head	X	X		X			X		X	X
Tail			X		X	X		X		
Ratio of Heads	$\frac{1}{1}$	$\frac{2}{2}$	$\frac{2}{3}$	$\frac{3}{4}$	$\frac{3}{5}$	$\frac{3}{6}$	$\frac{4}{7}$	$\frac{4}{8}$	$\frac{5}{9}$	$\frac{6}{10}$
Ratio of Tails	$\frac{0}{1}$	$\frac{0}{2}$	$\frac{1}{3}$	$\frac{1}{4}$	$\frac{2}{5}$	$\frac{3}{6}$	$\frac{3}{7}$	$\frac{4}{8}$	$\frac{4}{9}$	$\frac{4}{10}$
Per Cent of Heads	100	100	67	75	60	50	57	50	56	60
Per Cent of Tails	0	0	33	25	40	50	43	50	44	40

The graphical presentation of the results obtained from these 10 tosses gives a visual interpretation of the meaning of probability. Despite minor fluctuations, in the long run the graphs of the per cent of heads and tails will come closer and closer to the 50 per cent line.

That is, in the long run we expect to come close to having one-half of our tosses produce heads.

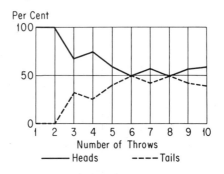

Number of Throws
——— Heads   ----- Tails

Exercises

1. Carry out an experiment for 15 tosses of a single coin and record the results on the following chart:

Number of Throws	1	2	3	4	5	6	7	8	9	10	11	12	13	14	15
Head															
Tail															
Ratio of Heads															
Ratio of Tails															
Per Cent of Heads															
Per Cent of Tails															

2. Draw a graph of the per cent of heads and tails obtained in Ex. 1:

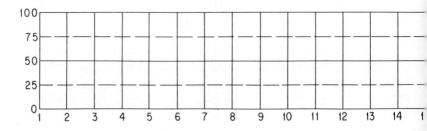

5–3 Sample Spaces

When several coins are tossed at one time, we must identify each of the possible outcomes before computing any of the probabilities. A listing of these possible outcomes is called a **sample space**. We shall illustrate first the case involving two coins.

Note that the toss of the first coin may produce either a head or a tail. Regardless of the result of this toss, the second coin may also be a head or a tail. This is summarized in the following chart:

First Coin	Second Coin
H	H
H	T
T	H
T	T

A convenient method for listing all logical possibilities is by means of a **tree diagram**, where the branches represent the possible choices. The following diagram is an illustration of this procedure:

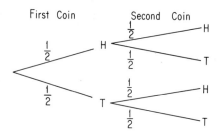

The number of terminal branches is the number of different ways in which the event can occur. The possible results HH, HT, TH, and TT may be read from the diagram. The probability of each of these results is the product of the probabilities along the path of the tree leading to the desired terminal point. Each of the possible results has probability $\frac{1}{4}$; $\frac{1}{2} \times \frac{1}{2} = \frac{1}{4}$. These results may now be summarized in terms of the probability of getting a specific number of heads, as seen in the following probability distribution. The number of tails need not be mentioned; since the total number of events is two, all cases that are not heads are obviously tails.

Event	Probability
0 heads	$\frac{1}{4}$
1 head	$\frac{2}{4}$
2 heads	$\frac{1}{4}$

Note that $\frac{1}{4} + \frac{2}{4} + \frac{1}{4} = 1$. This serves as a check on the computation.

For the case of three coins, the following tree diagram and array may be made:

First Coin	Second Coin	Third Coin
H	H	H
H	H	T
H	T	H
H	T	T
T	H	H
T	H	T
T	T	H
T	T	T

From the above we may list the probabilities of specific numbers of heads by means of the following distribution.

Event	Probability
0 heads	$\frac{1}{8}$
1 head	$\frac{3}{8}$
2 heads	$\frac{3}{8}$
3 heads	$\frac{1}{8}$

In each case, both for two coins and for three coins, the sum of the probabilities is 1; that is, no other possibilities exist outside of the ones listed. Also note that for two coins there were four possible outcomes, for three coins there were eight possible outcomes, and, in general, for n coins there would be 2^n possible outcomes.

Each of the preceding distributions was an example of a **binomial distribution**, that is, one in which only one of two events (heads or tails) is possible.

Exercises

1. Toss two coins 40 times and record the frequency of 0, 1, and 2 heads. Compare the results with the expected theoretical distribution.

2. Repeat Ex. 1 for three coins.

5-4 Pascal's Triangle

Rather than draw diagrams and list events for more than three coins, we may make use of a device called **Pascal's Triangle.** This is an array of numbers which actually represent the coefficients of the terms of $(a + b)^n$, where n is a positive integer. Generally ascribed to the French mathematician Blaise Pascal (1623–1662), this array of numbers is said to have been known to the Chinese in the early fourteenth century.

We start by looking at the coefficients in the binomial expansion of $(a + b)^n$:

$$(a + b)^1 = 1a + 1b$$
$$(a + b)^2 = 1a^2 + 2ab + 1b^2$$
$$(a + b)^3 = 1a^3 + 3a^2b + 3ab^2 + 1b^3$$
$$(a + b)^4 = 1a^4 + 4a^3b + 6a^2b^2 + 4ab^3 + 1b^4$$

$\cdot \ \cdot \ \cdot \ \cdot \ \cdot \ \cdot \ \cdot \ \cdot \ \cdot \ \cdot \ \cdot \ \cdot \ \cdot \ \cdot \ \cdot \ \cdot \ \cdot \ \cdot$

To form the following array known as Pascal's Triangle, we list the coefficients only. Note that each row begins with 1. The first row consists of 1, 1. On each succeeding row, each number is obtained as the sum of the two numbers appearing in the preceding row to the right and left of the position to be filled.

Thus, to obtain the seventh row, begin with 1. Then fill the next position by adding 1 and 6 from the sixth row. Then add 6 and 15 to obtain 21, add 15 and 20 to obtain 35, and so forth. (These entries will be the coefficients of the binomial expansion of $(a + b)^7$.)

```
              1   1

            1   2   1

          1   3   3   1

        1   4   6   4   1

      1   5  10  10   5   1

    1   6  15  20  15   6   1
      \ / \ / \ / \ /
  1   7  21  35 · · · · · · · · · · · · ·
```

Pascal's triangle may be used mechanically to compute probabilities as follows:

The elements of the second row are the numerators for the probabilities when two coins are tossed; the elements of the third row are the numerators when three coins are tossed; and so on. The denominator in each case is found as the sum of the elements in the row used. For example, when three coins are tossed, we examine the third row, (1, 3, 3, 1). The sum is 8. The probabilities of 0, 1, 2, and 3 heads are then given as $\frac{1}{8}$, $\frac{3}{8}$, $\frac{3}{8}$, and $\frac{1}{8}$, as in §5–3.

Note that the sum of the entries in the second row is 4, the sum in the third row is 2^3 or 8, the sum in the fourth row is 2^4 or 16, and, in general, the sum in the nth row will be 2^n.

As another example, we may obtain the probability of 0, 1, 2, 3, or 4 heads, when four coins are tossed, from the fourth row of Pascal's Triangle. The numerators are the entries 1, 4, 6, 4, 1; the denominator is 2^4 or 16 (that is, $1 + 4 + 6 + 4 + 1$). Thus, we have:

Event	Probability
0 heads	$\frac{1}{16}$
1 head	$\frac{4}{16}$
2 heads	$\frac{6}{16}$
3 heads	$\frac{4}{16}$
4 heads	$\frac{1}{16}$

(*Note:* The preceding analysis could also have been made for the probabilities of obtaining specific numbers of tails.)

Exercises

1. Continue Pascal's Triangle through the tenth row.

2. Make a tree diagram for the logical possibilities when four coins are tossed. From this, list the probabilities of obtaining 0, 1, 2, 3, and 4 heads. Verify your results, using Pascal's Triangle.

3. Make a table of probabilities for all the possible outcomes of heads when five coins are tossed.

4. Four coins are tossed. What is the probability of obtaining *at least* 2 heads? (This is the sum of the probabilities of obtaining 2, 3, and 4 heads.)

5. What is the probability of obtaining at least 2 heads in a single toss of 10 coins?

6. Five coins are tossed. What is the probability of obtaining *more than* 3 heads?

7. What is the probability of obtaining all heads on a single toss of 10 coins? On 10 tosses of a single coin?

5-5 Dependent Events

The probability of several events occurring, each dependent upon the preceding one, is generally found as the product of the several probabilities. This will be explained by means of the following illustrative example.

Example. A box contains two red and three white balls. Two balls are drawn in succession without replacement. What is the probability that both are red?

SOLUTION: The probability that the first is red is $\frac{2}{5}$. If a red ball is drawn, the probability that the second is red is $\frac{1}{4}$. The probability that both are red is $\frac{2}{5} \times \frac{1}{4} = \frac{1}{10}$.

This result could also have been deduced from the following tree diagram and sample space which give all logical possibilities. The subscripts are used to identify individual balls. The two red balls are denoted as R_1 and R_2; the white balls as W_1, W_2, and W_3.

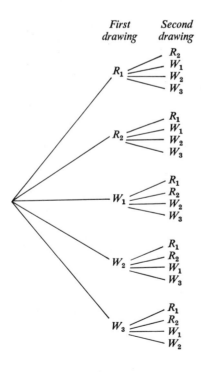

From the tree diagram, we list the following sample space:

$R_1 R_2$	$R_2 R_1$	$W_1 R_1$	$W_2 R_1$	$W_3 R_1$
$R_1 W_1$	$R_2 W_1$	$W_1 R_2$	$W_2 R_2$	$W_3 R_2$
$R_1 W_2$	$R_2 W_2$	$W_1 W_2$	$W_2 W_1$	$W_3 W_1$
$R_1 W_3$	$R_2 W_3$	$W_1 W_3$	$W_2 W_3$	$W_3 W_2$

Clearly, two out of twenty (that is, those encircled) produce the required two red balls, giving a probability of $\frac{2}{20}$ or $\frac{1}{10}$.

Exercises

1. For the Example in this section, what is the probability that: (a) exactly one white ball is drawn; (b) at least one white ball is drawn?

2. What is the probability of drawing two red balls in succession from a box which contains 3 red and 2 white balls?

3. What is the probability of selecting 2 aces in two successive draws from a deck of 52 bridge cards, assuming that no replacement is made?

4. Repeat Ex. 3 if the card is replaced after each drawing.

5. What is the probability of obtaining an ace followed by a king in two successive drawings from a deck of bridge cards with no replacement made?

6. Repeat Ex. 5 if the king must be of the same suit as the ace.

7. Repeat Exs. 5 and 6, assuming that a replacement is made after the first drawing.

5–6 Odds

The **odds in favor** of an event are defined as the ratio of the probability of success of an event to the probability of failure of that event to occur. The reciprocal of this ratio gives the **odds against** the occurrence of the event.

Example. Find the odds in favor of obtaining a 3 in one toss of a die.

SOLUTION: The probability of obtaining a 3 in one toss of a die is $\frac{1}{6}$; the probability of failure to obtain a 3 is $\frac{5}{6}$. The odds in favor of obtaining a 3 are $\frac{1}{6} \div \frac{5}{6}$, that is, $\frac{1}{5}$; these odds are often written as "1 to 5." (The odds against obtaining a 3 are "5 to 1.")

Exercises

1. What are the odds in favor of obtaining 3 heads in a single toss of three coins?

2. What are the odds against drawing an ace in a single draw from a deck of cards?

3. What are the odds in favor of rolling a 7 or an 11 in a single toss of a pair of dice?

5–7 Mathematical Expectation

Mathematical expectation is defined as the product of the probability that an event will occur and the amount to be received upon such occurrence. Suppose that you are to receive $2.00 each time you obtain two heads on a single toss of two coins. You do not receive anything for any other outcome. Then your mathematical expectation will be $\frac{1}{4} \times \$2.00$ or $0.50. This means that you should be willing to pay $0.50 each time you toss the coins if the game is to be a fair one. In the long run, both you and the person who is running the game would break even.

Note that the odds against tossing two heads are 3 to 1. Your mathematical expectation is $2.00, with ratio 4 to 1, because you pay $0.50 each time *before* you toss the coins. For each success your net return is $1.50, which is at the 3-to-1 rate.

If an event has several possible outcomes which occur with probabilities p_1, p_2, p_3, and so forth, and for each of these outcomes one may expect the amounts m_1, m_2, m_3, and so on, then the mathematical expectation, M, may be defined as:

$$M = m_1 p_1 + m_2 p_2 + m_3 p_3 + \cdots$$

Example. Suppose that you play a game wherein you are to toss a coin twice and are to receive 10 cents if two heads are obtained, 5 cents if one head is obtained, and nothing if both tosses produce tails. What is your expected value in this game?

SOLUTION: The probabilities of obtaining two, one, and no heads, respectively, are $\frac{1}{4}$, $\frac{1}{2}$, and $\frac{1}{4}$. Therefore, the expected value, M, in cents, is found as:

$$M = (10)(\tfrac{1}{4}) + (5)(\tfrac{1}{2}) + (0)(\tfrac{1}{4}) = 5.$$

This solution may be interpreted in several ways. For one thing, it is the price you should be willing to pay for the privilege of playing this game. It may also be interpreted as the average amount of winnings per game that one may expect when one is playing a large number of games.

Exercises

1. One hundred tickets are sold for a lottery. The grand prize is $1,000. What is a fair price to pay for a ticket?

2. What is your mathematical expectation in a game in which you will receive $10 if you toss a "double" (the same number on both dice) on a single toss of a pair of dice?

3. A box contains three dimes and two quarters. You are to reach in and select one coin, which you may then keep. Assuming that you are not able to determine which coin is which by its size, what would be a fair price for the privilege of playing this game?

4. There are three identical boxes on a table. One contains a five-dollar bill, one contains a one-dollar bill, and the third is empty. A man is permitted to select one of these boxes and to keep its contents. What is his expectation?

5. Four coins are tossed. What is the expected number of heads?

*6. Two bills are to be drawn from a purse which contains three five-dollar bills and two ten-dollar bills. What is the mathematical expectation for this drawing?

5–8 Control Charts

A **control chart** is a graph on which lines are drawn to represent the limits within which all data are expected to fall a given per cent of the time. In industry, for example, a chart like the following may be drawn on which data from samples are plotted.

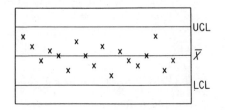

The middle horizontal line represents the **mean**, $(\bar{X})$, or average around which these data are expected to lie. The other horizontal lines, called the **upper control limit**, (UCL), and **lower control limit**, (LCL), represent the limits within which all the data are expected to fall most of the time. Occasionally data may fall outside of these limits; as long as most of the samples tested produce data which lie between these lines, the process is said to be "in control."

As a specific example, it can be shown that when a total of 100 coins is tossed, the number of heads which turn up will practically always be between 35 and 65. The theoretical average is, of course, 50. The lower control limit would be 35 and the upper control limit would be 65. We would suspect that something were wrong if a toss of 100 coins were to produce fewer than 35 or more than 65 heads. Such an event can take place just by chance, but it would be very unusual.

The control limits may be obtained from the **standard deviation** of a distribution. The standard deviation of a distribution is a measure of its spread or variability. The concept of the measure of the spread of data is an important one. Thus, a distribution may have a mean which is identical to that of a second distribution, yet the two may differ markedly because of the manner in which the data are dispersed. For example, the set of scores 60, 70, and 80 has the same mean (70) as the set 40, 70, and 100, yet differs in the manner in which the scores are dispersed. One way in which to measure this spread is to consider the **range**, the difference between the two extreme scores. For the two sets of scores just given, the ranges are 20 and 60, respectively. As can be clearly seen, the greater the range, the more dispersed the scores will be.

The standard deviation is a far more complicated measure of dispersion to compute than is the range, but a much more useful measure in statistical work. A full discussion of standard deviation is beyond the scope of this text; however, it is defined as the square root of the sum of the squares of the deviations of a set of scores from the mean of that distribution. For a binomial distribution (one in which only one of two events is possible), the standard deviation, (σ), is given by the formula $\sigma = \sqrt{p \cdot q \cdot n}$, where p is the probability of success, q is the probability of failure, and n is the number of trials.

For heads on 100 coins, we have $p = \frac{1}{2}$, $q = \frac{1}{2}$, $n = 100$. Therefore, $\sigma = \sqrt{(\frac{1}{2})(\frac{1}{2})(100)} = \sqrt{25} = 5$.

The mean of a binomial distribution, or the number of successes one may expect on the average, is found as the product of p, the probability that an event will occur, and *n*, the number of trials. For heads on 100 coins, we have $p = \frac{1}{2}$ and $n = 100$. Therefore, the mean or average number of heads expected is $(\frac{1}{2})(100) = 50$.

It can be shown for a binomial distribution that if three standard deviations are added to and subtracted from the mean, we have the limits within which almost all of the data will fall. For the example of 100 coins, the mean is 50, three times the standard deviation is 15, thus giving the limits 35 to 65. This is frequently stated in terms of **confidence limits**: we may say with "*almost* 100 per cent" confidence that the number of heads will be between 35 and 65. Furthermore, we may say with approximately 95 per cent confidence that the number of heads will be between 40 and 60, that is, within two standard deviations of the mean; we may say with approximately 68 per cent confidence that the number of heads will be between 45 and 55, that is, within one standard deviation of the mean.

Exercises

1. Toss 10 coins 100 times and record the results on a control chart.

2. A coin is tossed 64 times. Within what limits can we say, with 95 per cent confidence, that we will find the total number of heads?

3. A single die is tossed 180 times. What is the mean number of 3's which we might expect to find? What is the maximum number of 3's we can expect to obtain with "almost 100 per cent" confidence? What is the minimum number?

4. Test your answer to Ex. 3 experimentally by tossing a die a large number of times.

5–9 Laboratory Experiment

As a final example of an experiment related to sampling which might be conducted in a classroom, prepare an envelope with 10 white and 40 red chips. (Marbles, beads, colored slips of paper, and so forth, may be used just as well.)

Shake thoroughly; then have a student remove a sample of five chips. Record the number of white chips obtained, return the chips to the box, mix, and draw again. Repeat for 20 drawings.

After 20 such samples, the per cent of white chips in the box is to be estimated. (This information is not given to the student previously.)

Then add to the original distribution a collection of 50 white chips without telling the class the nature of the contents of this addition. Have them draw another 20 samples of five each in the manner described above and form another estimate of the contents of the envelope.

This experiment should serve to demonstrate that fluctuation is normal, but that this variation takes place about the average for the distribution from which the samples are drawn. Thus, in the first distribution described in this section, we can expect, in the long run, that $\frac{1}{5}$, or 1 out of every 5, of the chips will be white; in the second distribution, that $\frac{3}{5}$ of the chips will be white.

Nevertheless, it is possible to draw a sample from the first distribution which contains 3 white chips while a sample from the second distribution may have only 1 white chip. It would be unusual, however, to draw a sample from the first distribution with 4 or 5 white; it would also be unusual to have a sample from the second distribution with 0 white. There is a normal variation which emphasizes the meaning of probability as being expected occurrence whenever there are many repeated trials.

The following is a set of instructions which might be given to a class if this specific experiment is to be conducted under a typical laboratory situation. Each student or group of students is to be supplied with a manila envelope containing 10 white and 40 red chips. In addition, each manila envelope is to contain another white envelope in which there are 50 additional white chips.

Sample Classroom Instructions for a Laboratory Experiment*

Directions: Read the following set of instructions carefully *before* you begin the experiment. As the class period progresses, refer to these notes whenever any question arises as to procedure.

Part I:

1. Open the manila envelope and withdraw the white envelope which is contained inside. Do *not* look inside at the contents of either of these two envelopes. (They contain chips that are either white or red.) Set the white envelope aside temporarily. Reach inside of the manila envelope and mix the chips well.

---

* Anyone wishing to reproduce this experiment for classroom use, giving due credit for its source, is hereby authorized to do so.

2. Have one member of your group reach inside the manila envelope and take a sample of 5 chips. Count these *before* you look at them. Then look at the chips you have drawn and record the number of white chips in this sample.

3. Return the chips which you have drawn, mix well, and then draw another sample of 5. Record the number of white chips in this second sample.

4. Continue this process for a total of 20 times. Each time a sample of 5 is drawn, the number of white chips is recorded and the chips are replaced in the envelope and mixed well.

Method of recording data:

Have the data recorded on one sheet of graph paper for each student or group of students having a manila envelope. On the horizontal axis, number the drawings of chips from 1 to 20. On the vertical axis, number from 1 to 5 to represent the number of white chips drawn. Then plot each sample by means of dots. A typical chart might look like the following:

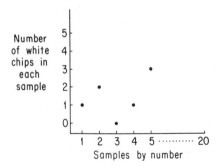

In the samples recorded on the chart, there was 1 white chip in the first sample, 2 in the second, none in the third, 1 in the fourth, and 3 in the fifth.

After you have completed this chart, stop and examine it carefully. On the basis of your 20 samples, make a prediction about the number of white chips in the manila envelope as compared to the total. That is, try to predict what per cent of the chips in the envelope are white. Make this a group decision which is arrived at by means of discussion and examination of the results of your samples.

Part II:

1. Open the white envelope but do not look at its contents. Pour the chips from the white envelope into the manila envelope and spend several moments mixing well.

2. Repeat the steps from the first part of the experiment; that is, take 20 samples of 5 chips each from the envelope and record the results for this second distribution on a chart similar to that used for the first distribution.

After you have completed the second chart, make a prediction concerning:

(a) The per cent of the chips in the second distribution which are white;

(b) Your notion as to the contents of the white envelope.

Finally, examine the two charts which you have drawn. In what ways are they alike? In what ways do they differ?

Application and Additional Readings

A course on probability and statistics has been recommended as suitable for the senior year in a college preparatory program by the Commission on Mathematics. Toward this end they have produced a textbook for students which is a good introductory text for teachers to read [12].

The point of view stressed in this chapter, however, is that such material can be effectively treated at a much earlier stage of the student's development if presented with a laboratory-type approach stressing student experimentation. Such approaches have proved to be quite successful with youngsters in the seventh and eighth grades, as well as with slow learners in ninth-grade non-academic courses. A unit on probability and statistics for this latter group not only serves to create interest and to develop important ideas, but also helps to provide an interesting setting for a review of the fundamentals of arithmetic.

A readable popular discussion of statistics is given in the text by Wallis and Roberts [51]. Misuses of statistics and popular misconceptions concerning the laws of probability are interestingly presented for the layman in the two books by Huff, [19] and [20].

The School Mathematics Study Group text written for junior high school students contains a unit on probability that may be adapted directly to the classroom, [42].

For an interesting but more advanced approach that makes use of the concepts of sets in treating probability, see the text by Kemeny, Snell, and Thompson, [27]. Another effective treatment for teachers may be found in [35]. Finally, the discussion of probability and statistics in the 24th Yearbook of the National Council of Teachers of Mathematics, [36], provides many ideas concerning the teaching of these topics at various grade levels.

Answers for Exercises

5–1 *Definition of Probability*

1. $\frac{1}{2}$ **2.** $\frac{2}{3}$ **3.** $\frac{1}{13}$ **4.** $\frac{1}{2}$ **5.** 0   **6.** $\frac{7}{8}$ **7.** $\frac{5}{6}$, 1   **8.** $\frac{6}{7}$

5–4 *Pascal's Triangle*

1. 7th row: 1, 7, 21, 35, 35, 21, 7, 1
    8th row: 1, 8, 28, 56, 70, 56, 28, 8, 1
    9th row: 1, 9, 36, 84, 126, 126, 84, 36, 9, 1
   10th row: 1, 10, 45, 120, 210, 252, 210, 120, 45, 10, 1

2.

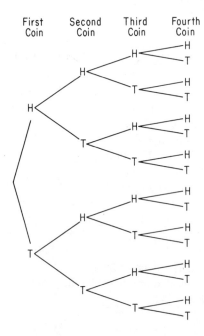

Number of Heads	0	1	2	3	4
Probability	$\frac{1}{16}$	$\frac{4}{16}$	$\frac{6}{16}$	$\frac{4}{16}$	$\frac{1}{16}$

3.

Number of Heads	0	1	2	3	4	5
Probability	$\frac{1}{32}$	$\frac{5}{32}$	$\frac{10}{32}$	$\frac{10}{32}$	$\frac{5}{32}$	$\frac{1}{32}$

4. $\frac{11}{16}$

5. The sum of the entries in the tenth row of Pascal's Triangle is 2^{10}, or 1,024. The probability of no heads or of 1 head is $\frac{1}{1024} + \frac{10}{1024}$ or $\frac{11}{1024}$. Therefore, the probability of at least 2 heads is $1 - \frac{11}{1024}$ or $\frac{1013}{1024}$.

6. The probability of getting more than 3 heads is equal to the sum of the probabilities of getting 4 and 5 heads: $\frac{5}{32} + \frac{1}{32} = \frac{6}{32}$.

7. Both are the same, $\frac{1}{1024}$.

5–5 Dependent Events

1. (a) 12 of the 20 results listed consists of one white and one red; therefore, the probability is $\frac{12}{20}$ or $\frac{3}{5}$.

    (b) The probability of two red is $\frac{1}{10}$; therefore, the probability of at least one white is $1 - \frac{1}{10}$ or $\frac{9}{10}$.

2. $\frac{3}{10}$

3. $\frac{4}{52} \times \frac{3}{51}$

4. $\frac{4}{52} \times \frac{4}{52}$

5. $\frac{4}{52} \times \frac{4}{51}$

6. $\frac{4}{52} \times \frac{1}{51}$

7. (a) $\frac{4}{52} \times \frac{4}{52}$ (b) $\frac{4}{52} \times \frac{1}{52}$

5–6 Odds

1. $\frac{1}{8} \div \frac{7}{8}$ or 1 to 7

2. $\frac{48}{52} \div \frac{4}{52}$ or 12 to 1

3. $\frac{8}{36} \div \frac{28}{36}$ or 2 to 7

5–7 *Mathematical Expectation*

1. $\frac{1}{100}$ of $1,000 is $10.

2. $\frac{6}{36}$ of $10, or approximately $1.67

3. $(10\cancel{c})(\frac{3}{5}) + (25\cancel{c})(\frac{2}{5}) = 6\cancel{c} + 10\cancel{c} = 16\cancel{c}$

4. $(\$5)(\frac{1}{3}) + (\$1)(\frac{1}{3}) + (0)(\frac{1}{3}) = \$2$

5. $(0)(\frac{1}{16}) + (1)(\frac{4}{16}) + (2)(\frac{6}{16}) + (3)(\frac{4}{16}) + (4)(\frac{1}{16}) = 2$

6. The probability both will be tens is $\frac{2}{5} \times \frac{1}{4} = \frac{1}{10}$. The probability both will be fives is $\frac{3}{5} \times \frac{2}{4} = \frac{3}{10}$. The probability that one will be a five and one a ten is found as $\frac{3}{5} \times \frac{2}{4} + \frac{2}{5} \times \frac{3}{4} = \frac{3}{5}$. The mathematical expectation is then found to be $(\$20)(\frac{1}{10}) + (\$10)(\frac{3}{10}) + (\$15)(\frac{3}{5}) = \$14$.

5–8 *Control Charts*

2. $\bar{X} = 32$; $\sigma = 4$; the 95 per cent confidence limits are found as $32 \pm 2(4)$, or 24 to 40.

3. $\bar{X} = 30$; $\sigma = 5$; the limits within which almost all of the data will fall are $30 \pm 3(5)$, or 15 to 45. The maximum number to be expected is 45; the minimum is 15.

PART
TWO

ALGEBRA

The subject matter of elementary algebra is essentially the same today as it has been for many years. The changes being recommended by various curriculum groups are those which would have us stress the development of concepts and meanings as being equal in importance to mechanical manipulations.

There has also been a certain amount of change with respect to vocabulary and symbolism. Thus, the concept of set is used early in the course and becomes a unifying and clarifying concept throughout the course. Inequalities are developed along with equations. The concept of a graph is broadened and used much more extensively than in the traditional program.

The chapters which follow in Part II are written with a special emphasis upon the new vocabulary. They include most of the essential non-traditional material which is finding its way into the algebra program in secondary schools.

Chapter 6. Basic Definitions of Sets.
Chapter 7. The Use of Sets in Elementary Algebra.
Chapter 8. The Use of Deductions in Algebra.
Chapter 9. An Introduction to Abstract Algebra.

CHAPTER

SIX

BASIC DEFINITIONS
OF SETS

The concept of a set is one of the major items being recommended for inclusion in the secondary school mathematics curriculum. It is claimed that this notion can be used as a unifying and clarifying concept throughout the mathematics curriculum. In this chapter we shall consider, in concise form, some of the basic definitions necessary for a clear understanding of sets.

6–1 Sets

A **set** is a collection of elements. We generally name a set with a capital letter and include the elements of the set within a pair of braces.

Example 1. List the elements in the set A of positive integers greater than 5 but less than 9.

SOLUTION: $A = \{6, 7, 8\}$.

Example 2. List the elements in the set B of positive odd integers.

SOLUTION: $B = \{1, 3, 5, 7, . . .\}$. *Note:* The three dots indicate that not all of the elements are listed. In this case, the set is an infinite one and continues in the pattern exhibited by the members listed.

Any set may be identified by a description or by a listing of its elements. Where it is possible to know just which elements are members of a set, we say that the set is **well defined**. Thus, the set of "interesting" numbers and the set of "pretty" colors are not well-defined sets. We shall hereafter consider only well-defined sets.

The following notation is used to show whether or not an element is a member of a set:

$y \in A$: "y is a member of the set A."
$y \notin B$: "y is not a member of the set B."

Thus, if $A = \{2, 3, 4\}$, we may write $2 \in A$ and $7 \notin A$.

Two sets are said to be **identical** if they consist of precisely the same elements. Thus, the following sets are identical:

$$A = \{2, 1, 3, 5\} \qquad B = \{3, 2, 5, 1\}$$

We write $A = B$ to show that A and B are two names for the same set.

Two sets, $X = \{x_1, x_2, \ldots\}$ and $Y = \{y_1, y_2, \ldots\}$ are said to be in **one-to-one correspondence** if we can find a pairing of the x's and y's such that each x corresponds to one and only one y and each y corresponds to one and only one x.

Two sets, A and B, which can be placed in a one-to-one correspondence are said to be **equivalent** (written $A \leftrightarrow B$). Thus, the following two sets are equivalent:

$$A = \{1, 3, 5, 9\} \qquad B = \{2, 4, 6, 7\}$$

These two sets have the same **cardinality**, that is, the same number of elements in each set. When such is the case, this implies that the sets are equivalent. As another example of equivalent sets, consider the set E of even integers and the set I of positive integers. The following scheme indicates one means of placing these two sets in a one-to-one correspondence:

$$E = \{2, \ 4, \ 6, \ 8, \ \ldots, \ 2n, \ \ldots\}$$
$$\updownarrow \ \updownarrow \ \updownarrow \ \updownarrow \qquad \updownarrow$$
$$I = \{1, \ 2, \ 3, \ 4, \ \ldots, \ n, \ \ldots\}$$

Exercises

1. List the elements in each of the following sets:

(a) The set of odd integers between 0 and 10.

(b) The set of even integers greater than 10.

(c) The set of fractions whose numerator is 1 and whose denominator is an integer between 1 and 5.

(d) The set of multiples of 5 between 11 and 14.

(e) The set of prime numbers less than 20.

2. Tell which of the following sets are well defined. For those which are not, explain why.

(a) The set of states now in the United States.

(b) The set of good bridge players in New York City.

(c) The set of exciting movies now playing in Chicago.

(d) The set of basketball players over 6′ 5″ tall on any given college team.

3. Are two identical sets necessarily equivalent? Are two equivalent sets necessarily identical? Explain your answer.

4. Display a one-to-one correspondence between the set of positive odd integers and the set of positive integral multiples of 5.

6–2 Subsets

A set A is said to be a **subset** of a set B if each element of A is an element of B. We write $A \subseteq B$ (read "A is included in B").

Thus, if $B = \{1, 2, 3\}$, there are many subsets which may be written, such as $A_1 = \{1, 2\}$, $A_2 = \{1, 3\}$, $A_3 = \{2, 3\}$, and so forth. Any set is a subset of itself, so that $A_4 = \{1, 2, 3\}$ may be classified as a subset of B.

A set A is said to be a **proper subset** of a set B if $A \subseteq B$ and there is at least one element of B which is not an element of A. We write $A \subset B$ (read "A is properly included in B"). Thus, if $B = \{1, 2, 3, 4, 5\}$, and $A = \{1, 2, 3\}$, then A is a proper subset of B inasmuch as there is at least one member of B which is not a member of A. Note that $4 \in B$ and $4 \notin A$; also, $5 \in B$ and $5 \notin A$.

The **empty set** or **null set** is the set which contains no elements and is denoted by the symbol $\emptyset$. Some examples of empty sets are:

The set of odd integers exactly divisible by 2.

The set of integral multiples of 5 with unit's digit 3.

The set of negative integers between 5 and 10.

The empty set is considered to be a subset of any set. For example:

if $A = \{1, 2, 3\}$ and $B = \{4, 7\}$, then $\emptyset \subseteq A$; $\emptyset \subseteq B$; $\emptyset \subseteq \emptyset$.

The set consisting of the totality of elements under discussion is called the **universal set**, U. Then $A \subset U$ for each set A under discussion.

Consider a universal set $U = \{1, 2, 3, 4, 5, 6, 7\}$ and a subset $A = \{1, 2, 3, 4\}$. The set of elements of U which are not elements of A

form a set, written as A' or $\bar{A}$, which is called the **complement** of A relative to U. For the example just given, $A' = \{5, 6, 7\}$. Again, if U is the set of positive integers and A is the set of even integers, then A' is the set of odd integers.

Example. Given $U = \{1, 3, 5, 7, 9\}$ and $A = \{1, 3, 5\}$, find A'.
SOLUTION: $A' = \{7, 9\}$.

In general, for any given universal set U, each set A has a complement A' consisting of the elements of U which are not elements of A. If $A = U$, then $A' = \emptyset$; if $A = \emptyset$, then $A' = U$. In all cases, the complement of A' is A.

Exercises

1. List all of the possible subsets of the set $A = \{1, 2, 3\}$.

2. Repeat Ex. 1 for $B = \{1, 2, 3, 4\}$, and for $C = \{1, 2, 3, 4, 5\}$.

3. Use the information gained from the preceding two exercises to conjecture a formula for the number, N, of subsets which can be formed from a set consisting of n elements.

4. Give three examples of empty sets.

5. Is the set consisting of the integer, 0, equivalent to the empty set? Explain your answer.

6. Let $U = \{1, 2, 3, 4, 5\}$. List the elements in both B' and C' for B and C as in Ex. 2.

6–3 Relationships Between Sets

The **union** of two sets A and B (written $A \cup B$) is the set of elements which are members of at least one of the given sets. Each of the given sets is a subset of their union.

Example 1. If $A = \{1, 2, 3, 4, 5\}$ and $B = \{4, 5, 6, 7\}$, find $A \cup B$.
SOLUTION: $A \cup B = \{1, 2, 3, 4, 5, 6, 7\}$.

The **intersection** of two sets A and B (written $A \cap B$) is the set of elements which are members of both sets. The intersection is a subset of A and also a subset of B.

Example 2. If $A = \{1, 2, 3, 4, 5\}$ and $B = \{4, 5, 6, 7\}$, find $A \cap B$.
SOLUTION: $A \cap B = \{4, 5\}$.

Two sets whose intersection is the null set have no elements in common and are said to be *disjoint* or mutually exclusive. Thus, the sets $A = \{1, 2, 3\}$ and $B = \{4, 5, 6\}$ are disjoint sets, and we write $A \cap B = \emptyset$.

We can represent the elements of a set as points. A visual interpretation of sets and relationships among sets can be given by means of figures known as **Venn diagrams**. We may represent the set of elements in the universe under discussion by the points within a rectangle; we then represent various subsets in this universe as sets of points interior to circles within the rectangle. The following diagram illustrates two disjoint sets, A and B, as subsets of a universal set U.

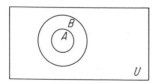

To show set A as a proper subset of set B, we merely include the elements of A within B:

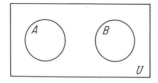

The union of sets A and B is shaded in the diagram which follows:

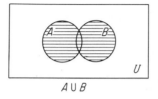

$$A \cup B$$

Note that $A \cup B$ includes all of the points that are in the set A as well as all of those in the set B.

The intersection of sets A and B is shaded in the next diagram.

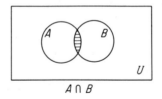

$$A \cap B$$

Note that $A \cap B$ includes only those points that are in both set A and set B.

We can represent the complement of a set A by shading the points in U which are outside of A:

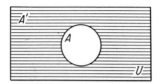

Venn diagrams also can be used to establish the equivalence of two sets. Two sets are equivalent if they are represented by the same points in Venn diagrams.

Example 3. Show that $A \cap (B \cup C) = (A \cap B) \cup (A \cap C)$.

SOLUTION: Set A is shaded with vertical lines; $B \cup C$ is shaded with horizontal lines. The intersection of these sets, $A \cap (B \cup C)$, is the subset of U which has both vertical and horizontal shading.

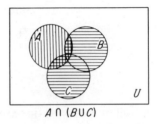

$$A \cap (B \cup C)$$

The set $A \cap B$ is shaded with horizontal lines; $A \cap C$ is shaded with vertical lines. The union of these sets is the subset of U which is shaded with lines in either or in both directions.

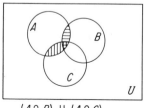

$$(A \cap B) \cup (A \cap C)$$

Note that the final results in the two diagrams are the same, thus showing the equivalence of $A \cap (B \cup C)$ and $(A \cap B) \cup (A \cap C)$.

Exercises

1. Let $U = \{1, 2, 3, \ldots\}$; $A = \{1, 2, 3, 4, 5\}$; $B = \{3, 4, 5, 6, 7\}$. List the elements in:

(a) $A \cup B$ (b) $A \cap B$ (c) $A' \cap B'$ (d) $A' \cup B'$

2. Show by means of Venn diagrams:

(a) $A \cup (B \cup C) = (A \cup B) \cup C$

(b) $A \cap (B \cap C) = (A \cap B) \cap C$

(c) $A \cup (B \cap C) = (A \cup B) \cap (A \cup C)$

(d) $(A \cap B)' = A' \cup B'$

(e) $(A \cup B)' = A' \cap B'$

3. Describe the union and the intersection of sets A and B, where A is the set of all even integers and B is the set of all odd integers.

6–4 Graphs on a Line

We shall, in this section, discuss means of describing sets of numbers through the use of graphs on a line. To do this, we assume the existence of a one-to-one correspondence between the sets of points on a number line and the set of real numbers. (A systematic development of the structure of the real number system will be given in Chapter 9.)

Occasionally the symbolism [*a*, *b*] is used to represent a set of points on a line in the interval from *a* to *b*, with both end-points *a* and *b* included in the set. Thus, for integral points, [2, 6] = {2, 3, 4, 5, 6}. The graph of this set may be drawn by placing solid dots on the number line at each of the corresponding points of the set as follows:

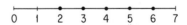

If we consider the set of real numbers as our universal set, then [2, 6] represents all of the real numbers from 2 through 6 inclusive. The graph of this set is drawn by placing solid dots at the end-points and shading the interval between:

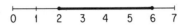

Note that the symbol [2, 6] may be used for both integers and real numbers, and, indeed, for other sets of numbers. However, the universe must be specified if we are to know which set of numbers we are to consider.

We use the symbolism (*a*, *b*) to represent the points on the interval from *a* to *b*, exclusive of these two end-points. Thus, for integral points, (2, 6) = {3, 4, 5}. Similarly, for an interval of real numbers, (2, 6) represents all of the numbers *between* 2 and 6. This may be graphed by placing hollow dots at the end-points of the interval to indicate that they are not members of the set:

```
 ├──┼──○━━━━━━━━━○──┤
 0  1  2  3  4  5  6  7
```

A combination of these symbols may be used to indicate that one end-point is included but not the other. Thus, for intervals of integers, we have:

$$[2, 6) = \{2, 3, 4, 5\} \quad \text{and} \quad (2, 6] = \{3, 4, 5, 6\}.$$

For intervals of real numbers, the preceding two sets may be graphed as shown at the top of the next page.

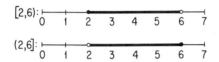

Example 1. Find the integral elements in the set: $[3, 7] \cup (1, 6)$.

SOLUTION: $[3, 7] = \{3, 4, 5, 6, 7\}$; $(1, 6) = \{2, 3, 4, 5\}$; $[3, 7] \cup (1, 6)$ $= \{2, 3, 4, 5, 6, 7\}$. This solution can be represented by the symbol $[2, 7]$, by $(1, 8)$, and in other ways as well. These two representations of the solution are equivalent for intervals of integers. They would not be equivalent for intervals of real numbers.

Example 2. Let $U = [-10, 10]$, an interval of real numbers, and graph the set $[-10, 2] \cap (0, 5)$.

SOLUTION: The graph of $[-10, 2]$ is:

The graph of $(0, 5)$ is:

The graph of their inter-
section is:

Using the symbolism just described, this intersection may be written for an interval of real numbers as $(0, 2]$.

Exercises

List and then show on a number line the integral elements in each set:

1. $[2, 4] \cup [1, 5]$ **2.** $[3, 7] \cup [1, 3]$

3. $[2, 5] \cap [3, 7]$ **4.** $[3, 5] \cap (5, 8]$

5. $(2, 5] \cup [3, 7)$ **6.** $[4, 9) \cap [8, 10)$

For each of the following, let $U = [-10, 10]$, *an interval of real numbers. Draw the graph of each set and state the results, using the symbolism for intervals of real numbers.*

7. $[-10, 3) \cup (5, 10]$

8. $[-5, 2]'$; that is, the complement of the interval $[-5, 2]$

9. $\{[-7, 2] \cap [3, 5]\}'$

10. $[-10, 10]'$

★11. $\{[-2, 5] \cup [3, 8]\} \cap \{[-5, 7] \cap [-3, 3]\}$

★12. $\{(3, 7] \cap [-1, 2)\} \cup \{[-1, 2] \cap [-2, 1]\}$

Application and Additional Readings

Although the basic definitions developed in this chapter were presented primarily for the teacher's own background, many of these concepts, as well as the vocabulary involved, are finding their way very early into the high school mathematics curriculum. Thus, the concepts of union and intersection of sets plays an important role in the development of the seventh- and eighth-grade materials of the School Mathematics Study Group [42]. Indeed, some of the concepts of sets are being introduced on an experimental basis in the elementary grades, even in the primary grades [44].

At the secondary level, the concept of set plays a major role in the treatment of the first course in algebra, as will be discussed in detail in Chapter 7. Not all of the symbolism developed in this chapter need be or should be provided at an early stage of a student's mathematical development. However, most of the concepts can be and should be provided early on an intuitive basis.

A number of sources present the basic definitions of sets. For readable accounts, see Allendoerfer and Oakley [4], Kemeny, Snell, and Thompson [27], and *Introductory Probability and Statistical Inference* (Appendix 1) [12]. In addition, a number of pamphlets on sets have been written for high school students: [3], [22], and [53]. For a more detailed account, see Breuer [11].

Answers for Exercises

6–1 *Sets*

1. (a) $\{1, 3, 5, 7, 9\}$ (b) $\{12, 14, 16, \ldots\}$
   (c) $\{\frac{1}{2}, \frac{1}{3}, \frac{1}{4}\}$ (d) There are none.
   (e) $\{2, 3, 5, 7, 11, 13, 17, 19\}$

2. (a) and (d) are well-defined sets. In (b) and (c) the words "good" and "exciting" are not clearly defined.

3. If two sets are identical, they can be placed in one-to-one correspondence and are thus necessarily equivalent. Two equivalent sets are not necessarily identical. For example, the set of even integers is equivalent, but not identical, to the set of positive integers.

4. 1,   3,   5,   7,   9, . . . , $2n - 1$

$\updownarrow$ $\updownarrow$ $\updownarrow$ $\updownarrow$ $\updownarrow$ $\updownarrow$

5, 10, 15, 20, 25, . . . , $5n$

6–2 Subsets

1. {1}, {2}, {3}, {1, 2}, {1, 3}, {2, 3}, {1, 2, 3}, ∅.

2. Set B will have 16 subsets; set C will have 32 subsets.

3. $N = 2^n$.

4. The set of odd integers divisible by 2; the set of integers between 5 and 6; the set of even integers between 6 and 8; and so forth.

5. No. The empty set has no members; the set {0} consists of the element 0.

6. $B' = \{5\}$, $C' = \emptyset$.

6–3 Relationships Between Sets

1. (a) {1, 2, 3, 4, 5, 6, 7}   (b) {3, 4, 5}

(c) {8, 9, 10, . . .}   (d) {1, 2, 6, 7, 8, . . .}

2. In each of the following pairs of diagrams, the final result is the same, showing the equivalence of the statements given.

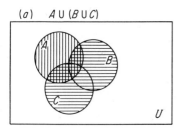

(a) $A \cup (B \cup C)$

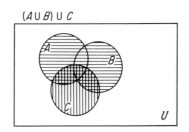

$(A \cup B) \cup C$

Set A is shaded with vertical lines; $B \cup C$ is shaded with horizontal lines. The union of these sets is the subset of U which is shaded with lines in either or both directions.

Set C is shaded with vertical lines; $A \cup B$ is shaded with horizontal lines. The union of these sets is the subset of U which is shaded with lines in either or both directions.

(b) $A \cap (B \cap C)$

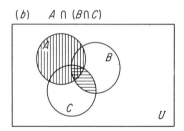

$(A \cap B) \cap C$

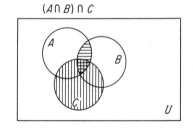

Set A is shaded with vertical lines; $B \cap C$ is shaded with horizontal lines. The intersection of these sets is the subset of U which has both horizontal and vertical shading.

Set C is shaded with vertical lines; $A \cap B$ is shaded with horizontal lines. The intersection of these sets is the subset of U which has both horizontal and vertical shading.

(c) $A \cup (B \cap C)$

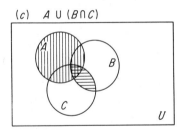

$(A \cup B) \cap (A \cup C)$

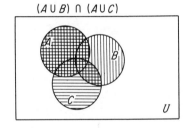

Set A is shaded with vertical lines; $B \cap C$ is shaded with horizontal lines. The union of these sets is the subset of U which is shaded with lines in either or both directions.

Set $A \cup B$ is shaded with vertical lines; $A \cup C$ is shaded with horizontal lines. The intersection of these sets is the subset of U which has both horizontal and vertical shading.

(d)   (A ∩ B)'

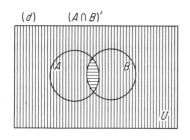

A' ∪ B'

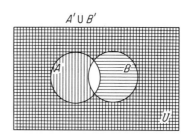

Set $A \cap B$ is shaded with horizontal lines. The complement of this set, $(A \cap B)'$, is the remaining portion of U, shaded with vertical lines.

Set A' is shaded with horizontal lines; B' is shaded with vertical lines. The union of these sets is the subset of U which is shaded with lines in either or both directions.

(e)   (A ∪ B)'

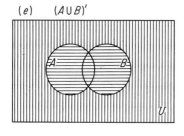

A' ∩ B'

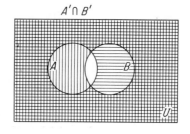

Set $A \cup B$ is shaded with horizontal lines. The complement of this set, $(A \cup B)'$, is the remaining portion of U, shaded with vertical lines.

Set A' is shaded with horizontal lines; B' is shaded with vertical lines. The intersection of these sets is the subset of U which has both horizontal and vertical shading.

3. The union of sets A and B is the set of all integers; the intersection is the empty set.

6–4 Graphs on a Line

1. {1, 2, 3, 4, 5}.

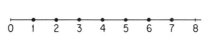

2. {1, 2, 3, 4, 5, 6, 7}.

3. {3, 4, 5}.
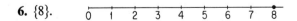

4. Ø.

5. {3, 4, 5, 6}.

6. {8}.
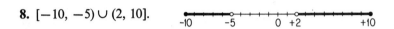

7. [3, 5]′.
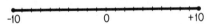

8. [−10, −5) ∪ (2, 10].
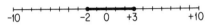

9. [−7, 2] and [3, 5] are disjoint sets; their intersection is the empty set. The complement of the empty set is the universal set, namely, [−10, 10].

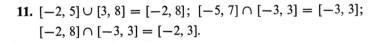

10. The complement of the universal set is the empty set, Ø.

11. [−2, 5] ∪ [3, 8] = [−2, 8]; [−5, 7] ∩ [−3, 3] = [−3, 3]; [−2, 8] ∩ [−3, 3] = [−2, 3].

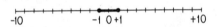

12. (3, 7] ∩ [−1, 2) = Ø; [−1, 2] ∩ [−2, 1] = [−1, 1]; Ø ∩ [−1, 1] = [−1, 1].

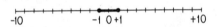

CHAPTER

SEVEN

THE USE OF SETS IN ELEMENTARY ALGEBRA

Now that the basic definitions of sets have, been provided in Chapter 6, we can exhibit here some of the specific ways in which the language and notation of sets may be used in a study of the elements of algebra. Primarily, we shall show how sets may be used effectively in the presentation of a unit on statements of linear equations and inequalities in one or two variables.

The concept of sets is often considered to be a unifying concept for all of mathematics. For example, in addition to the uses considered in this chapter, sets may be used in the development of number concepts in elementary arithmetic, in the study of probability, and in the study of geometry (see Chapter 10.) Details of the use of sets at various grade levels are considered in the Twenty-fourth Yearbook of the National Council of Teachers of Mathematics [36].

7–1 Sentences and Statements

We shall consider two types of sentences: **statements**, those which can be identified as true or identified as false; and **open sentences**, those which cannot be identified as true or false without the insertion of additional information.

Sentences that are true and sentences that are false are called statements. A statement cannot be both true and false. These are examples of statements:

1. George Washington is President of the United States.
2. $8 \times 2 = 16$ (a true statement of equality).
3. $7 - 3 = 5$ (a false statement of equality).

Statements of equality, whether true or false, are called *equations.* We may also write statements of inequality using the following symbolism:

$$\neq: \text{ is not equal to;}$$
$$>: \text{ is greater than;}$$
$$<: \text{ is less than.}$$

Consider these examples:

1. $5 - 2 \neq 4$ (a true statement of inequality);
2. $8 \times 3 \neq 24$ (a false statement of inequality);
3. $12 > -3$ (a true statement of inequality);
4. $-3 < -5$ (a false statement of inequality);
5. $|-3| < 2$ (a false statement of inequality).

Note that $|-3|$ is read "the **absolute value** of -3" and is equal to $+3$. In general, $|k|$ is read "the absolute value of k." By definition, $|k| = +k$ if k is positive, $|k| = -k$ if k is negative, and $|k| = 0$ if k is zero. Thus, $|+3| = +3$, and $|-3| = +3$. (Any number symbol with a plus sign may be written without the sign; any number symbol without a sign is assumed to have a plus sign. Thus, $+3 = 3$, $+(-5) = -5$, and $+k = k$ whether k is positive, negative, or zero.)
6. $x + y = y + x$ (a true statement of equality).
Such a general statement, frequently called a law, is considered to be true if and only if it is true for all possible replacements of x and y.

Sentences that are neither true nor false are called **open sentences.** These are examples of open sentences:

1. _____ is President of the United States;
2. Mr. _____ is a teacher in this school;
3. $x + 2 = 7$;
4. $x - 3 = 4$.

In the preceding examples of open sentences, the blank spaces and the symbols x are called *variables.* In each case, the sentence is neither true nor false until a replacement is made for the variable. After such a replacement is made, we have a statement, that is, a sentence which can be classified as either true or false.

A **variable** is a placeholder for its replacements. Each blank in Examples 1 and 2 held a place for the name of a person. Each x in Examples 3 and 4 held a place for the name of a number, that is, for a numeral such as 5 or 7. When a replacement is a number, it is often called a **value** for the variable. We may abbreviate such statements and say that the variable is a placeholder for the name of a person or a number. Given any open sentence, there are certain names of people, numbers, and so forth, which may be used as possible replacements. In each case, this given set of possible replacements is called the **domain** of the variable. For example:

1. Christmas is in the month of ——————.

The domain of the variable is the set of names of the 12 months. The statement is true when the replacement is "December"; the statement is false for other replacements.

2. A two-digit number may be represented as $10x + y$.

The domain of x is the set of digits $\{1, 2, 3, 4, 5, 6, 7, 8, 9\}$ and the domain of y is the set $\{0, 1, 2, 3, 4, 5, 6, 7, 8, 9\}$. Why is 0 excluded from the domain of x?

Exercises

Tell whether each statement is true or false:

1. $8(5 + 3) = 8 \times 5 + 8$
2. $(3) - (2) = (-2) - (3)$
3. $|-2|^2 = |(-2)^2|$
4. $|-2| \times |-3| = |-6|$
5. $7 - 3 \neq 9 - 5$
6. $|-3| < |-9|$
7. $\frac{432}{796} > \frac{432}{795}$
8. $-\frac{432}{796} < -\frac{432}{795}$
9. $|x| \times |y| = |xy|$
10. $|x| + |y| = |x + y|$

Write an expression for each of the following and give the domain of each variable used:

11. A number which exceeds 5 by a positive integral number of units.

12. The perimeter of an equilateral triangle whose side is always an odd integer.

13. A three-digit integer.

14. The cost, C, in dollars of n four-cent postage stamps.

*15. The perimeter of an equilateral triangle in terms of its side and such that the perimeter is always an even integer.

7–2 Solution Sets

Given an open sentence, the set of replacements which makes the sentence true is called the **solution set** of the sentence. Each of the elements of the solution set is said to satisfy the open sentence. Thus, consider the sentence:

_____ is a vowel.

The solution set consists of the elements $\{a, e, i, o, u\}$.

The following examples are presented in detail to illustrate the meaning of solution sets and their graphs in equations and inequalities. In each one, we are asked to find and graph the solution set.

Example 1. $x + 3 = 5$. Domain of x: integers.

SOLUTION: The solution set consists of the single element $\{2\}$. We can graph this solution set on a number scale by drawing a solid dot at 2.

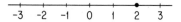

Example 2. $x + 3 = 5$. Domain of x: negative integers.

SOLUTION: We have an impossible equation; that is, no element in the domain will produce a true statement when used as a replacement for x. We say that the solution set is the empty set.

Example 3. $x + 2 > 3$. Domain of x: real numbers.

SOLUTION: The solution set consists of all the real numbers greater than 1. The graph of the solution set is drawn by placing a hollow dot at 1 on the number scale to indicate that this is not a member of the solution set, and drawing a heavily shaded arrow to show that all numbers greater than 1 satisfy the given inequality.

Example 4. $x \leq 5$ (read "x is less than or equal to 5"). Domain of x: positive integers.

SOLUTION: The solution set of this inequality consists of the elements $\{1, 2, 3, 4, 5\}$. The graph of the solution set follows:

The sentence "$x \leq 5$" may also be written as "$x < 5$ *or* $x = 5$." Notice the use of "or" in these open sentences. If *at least one* of these two open sentences is true when x is replaced by a numeral, the number is a member of the solution set of $x \leq 5$. For instance, when x is replaced by 5 in $x = 5$, the true statement $5 = 5$ is obtained; hence, 5 is a member of the solution set even though replacing x by 5 in $x < 5$ gives the false statement $5 < 5$. Similarly, when x is replaced by 3 in $x < 5$, the true statement $3 < 5$ is obtained; hence, 3 is a member of the solution set, even though replacing x by 3 in $x = 5$ gives a false statement.

For the domain given in this Example, the solution set for $x < 5$ is $\{1, 2, 3, 4\}$; the solution set for $x = 5$ is $\{5\}$. Then the solution set for $x \leq 5$ may be considered as the *union* of these two sets.

Example 5. $x \not> 5$ (read "x is not greater than 5"). Domain of x: positive integers.

SOLUTION: Since, for any real number x, exactly one of the statements $x < 5$, $x = 5$, or $x > 5$ must hold; here x must be less than or equal to 5. This reduces to the same statement as in Example 4 and has the same domain. Thus, the solution set is the same as for Example 4.

Example 6. $-1 < x \leq 3$. Domain of x: integers.

SOLUTION: This inequality states that x is greater than -1 but is less than or equal to 3. The solution set consists of the elements $\{0, 1, 2, 3\}$. The graph of the solution set is:

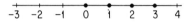

For the domain given in this Example, the solution set for $x \leq 3$ is $\{\ldots, -1, 0, 1, 2, 3\}$; the solution set for $-1 < x$ is $\{0, 1, 2, 3, \ldots\}$. Then the solution set for $-1 < x \leq 3$ may be considered as the *intersection* of these two sets.

Example 7. $-1 < x \leq 3$. Domain of x: real numbers.

SOLUTION: This is the same sentence as in Example 6, but with a different domain. The graph of the solution set now includes all of the points on the number line between -1 and $+3$, including $+3$ but not -1, that is, the points of the interval $(-1, 3]$:

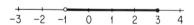

Example 8. $x + 3 < 5$. Domain of x: negative integers.

SOLUTION: The solution set consists of the elements $\{-1, -2, -3, -4, -5, \ldots\}$. The graph of the solution set is:

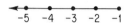

Example 9. $x + 2 = 2 + x$. Domain of x: real numbers.

SOLUTION: This sentence is true for all replacements of x and thus is classified as an identity. The solution set is the entire domain, that is, the set of all real numbers. The graph of the solution set follows:

We now summarize the concepts considered in this section. An open sentence in one variable divides the domain of the variable into two *subsets*: one subset consists of replacements which make the sentence true; the other subset consists of the replacements which make the sentence false. A replacement that makes the sentence true is a *solution* of the sentence. The set of all solutions is the *solution set* of the sentence; the solution set is a subset of the domain. The complement of the solution set relative to the domain is the set of replacements which make the sentence false. The *graph* of an equation or an inequality is the graph of its solution set.

We can think of an equation such as $x + 2 = 5$ as a **set selector**; it selects from the domain of x just those members which make the sentence true when used as replacements for x. The selected set is the solution set of the equation.

Exercises

Describe the solution set of each equation and inequality for the domain given. Then graph the solution set on a number scale.

1. $2x - 1 = 11$ Domain of x: real numbers.

2. $2y < 12$ Domain of y: positive integers.

3. $y + 3 \geq 5$ Domain of y: negative integers.

4. $9 + x < 9$ Domain of x: real numbers.

5. $x < -3$ Domain of x: negative numbers.

6. $3x \neq 15$ Domain of x: real numbers.

7. $-2 \leq x < 3$ Domain of x: real numbers.

8. $4 > x > -1$ Domain of x: real numbers.

9. $|x| < 2$ Domain of x: real numbers.

10. $|x| \geq 3$ Domain of x: real numbers.

11. $x^2 = 16$ Domain of x: real numbers.

12. $x + 2 \neq x$ Domain of x: real numbers.

13. $5x \geq 10$ Domain of x: real numbers.

14. $2m \geq 6$ Domain of m: positive integers.

15. $x + 2 < 5 + 2$ Domain of x: negative integers.

16. $2t + 1 = 4$ Domain of t: positive integers.

17. $3 + r = r + 2$ Domain of r: real numbers.

18. $x^2 \neq 9$ Domain of x: real numbers.

19. $x^2 < 9$ Domain of x: real numbers.

20. $x^2 > 9$ Domain of x: real numbers.

7–3 Set-builder Notation

The statement of Example 1 in §7–2 was given as "$x + 3 = 5$. Domain of x: integers." The solution set was found to be $\{2\}$. The equation served to select a subset, $\{2\}$, of the domain. We now introduce the set-builder notation as a means of naming the desired solution set. For example, we may write

$$\{x \mid x + 3 = 5, \ x \text{ an integer}\},$$

and read it as "the set of all x such that $x + 3 = 5$, where x is an integer." Usually the domain is specified in advance and the set-builder notation is abbreviated as

$$\{x \mid x + 3 = 5\};$$

that is, "the set of all x such that $x + 3 = 5$." Notice that the variable is given at the left of the bar; the set-selector sentence is given at the right. Some texts use a colon instead of a bar; however, the meaning is the same.

The sentence $x \leq 5$ was used in Example 4 of §7–2. We may use set-builder notation and name the solution set of this sentence as

$$\{x \mid x \leq 5\},$$

read as "the set of all x such that x is less than or equal to 5." We may also write this in the form

$$\{x \mid x = 5 \quad or \quad x < 5\},$$

read as "the set of all x such that x equals 5 or x is less than 5."

Here are several examples to further illustrate the use of this notation. For each open sentence given, we are to name the solution set, using set-builder notation, and then to graph the solution set.

Example 1. $\{x \mid x^2 > 4\}$. Domain of variable: real numbers.
SOLUTION: The solution set can be named for real numbers x as:

$$\{x \mid x > 2 \quad or \quad x < -2\}.$$

Here the solution set may be thought of as the *union* of the two sets $\{x \mid x > 2\}$ and $\{x \mid x < -2\}$. The graph of the solution set is:

Example 2. $\{x \mid x^2 \leq 1\}$. Domain of variable: real numbers.
SOLUTION: The solution set can be named for real numbers x as:

$$\{x \mid x \leq 1 \quad and \quad x \geq -1\}.$$

Here the solution set may be thought of as the *intersection* of the two sets $\{x \mid x \leq 1\}$ and $\{x \mid x \geq -1\}$. The graph of the solution set is:

Example 3. $\{x \mid |x - 5| \leq 2\}$. Domain of variable: real numbers.

SOLUTION: The solution set may be thought of as the intersection of two sets:

$$\{x \mid x \leq 7\} \quad \text{and} \quad \{x \mid x \geq 3\}.$$

This may also be written as $\{x \mid 3 \leq x \leq 7\}$. The solution set may be thought of as the set of points on the number line whose distance from 5 is less than or equal to 2. The graph of the solution set is:

Exercises

In these exercises, the domain of each variable is the set of real numbers. In Exercises 1 through 30, draw the graph of the solution set for each of the given open sentences.

1. $\{x \mid x \geq 1\}$

2. $\{y \mid y \leq 5\}$

3. $\{a \mid 2a \geq 8\}$

4. $\{b \mid 3b \leq 3\}$

5. $\{m \mid m + 5 \geq 2\}$

6. $\{n \mid n + 3 \leq 2\}$

7. $\{x \mid 9 \geq x - 2\}$

8. $\{k \mid 13 \leq 2 - k\}$

9. $\{k \mid 6 + k \geq k\}$

10. $\{x \mid 9 + x \leq x\}$

11. $\{x \mid x \not\geq 10\}$

12. $\{x \mid -1 < x \leq 3\}$

13. $\{u \mid u \not\geq -3\}$

14. $\{t \mid -3 \leq t \leq 0\}$

15. $\{u \mid u + 5 \geq 7\}$

16. $\{u \mid u + 3 \not\geq 8\}$

17. $\{u \mid u + 3 > 8\}$

18. $\{x \mid |x| \geq 3\}$

19. $\{a \mid |a| < -2\}$

20. $\{x \mid |x| \leq 2\}$

21. $\{x \mid |x^2| < 4\}$

22. $\{x \mid |x^2| > 9\}$

⋆23. $\{x \mid |x + 1| < 5\}$

⋆24. $\{x \mid (x - 1)(x - 3) > 0\}$

⋆25. $\{x \mid x + |x| = 0\}$

⋆26. $\{x \mid (x - 1)(x + 2) \geq 0\}$

⋆27. $\{x \mid (x + 3)(x + 1)(x - 2) < 0\}$

⋆28. $\{x \mid 1 \leq |x - 5| \leq 3\}$

⋆29. $\{b \mid |b + 5| > 7\}$

⋆30. $\{x \mid (x)(x - 1)(x - 2)(x - 3) \ldots = 0\}$

Express in terms of the union or intersection of sets:

31. $\{x \mid x^2 > 9\}$ **32.** $\{x \mid x^2 \leq 9\}$

33. $\{x \mid |x| \leq 2\}$ **34.** $\{x \mid |x| > 2\}$

Draw the graphs of $A \cup B$ *as well as* $A \cap B$:

★35. $A = \{x \mid x + 2 > 3\};$ $B = \{x \mid x - 2 \leq 5\}$

★36. $A = \{x \mid |x - 1| \leq 2\};$ $B = \{x \mid |x + 2| \geq 3\}$

7–4 Classification of Equations

One use of sets in algebra as a unifying concept is indicated by the following classification of equations in one variable. Inequalities are included to show an extension of the classification.

An equation in one variable is an **identity** (an inequality is an **absolute inequality**) if its solution set includes all elements of the domain of the variable for which the terms are defined. These are examples:

1. $x^2 - 4 = (x + 2)(x - 2)$ 3. $x + 3 \neq x$
2. $x + 2 = 2 + x$ 4. $x + 5 > x''$

In each case, each element in the domain of the variable may be used as a replacement for x to form a true statement; that is, the solution set is the domain of the variable.

An equation in one variable is an **impossible equation** (an inequality is a **false statement of inequality**) if the solution set is the empty set. These are examples:

1. $x + 3 = x$ 3. $x + 1 \neq x + 1$
2. $x + 2 = x + 3$ 4. $x + 5 > x''$

In each case, regardless of the element used as a replacement for x, the resulting statement is a false one; that is, the solution set is the empty set.

An equation in one variable is a **conditional equation** (an inequality is a **conditional inequality**) if the solution set is a non-empty proper subset of the domain of the variable. These are examples:

1. $x - 2 = 5$ 3. $x \neq x^2$
2. $x + 3 = 7$ 4. $x - 1 > 5$

If the domain of the variable is the set of real numbers, then each of the preceding examples has a solution set consisting of at least one, but not all, of the elements of the domain; that is, the solution set is a nonempty subset of the domain of the variable.

Exercises

Classify each of the following as an identity, an impossible equation, or a conditional equation. (In each case, the domain of the variable is the set of real numbers.)

1. $x + 5 = 3$ 2. $x - 3 > 2$

3. $x + 3 = 3 + x$ 4. $x - 2 = 2 - x$

5. $x - 1 \neq 1 - x$ 6. $|x| = -2$

7. $x \neq x + 1$ 8. $x - |x| = 0$

7–5 Linear Equations and Inequalities in Two Variables

An open sentence such as $x + y = 8$ remains an open sentence if a replacement is made for only one of the variables. For example, if x is replaced by 5, the sentence becomes $5 + y = 8$, which is an open sentence. Thus, a pair of replacements is needed for an open sentence in two variables in order to determine whether it is true or false for these replacements.

If x is replaced by 5 and y is replaced by 3, the sentence $x + y = 8$ is true. Usually we think of the variables as an ordered pair (x, y) and speak of the replacements as an ordered pair of numbers, $(5, 3)$. By convention the variable x is assumed to be the first of the two variables, and the first number in the ordered pair of numbers is taken as the replacement for x; the variable y is then taken as the second variable, and the second number in the ordered pair is taken as the replacement for y.

Thus, the sentence $x + y = 8$ is true or false for certain ordered pairs of numbers. It is true for $(5, 3)$; it is false for $(2, 7)$. The solution set for the sentence $x + y = 8$ is a set of ordered pairs of numbers for which the sentence is true. This solution set of the sentence may be indicated in the set-builder notation as follows:

$$\{(x, y) \mid x + y = 8\}.$$

This is read as "the set of ordered pairs (x, y) such that $x + y = 8$." The solution set for any sentence in two variables is a set of ordered pairs.

A set of ordered pairs may be obtained from any set of numbers. For example, consider the set of numbers:

$$U = \{1, 2, 3\}.$$

Then the set of all ordered pairs of numbers from U consists of those pairs of numbers whose members are both elements of U. This set of ordered pairs is called the **Cartesian product** of U and U, is written as $U \times U$, and is read "U cross U." The set of all ordered pairs whose coordinates belong to the given set U is:

$$\{(1, 1), (1, 2), (1, 3), (2, 1), (2, 2), (2, 3), (3, 1), (3, 2), (3, 3)\}.$$

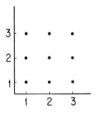

The graph of $U \times U$ is given by the nine-point **lattice** in the accompanying figure. When U is the set of all real numbers, $U \times U$ has as its graph the entire Cartesian coordinate plane.

Next we shall consider a number of specific examples of equations and inequalities in two variables. For each we are to draw the graph of the solution set.

Example 1. $\{(x, y) \mid y = x + 1\}; \ U = \{1, 2, 3, 4\}.$

SOLUTION: Here the set of possible replacements consists of a set of 16 ordered pairs of numbers, that is, a lattice of 16 points. The set of ordered pairs which make the sentence true—the solution set—is:

$$\{(1, 2), (2, 3), (3, 4)\}.$$

These are indicated by heavily shaded dots in the accompanying graph of the solution set.

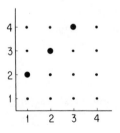

Example 2. $\{(x, y) \mid x + y \geq 6\}$; $U = \{1, 2, 3, 4\}$.

SOLUTION: For $x = 1$, there is no value in the domain of y which will satisfy this inequality. For $x = 2$, $y = 4$; for $x = 3$, $y = 3$ or 4; and for $x = 4$, $y = 2$, 3, or 4. The solution set is:

$$\{(2, 4), (3, 3), (3, 4), (4, 2), (4, 3), (4, 4)\}.$$

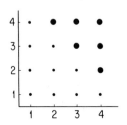

Example 3. $\{(x, y) \mid y \geq x + 2\}$; $U = \{-3, -2, -1, 0, 1, 2, 3\}$.

SOLUTION: The set of ordered pairs $U \times U$ is represented by a lattice of 49 points. The graph of the solution set is given in the accompanying figure.

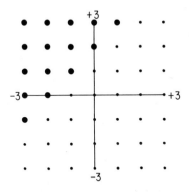

The lattice of points used need not necessarily be a square one. Thus, consider the following sets of numbers:

$$A = \{1, 2, 3\};$$
$$B = \{1, 2\}.$$

Then $A \times B = \{(1, 1), (1, 2), (2, 1), (2, 2), (3, 1), (3, 2)\}$.

Example 4. $\{(x, y) \mid y \geq x\}$; $U = A \times B$, where $A = \{1, 2, 3\}$ and $B = \{1, 2\}$.

SOLUTION: The solution set consists of the ordered pairs:

$$\{(1, 1), (1, 2), (2, 2)\}.$$

When we make the extension of U to the set of real numbers, our solution sets usually become infinite sets of ordered pairs. Note the following illustrations:

Example 5. $\{(x, y) \mid y \leq x - 1\}$; U is the set of real numbers.

SOLUTION:

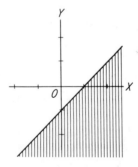

Here the solution set consists of all the points on the line $y = x - 1$ as well as the points in the half-plane indicated by the shaded portion of the graph.

Example 6. $\{(x, y) \mid y = |x + 1|\}$; U is the set of real numbers.
SOLUTION:

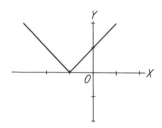

Any sentence in two variables can be considered as a *set-selector*. The set of ordered pairs selected is a *subset* of $U \times U$. If U is the set of real numbers, the solution set corresponds to the set of points satisfying a given condition on a coordinate plane. Thus, the graph of an equation or inequality is commonly called the **locus** of the equation or inequality; that is, the locus is the set of points which correspond to the solution set.

Exercises

Draw the graph of the solution set on a plane lattice where $U = \{1, 2, 3, 4\}$:

1. $\{(x, y) \mid x + y = 5\}$
2. $\{(x, y) \mid y \leq x - 1\}$
3. $\{(x, y) \mid y < x\}$
4. $\{(x, y) \mid y \geq x + 1\}$

Graph the solution sets with $U = \{-3, -2, -1, 0, 1, 2, 3\}$:

5. $\{(x, y) \mid y = x\}$
6. $\{(x, y) \mid x - y = 1\}$
7. $\{(x, y) \mid y - x = 2\}$
8. $\{(x, y) \mid y < x - 1\}$
9. $\{(x, y) \mid y \geq x\}$
10. $\{(x, y) \mid x + y = 7\}$
11. $\{(x, y) \mid y \geq |x|\}$
12. $\{(x, y) \mid y > |x + 1|\}$

13. Let $A = \{(x, y) \mid x > 1$ and $y < -2\}$. Let $B = \{(x, y) \mid x \leq 3$ and $y > -1\}$. Draw the graphs of and tell the number of points in A, B, $A \cup B$, and $A \cap B$.

For the following, let U *be the set of real numbers and draw the graph of the solution sets:*

14. $\{(x, y) \mid y = |x|\}$
15. $\{(x, y) \mid y \geq x + 1\}$
16. $\{(x, y) \mid y = -x^2\}$
17. $\{(x, y) \mid y = |x + 3|\}$

18. $\{(x, y) \mid x^2 + y^2 = 9\}$

19. $\{(x, y) \mid x^2 + y^2 = 9$ and $x \le 0, y \ge 0\}$

*20. $\{(x, y) \mid |x - 3| = y$ and $|y + 2| = -x\}$

*21. $\left\{(x, y) \mid y = \dfrac{x}{|x|}\right\}$

*22. $\{(x, y) \mid |x| + |y| = 1\}$

*23. $\{(x, y) \mid x + y = y + x$ and $x - y = y - x\}$

Draw the graphs of A ∪ B as well as A ∩ B, the universe being the set of real numbers:

24. $A = \{(x, y) \mid y \ge x^2\}$; $B = \{(x, y) \mid y \le 4\}$

*25. $A = \{(x, y) \mid x = y^2\}$ $B = \{(x, y) \mid |y + x| = 1\}$

*26. $A = \{(x, y) \mid y = x \cdot |x|\}$; $B = \{(x, y) \mid y \ge x + 1\}$

7–6 Relations and Functions

A **relation** may be defined as any subset of $U \times U$; thus, a relation is a set of ordered pairs of numbers. It is most often defined as a rule. Consider, for example,

$$\{(x, y) \mid y > x - 1\}, \qquad \text{where } U = \{1, 2, 3\}.$$

This solution set is:

$$\{(1, 1), (1, 2), (1, 3), (2, 2), (2, 3), (3, 3)\}.$$

It may be graphed as in the accompanying figure.

The relation may be defined by the solution set, by the graph, or by a table of values for the variable:

x	1	1	1	2	2	3
y	1	2	3	2	3	3

Here is the table and graph for another relation:

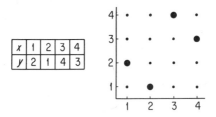

| x | 1 | 2 | 3 | 4 |
| y | 2 | 1 | 4 | 3 |

Note that the second relation differs from the first in that, for any value of x, there is at most one value for y. We call this special type of relation a *function*.

A **function** is a set of ordered pairs (x, y) such that for each value of x there is at most one value of y; that is, no first element appears with more than one second element. You may think of the first element as the independent variable and the second element as the dependent variable. Each variable has a set of possible values. The set of all first elements of the ordered pairs of numbers is called the **domain**; the set of all second elements is called the **range** of the function. In terms of its graph, any vertical line drawn meets the graph of a function in, at most, one point.

Here are the graphs of two relations, $\{(x, y)\}$, which are also functions:

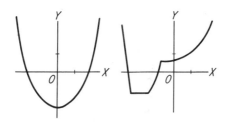

Here are the graphs of two relations, $\{(x, y)\}$, which are not functions:

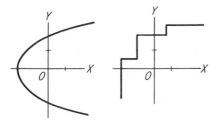

Although formulas such as $y = x^2$ may define a function, they are not strictly functions. We have defined the function to be a set of ordered pairs (x, y), such as those obtained from the formula $y = x^2$ for the real variable x. Thus, a formula may provide a rule by which the function may be determined. In other words, a formula may provide a means for associating a unique element in the range with each element in the domain.

Note: Unfortunately the word "function" is used in several ways. Basically, the term does not yet have a universally accepted definition. There are several quite different and equally proper definitions. Whenever you encounter the word "function" in the literature, you should check to see what definition (or definitions) the author is using.

Exercises

Draw the graph of the solution set for each relation and identify those which are functions; U *is the set of real numbers.*

1. $\{(x, y) \mid y^2 = x - 1\}$ 2. $\{(x, y) \mid x + y = y + x\}$

3. $\{(x, y) \mid y = x^2 - 1\}$ 4. $\{(x, y) \mid xy = 1\}$

5. $\{(x, y) \mid y \le x^2\}$ 6. $\{(x, y) \mid |x + y| = 1\}$

7. $\{(x, y) \mid y \ge |x|\}$ 8. $\{(x, y) \mid xy = 0\}$

9. $\{(x, y) \mid x = 2\}$ 10. $\{(x, y) \mid |x - 1| = 2\}$

11. $\{(x, y) \mid |x + y| = 2\}$ 12. $\{(x, y) \mid |y - x| = 2\}$

13. $\{(x, y) \mid |y - (x - 1)| = 2\}$ 14. $\{(x, y) \mid |y - (x + 1)| = 3\}$

Describe the graphs of:

★15. $\{(x, y) \mid |x| = k\}$ ★16. $\{(x, y) \mid |x - b| = k\}$

★17. $\{(x, y) \mid |x + y| = k\}$ ★18. $\{(x, y) \mid |y - x| = k\}$

★19. $\{(x, y) \mid |y - (x + b)| = k\}$ ★20. $\{(x, y) \mid |y - (mx + b)| = k\}$

7-7 Inverse Relations

Given any relation, the **inverse relation** is the set of ordered pairs obtained by interchanging the elements of each of the ordered pairs of the given relation. Thus, suppose we are given the relation:

$$R = \{(2, 1), (3, 2), (4, 3), (4, 5)\}.$$

The inverse relation of R then consists of the set of ordered pairs

$$\{(1, 2), (2, 3), (3, 4), (5, 4)\}.$$

In a similar manner, we may find the inverse of a function, inasmuch as a function is nothing more than a special type of relation. That is, the inverse of a function is obtained by interchanging the elements of each of the ordered pairs of numbers which comprise the function. The inverse of a function is a relation; however, it may or may not be a function. It will be a function if and only if, for each y of the original function, we have at most one x.

Example 1. Find the inverse of the function

$$F = \{(1, 2), (2, 3), (3, 4)\}.$$

SOLUTION: The inverse of this function is another function, F', where

$$F' = \{(2, 1), (3, 2), (4, 3)\}.$$

Example 2. Find the inverse of the function

$$A = \{(1, 3), (2, 4), (3, 4), (4, 7)\}.$$

SOLUTION: The inverse, A', of this function is a relation, but it is not a function.

$$A' = \{(3, 1), (4, 2), (4, 3), (7, 4)\}.$$

If a relation is given by a formula, then a formula for its inverse may be obtained by interchanging the variables.

Example 3. Find a formula for the inverse of the function

$$F = \{(x, y) \mid y = 2x\}.$$

SOLUTION: The inverse of F is $F' = \{(x, y) \mid x = 2y\}$. We may also write it as $F' = \left\{(x, y) \mid y = \dfrac{x}{2}\right\}$. Here the inverse of the given function is also a function.

Example 4. Find the inverse of $F = \{(x, y) \mid y = x^2\}$.

SOLUTION: $\{(x, y) \mid x = y^2\}$. We may also write the solution as $\{(x, y) \mid y = \pm\sqrt{x}\}$. Note that the inverse of the given function is a relation but it is not a function. Explain why not.

Exercises

Find the inverse for each of the following relations. Tell whether or not each inverse is a function.

1. $\{(1, 2), (3, 2), (5, 3)\}$ **2.** $\{(2, 1), (3, 4), (5, 2)\}$

3. $\{(1, 1), (2, 2), (3, 3), (4, 4)\}$ **4.** $\{(1, 2), (2, 2), (3, 4), (5, 3)\}$

Draw the graph of each relation and the graph of the inverse of each relation. For Exercises 7 through 12, the universe is the set of real numbers.

5. $\{(x, y) \mid y = x\};\ U = \{1, 2, 3\}$

6. $\{(x, y) \mid y = x + 1\};\quad U = \{1, 2, 3, 4\}$

7. $\{(x, y) \mid y = 4x^2\}$ **8.** $\{(x, y) \mid y = |x|\}$

★9. $\{(x, y) \mid y = 2^x\}$ **★10.** $\{(x, y) \mid y = \log x\}$

★11. $\{(x, y) \mid y = 2^{x-1}\}$ **★12.** $\{(x, y) \mid y - 3 = 2^x\}$

Application and Additional Readings

Almost all of the material in this chapter is suitable for courses in elementary and intermediate algebra. The use of sets in elementary algebra is treated in a number of pamphlets written explicitly for secondary schools, such as [3], [22], and [53]. It is also treated in a publication of the Commission on Mathematics, [14], as well as in the material prepared by the SMSG, [42]. An interesting approach may be read in the publications of UICSM, [48]. References can also be found in articles in professional periodicals, such as [7], [8], and [9]. Specific applications of this material at various grade levels may be read in the third chapter of [36].

Answers for Exercises

7–1 *Sentences and Statements*

1. False   **2.** False   **3.** True   **4.** True   **5.** False

6. True   **7.** False   **8.** False   **9.** True   **10.** False

11. $5 + x$; domain of x: $\{1, 2, 3, \ldots\}$

12. $3s$; domain of s: $\{1, 3, 5, \ldots\}$

13. $100h + 10t + u$; domain of h: $\{1, 2, 3, \ldots, 9\}$; domain of t and u: $\{0, 1, 2, 3, \ldots, 9\}$

14. $0.04n$; domain of n: $\{1, 2, 3, \ldots\}$

15. $3s$; domain of s: $\{\frac{2}{3}, \frac{4}{3}, \frac{6}{3}, \frac{8}{3}, \ldots\}$

7–2 Solution Sets

1. $\{6\}$

2. $\{1, 2, 3, 4, 5\}$

3. $\emptyset$

4. All negative numbers.

5. All real numbers less than -3.

6. All real numbers except 5.

7. All real numbers greater than or equal to -2 but less than 3.

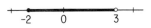

8. All real numbers between −1 and 4.

9. All real numbers between −2 and 2.

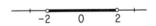

10. All real numbers less than or equal to −3 and all real numbers greater than or equal to 3.

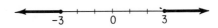

11. {−4, 4}

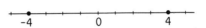

12. All real numbers.

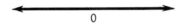

13. All real numbers greater than or equal to 2.

14. {3, 4, 5, . . .}

15. All negative integers.

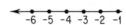

16. ∅

17. ∅

18. All real numbers except −3 and 3.

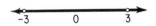

19. All real numbers between −3 and 3.

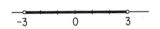

20. All real numbers less than −3 and all real numbers greater than 3.

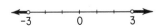

7–3 Set-Builder Notation

1.

2.

3.

4.

5.

6.

7.

8.

9.

10. The solution set is ∅.

11.

12.

13.

14.

15.

16.

17.

18.

19. The solution set is ∅.

20.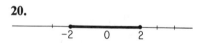

21.

22.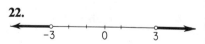

23.

24.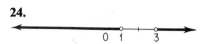

25.

26.

27.

28.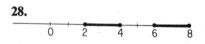

29.

30.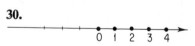

31. $\{x \mid x > 3\} \cup \{x \mid x < -3\}$

32. $\{x \mid x \le 3\} \cap \{x \mid x \ge -3\}$

33. $\{x \mid x \le 2\} \cap \{x \mid x \ge -2\}$

34. $\{x \mid x > 2\} \cup \{x \mid x < -2\}$

35.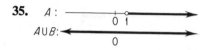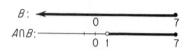

36.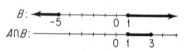

7–4 *Classification of Equations*

1. Conditional.   **2.** Conditional.   **3.** Identity.   **4.** Conditional

(true for $x = 2$).   **5.** Conditional.   **6.** Impossible equation.

7. Identity.   **8.** Conditional.

7–5 *Linear Equations and Inequalities in Two Variables*

1.

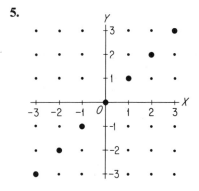

2.

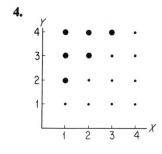

3.

4.

5.

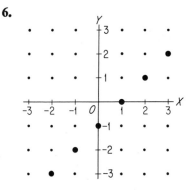

6.

7.

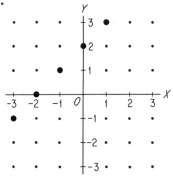

8.

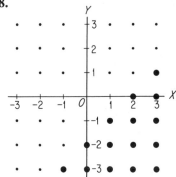

9.

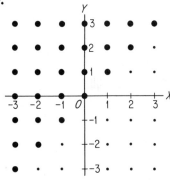

10. The solution set is Ø.

11.

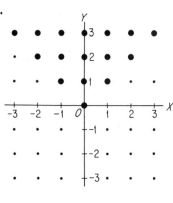

12.

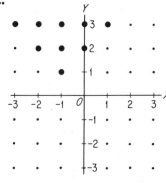

13. *A* has 2 points; *B* has 28 points; *A* ∩ *B* is the empty set; *A* ∪ *B* has 30 points. The graph of *A* ∪ *B* is:

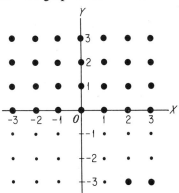

14.

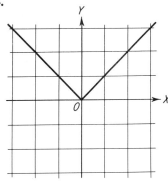

15.

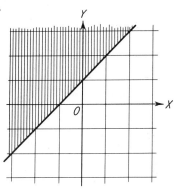

16.

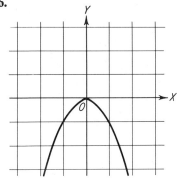

17.

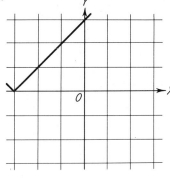

18.

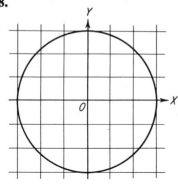

19.

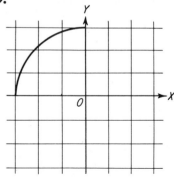

20. The solution set is Ø.

21.

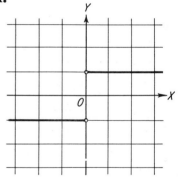

22.

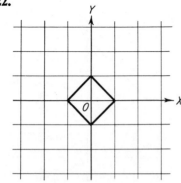

23.

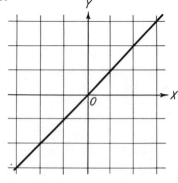

24.

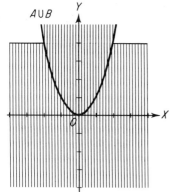

25.

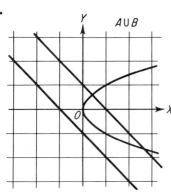   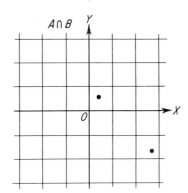

The intersection may be found algebraically by solving simultaneously the equations $x = y^2$ and $x + y = 1$. We note that $|y + x| = 1$ is equivalent to $y + x = 1$ or $y + x = -1$; however, the graphs of $x = y^2$ and $x + y = -1$ have no points in common.

26.

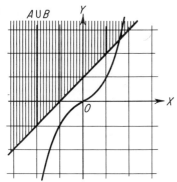   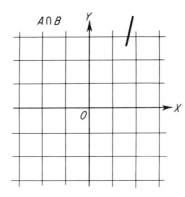

7–6 *Relations and Functions*

1.

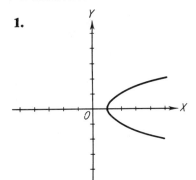

Not a function.

2. The solution set is the entire coordinate plane; this is not a function.

3.

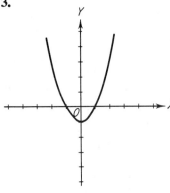

A function.

4.

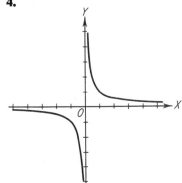

A function.

5.

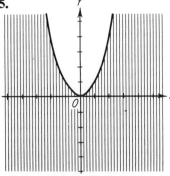

Not a function.

6.

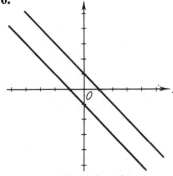

Not a function.

7.

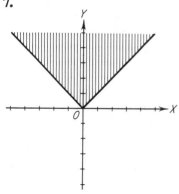

Not a function.

8. The graph of the solution set consists of the *x*- and *y*-axes; this is not a function.

9.

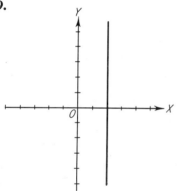

Not a function.

10.

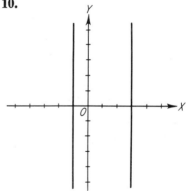

Not a function.

11.

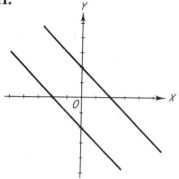

Not a function.

12.

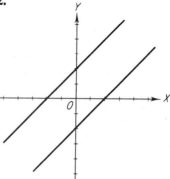

Not a function.

13.

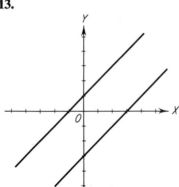

Not a function.

14.

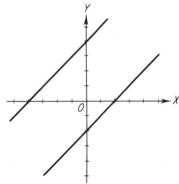

Not a function.

15. The graph consists of two straight lines parallel to the y-axis, namely: $x = k$ and $x = -k$.

16. The graph consists of two straight lines parallel to the y-axis, namely: $x - b = k$ and $x - b = -k$.

17. The graph consists of two parallel lines with slope -1 and y-intercepts k and $-k$: $x + y = k$ and $x + y = -k$.

18. The graph consists of two parallel lines with slope 1 and y-intercepts k and $-k$: $y - x = k$ and $y - x = -k$.

19. The graph consists of two parallel lines with slope 1 and y-intercepts $b + k$ and $b - k$: $y - x - b = k$ and $y - x - b = -k$.

20. The graph consists of two parallel lines with slope m and y-intercepts $b + k$ and $b - k$: $y - mx - b = k$ and $y - mx - b = -k$.

7–7 Inverse Relations

1. $\{(2, 1), (2, 3), (3, 5)\}$; not a function.

2. $\{(1, 2), (4, 3), (2, 5)\}$; a function.

3. $\{(1, 1), (2, 2), (3, 3), (4, 4)\}$; a function.

4. $\{(2, 1), (2, 2), (4, 3), (3, 5)\}$; not a function.

5.

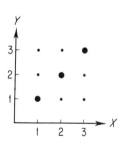

The graph of the inverse of this relation is the same as for the given relation. It consists of the set: {(1, 1), (2, 2), (3, 3)}.

6.

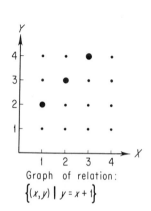

Graph of relation:
$$\{(x,y) \mid y = x + 1\}$$

Graph of inverse of relation:
$$\{(x,y) \mid x = y + 1\}$$

7.

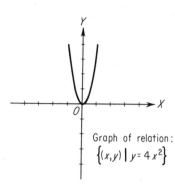

Graph of relation:
$$\{(x,y) \mid y = 4x^2\}$$

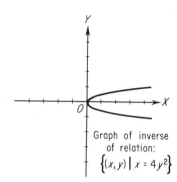

Graph of inverse of relation:
$$\{(x,y) \mid x = 4y^2\}$$

8.

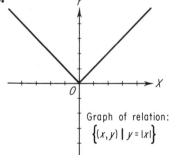

Graph of relation:
$$\{(x,y) \mid y = |x|\}$$

Graph of inverse
of relation:
$$\{(x,y) \mid x = |y|\}$$

9.

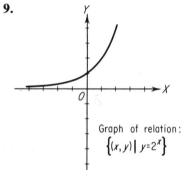

Graph of relation:
$$\{(x,y) \mid y = 2^x\}$$

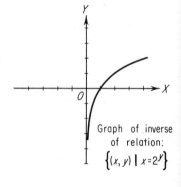

Graph of inverse
of relation:
$$\{(x,y) \mid x = 2^y\}$$

10.

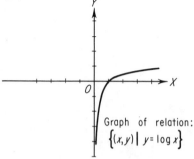

Graph of relation:
$$\{(x,y) \mid y = \log x\}$$

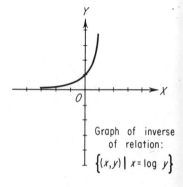

Graph of inverse
of relation:
$$\{(x,y) \mid x = \log y\}$$

11.

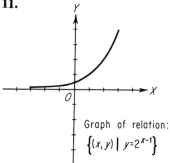

Graph of relation:
$$\{(x,y) \mid y=2^{x-1}\}$$

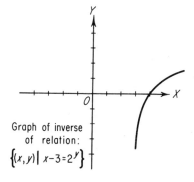

Graph of inverse
of relation:
$$\{(x,y) \mid x=2^{y-1}\}$$

12.

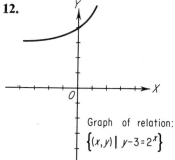

Graph of relation:
$$\{(x,y) \mid y-3=2^{x}\}$$

Graph of inverse
of relation:
$$\{(x,y) \mid x-3=2^{y}\}$$

THE USE OF DEDUCTIONS IN ALGEBRA

In Chapter 7 we saw how the language and notation of sets may be used in a study of the elements of algebra. Let us consider now the deductive development of algebra and the ways in which deductive proof may be used in the study of high school algebra. We should recognize that the abstract nature of deductive logic makes this material less familiar to most teachers than the material in the previous chapters.

The material in this chapter is presented with two goals in mind. One goal is for the reader to familiarize himself with the development of algebra as a logical system. The other goal is for the reader to identify the parts of this deductive development of algebra which are suitable for use in his high school classroom.

Deductions and the testing of conjectures with reference to a given set of axioms or assumptions are important in all branches of mathematics. Indeed, they are important in any logical system and also in everyday living.

8–1 Equations and Natural Numbers

When a statement is in the form of an equation, we interpret the statement to mean that the expressions on either side of the symbol, $=$, stand for the same number. Three properties of equations are of special importance: Any equation is **reflexive**; that is, for any expression a, we may write $a = a$. Any equation is **symmetric**; that is, for any two expressions a and b, if $a = b$, then $b = a$. Any equation is **transitive**; that is, for any expressions a, b, and c, if $a = b$ and $b = c$, then $a = c$.

The transitive property is often stated as: if two expressions are each equal to the same expression, they are equal to each other. We use the transitive property and assume that we may substitute any expression for an equal expression at any time.

The numbers used in counting are often called **natural numbers** or **counting numbers**. Notice that zero is not considered to be a natural number. We first consider the properties of these numbers under the operations of addition and multiplication. We shall use letters to stand for numbers so that we may make general statements of their properties.

We postulate these properties for the operation *addition* (written $+$):

Closure: For any two natural numbers a and b, there exists one and only one natural number c such that $a + b = c$.

Commutative: For any two natural numbers a and b, we have

$$a + b = b + a.$$

Associative: For any natural numbers a, b, and c, we have

$$a + (b + c) = (a + b) + c.$$

We postulate these properties for the operation *multiplication* (written $\times$, $\cdot$, or without any symbol):

Closure: For any two natural numbers a and b, there exists one and only one natural number c such that $a \times b = c$.

Commutative: For any two natural numbers a and b, we have

$$a \times b = b \times a.$$

Associative: For any natural numbers a, b, and c, we have

$$a(bc) = (ab)c.$$

We also postulate that the multiplication of natural numbers is *distributive* with respect to addition; that is,

$$a(b + c) = ab + ac.$$

By the reflexive property of equations, $ab + ac = a(b + c)$; since multiplication is commutative, $(b + c)a = ba + ca$.

Each of the operations, addition and multiplication, provides a means of associating a third number (the sum or product) with *two* given numbers. Hence, addition and multiplication are called **binary** operations. Notice that, when three or more numbers are to be added, you add two of them and then add the third to this sum:

$$2 + 3 + 6 = (2 + 3) + 6 = 5 + 6 = 11.$$

Fortunately, you can start with any two of the numbers:

$$2 + 3 + 6 = (2 + 3) + 6 = 2 + (3 + 6) = 2 + 9 = 11,$$

using the associative law, and:

$$2 + 3 + 6 = (2 + 6) + 3 = 8 + 3 = 11,$$

using the commutative and associative laws. However, in all cases, only two numbers are added at a time. Similar statements may be made for the binary operation of multiplication.

$$2 \times 3 \times 5 = 2 \times (3 \times 5) = (2 \times 3) \times 5$$
$$= (2 \times 5) \times 3 = 3 \times (2 \times 5) = 30.$$

In both addition problems and multiplication problems, we may omit the parentheses, since the manner in which we associate the numbers does not affect the answer.

Subtraction is defined as the inverse of addition; $a - b = c$ if and only if $a = b + c$. Thus, $6 - 2 = 4$ because $6 = 2 + 4$. However, notice that, for natural numbers, subtraction is frequently not possible. For example, $2 - 5$ does not represent a natural number; if $a - b = c$, where a, b, and c are natural numbers, then $b - a$ does not represent a natural number. We assume two properties of subtraction:

If $a - b$ represents a natural number, there is one and only one natural number $a - b$; and

For any natural numbers a and b, we have $(a - b) + b = a$ and $(a + b) - b = a$.

Division is defined as the inverse of multiplication; $a \div b = c$ if and only if $a = bc$. Thus, $6 \div 2 = 3$ because $6 = 2 \times 3$. However, notice that, for natural numbers, division is frequently not possible. For example, $2 \div 5$ does not represent a natural number. We assume two properties of division:

If $a \div b$ represents a natural number, there is one and only one
natural number $a \div b$; and

For any natural number a and any natural number $b \neq 0$, we have
$(a \div b) \times b = a$ and $(ab) \div b = a$.

The definitions of subtraction and division have been made over the
set of natural numbers; they will also hold for other sets of numbers.
Note that division by 0 has been excluded. If $b = 0$ and $a = bc$, then
$a = 0$ and c may have any value. Thus, if $b = 0$, the equality $a = bc$
used to define division of a by b cannot hold when $a \neq 0$; and division
by 0 of a number different from 0 is impossible for any set of numbers
that we shall consider. Also, if $b = 0$ and $a = 0$, then the quotient has
the form $\dfrac{0}{0}$ and may have any value c; that is, $\dfrac{0}{0}$ does not have a unique
answer and is said to be indeterminate. We avoid this situation by
excluding all division by zero. The impossible case $\dfrac{a}{0}$ where $a \neq 0$
corresponds to seeking the intersection of two distinct parallel lines in
geometry; the indeterminate case $\dfrac{0}{0}$ corresponds to seeking the intersection of two coincident lines.

The smallest natural number, 1, has these special properties under
multiplication and division: For any natural number b,

$$b \times 1 = b = 1 \times b; \qquad b \div 1 = b;$$

for any natural number $b \neq 0$, $b \div b = 1$.

Example 1. State the addition fact that is related to the difference
$11 - 5$.

SOLUTION: $6 + 5 = 11$.

Example 2. State the multiplication fact that is related to the
quotient $18 \div 2$.

SOLUTION: $9 \times 2 = 18$.

We next compare natural numbers in terms of their order on a
number scale. Two natural numbers are in the *order* $a < c$ if and
only if there exists a natural number b such that $a + b = c$. Thus, we
assume that any two natural numbers a and c must satisfy exactly one
of the relations $a < c$, $a = c$, and $a > c$. This ordering makes it
possible to graph the natural numbers on a number line.

If $a > c$, then $c < a$; if $a < c$, then $c > a$. Notice that this ordering of natural numbers is not reflexive, since $a < a$ does not hold; that is, $a \not< a$ (read, "a is not less than a"). This ordering is also not symmetric, since $a > c$ does not imply $c > a$. However, this ordering is transitive, as we shall now prove.

Example 3. Prove for all natural numbers a, b, and c: if $a < b$ and $b < c$, then $a < c$.

Proof: From the definition of the order of natural numbers,

$a < b$ means $a + d = b$ for some natural number d;
$b < c$ means $b + e = c$ for some natural number e.

Then, substituting $a + d$ for b, we have

$$(a + d) + e = c;$$

and, by the associative property of addition,

$$a + (d + e) = c.$$

Since the natural numbers are closed under addition, there is a natural number $d + e$ which, when added to a, gives c. Thus, by the definition of order, $a < c$.

Proofs may also be given for statements of equality.

Example 4. Prove for all natural numbers a, b, and c: if $a = b$, then $a + c = b + c$.

Proof: We have assumed that there is one and only one sum $a + c$ for any two natural numbers a and c. Note that this is a property of the numbers rather than of the symbols. Thus, if a and b stand for the same number, then $a + c$ and $b + c$ each stand for the sum of that number and c. Since these two numbers have one and only one sum, the expressions $a + c$ and $b + c$ must both stand for that sum; that is, $a + c = b + c$.

Exercises

State the addition fact that is related to each difference:

1. $13 - 7$ **2.** $17 - 9$ **3.** $501 - 497$

State the multiplication fact that is related to each quotient:

4. $10 \div 5$ **5.** $96 \div 32$ **6.** $1{,}256 \div 4$

Tell whether each of the following relations is necessarily (a) *reflexive,* (b) *symmetric,* (c) *transitive:*

7. $<$ **8.** $\leq$ **9.** $>$ **10.** $\neq$

11. $\approx$, "is approximately equal to."

12. Is an ancestor of.

13. Is the father of.

Give the property which may be used as a reason for each of the following statements:

14. $a(x + y) = ax + ay$.   **15.** $x + y = y + x$.

16. $(m + x) + r = m + (x + r)$.   **17.** $a \times (c \times d) = a \times (d \times c)$.

18. $ax + ay = ay + ax$.   **19.** If $ac = bd$, then $bd = ac$.

20. $x(yz) = (xy)z$.   **21.** $bc + ac = (b + a)c$.

22. If $a = b$ and $b = c$, then $a = c$. **23.** $d = d$.

24. $ay + ax = ay + xa$.

Supply a reason for each step of the following proof that
$$a(cx + cy) = c(ay + ax):$$

25. $a(cx + cy) = a(cx) + a(cy)$.

26. $= (ac)x + (ac)y$.

27. $= (ca)x + (ca)y$.

28. $= c(ax) + c(ay)$.

29. $= c(ax + ay)$.

30. $= c(ay + ax)$.

As in illustrative Examples 3 and 4 of this section, prove, for all natural numbers a, b, c, *and* d:

31. If $a < b$, then $a + c < b + c$.

32. If $a = b$, then $ac = bc$.

33. If $a < b$, then $ac < bc$.

34. If $a = b$, then $a^2 = b^2$.

35. If $a = b$ and $c = d$, then $a + c = b + d$.

36. If $a = b$ and $c = d$, then $ac = bd$.

37. If $a - c = b - c$, then $a = b$.

38. If $a \div c = b \div c$, then $a = b$.

39. If $a + c = b + c$, then $a = b$.

40. If $a + c = b + d$ and $a = b$, then $c = d$.

41. If $ac = bc$, then $a = b$.

42. If $ac = bd$ and $a = b$, then $c = d$.

8–2 Integers

The notation $[a - b]$ is used to identify differences "$a - b$" of natural numbers as integers and to avoid more abstract notations. We define $[b - b] = 0$, zero, for every natural number b. Then the *integers* may be defined in terms of differences of natural numbers and zero. For any natural number b, we write:

$$[b - 0] = +b, \text{ where } +b \text{ is a } positive\ integer;$$
$$[0 - b] = -b, \text{ where } -b \text{ is a } negative\ integer.$$

We define the operations and relations for integers in terms of the operations $(+, -, \times, \div)$ and relations $(=, <, >)$ for the natural numbers and zero. The number zero has the properties:

$$b + 0 = b; \qquad b \times 0 = 0;$$
$$bc = 0 \text{ if and only if } b = 0 \text{ or } c = 0, \text{ or both.}$$

Then the properties of the integers may be deduced from these definitions where the letters stand for natural numbers:

$[a - b] = [c - d]$ if and only if $a + d = b + c$;
$[a - b] + [c - d] = [(a + c) - (b + d)]$;
$[a - b] \times [c - d] = [(ac + bd) - (ad + bc)]$;
$[a - b] < [c - d]$ if and only if $a + d < b + c$.

The definitions have been chosen so that most of the properties of natural numbers are preserved, and also so that positive integers may be identified with natural numbers.

Example 1. Prove that the set of integers is closed under addition.

PROOF: Each integer, say, p and q, may be expressed as a difference of natural numbers. Suppose $p = [a - b]$ and $q = [c - d]$. Then,

$$p + q = [a - b] + [c - d]$$

and

$$p + q = [(a + c) - (b + d)],$$

where $a + c$ and $b + d$ stand for natural numbers, since the sum of any two natural numbers is a natural number. Thus, $p + q$ can be expressed as a difference of natural numbers and therefore is, by definition, an integer. We have proved that the sum of any two integers is an integer; in other words, the set of integers is closed under addition.

Example 2. Prove that multiplication of any two integers is commutative.

PROOF: We must prove that, for any two integers p and q, $pq = qp$. We know that multiplication of two natural numbers is commutative. Suppose that $p = [a - b]$ and $q = [c - d]$. Then,

$$
\begin{aligned}
pq &= [a - b] \times [c - d] \\
   &= [(ac + bd) - (ad + bc)],
\end{aligned}
$$

by the definition of a product of integers;

$$= [(ca + db) - (da + cb)],$$

since multiplication of natural numbers is commutative (used 4 times);

$$= [(ca + db) - (cb + da)],$$

since addition of natural numbers is commutative;

$$= [c - d] \times [a - b] = qp,$$

by the definition of a product of integers.

Exercises

Prove:

1. The set of integers is closed under multiplication.

2. The addition of integers is commutative.

3. The addition of integers is associative.

4. The multiplication of integers is associative.

5. An integer is positive, negative, or zero. *Hint:* Consider the order relations for natural numbers.

6. The product of any two positive integers is positive.

7. The product of any two negative integers is positive.

8. For any integer m, we have $m \times 0 = 0$ and $m + 0 = m$.

9. The product of a positive integer and a negative integer must be negative.

10. Give a definition for subtraction of integers and show that it is always possible.

11. The subtraction of integers is not commutative.

12. The subtraction of integers is not associative.

13. Each integer p has a negative $(-p)$ such that $p + (-p) = 0$.

14. For any integers a and b, we have $a - b = a + (-b)$.

15. The equality of integers is reflexive, symmetric, and transitive.

16. The distributive property of multiplication with respect to addition holds for integers.

8–3 Even and Odd Integers

We assume that, when an integer m is divided by an integer n, the quotient is an integer and the remainder is one of the integers 0, 1, 2, 3, . . ., $n - 1$.

Then, an integer is **odd** if, when it is divided by 2, the remainder is 1. An integer is **even** if, when it is divided by 2, the remainder is 0. Note that 0 is an even integer; thus, any integer is either even or odd.

Example: Prove that each even integer can be written in the form $2k$, where k is an integer.

PROOF: By definition of an even integer, $m = 2k + 0$; by Ex. 8 of §8–2, $2k = 2k + 0$; by the transitive property of "=," $m = 2k$.

Exercises

Prove (it is suggested that the results proved in early exercises be used in subsequent exercises):

1. Any integer is either even or odd.

2. The square of an even integer is even.

3. The square of an odd integer is odd.

4. If the square of an integer is odd, the integer is odd; if the square of an integer is even, the integer is even.

5. The sum of two even integers is even; the sum of two odd integers is even.

6. The sum of an even integer and an odd integer is odd.

7. The product of two odd integers is odd.

8. If the product of two integers is even, at least one of the integers is even.

9. If p is an integer and 3 is a factor of p^2, then 3 is a factor of p.

10. If p is an integer and 5 is a factor of p^2, then 5 is a factor of p.

8–4 Rational Numbers

The rational numbers may be defined in terms of quotients of integers. Any quotient of integers $\frac{a}{b}$, $b \neq 0$, stands for a rational number. Conversely, any rational number can be expressed as a quotient $\frac{a}{b}$ of integers where $b \neq 0$.

We define our operations and relations for rational numbers in terms of those for integers. The letters stand for integers.

$$\frac{a}{b} = \frac{c}{d} \text{ if and only if } ad = bc;$$

$$\frac{a}{b} + \frac{c}{d} = \frac{ad + bc}{bd};$$

$$\frac{a}{b} \times \frac{c}{d} = \frac{ac}{bd};$$

$$\frac{a}{b} < \frac{c}{d} \text{ if and only if } abd^2 < b^2cd.$$

Notice that

$$\frac{2}{3} < \frac{5}{4} \quad \text{and} \quad 2(4) < 3(5);$$

also,

$$\frac{-5}{4} < \frac{2}{-3}, \text{ but } (-5)(-3) > 4(2).$$

The form of the definition of order of rational numbers has been chosen so that the integers may be either positive or negative. Each of these definitions has been chosen so that the properties of integers are preserved and so that each rational number of the form $\frac{a}{1}$ may be identified with the integer a.

Example 1. Prove that the set of rational numbers is closed under addition.

PROOF: We know that the set of integers is closed under addition. We are to prove that the sum of any two rational numbers is a rational number.

Consider two rational numbers $\frac{r}{s}$ and $\frac{p}{q}$. By definition, their sum is $\frac{rq + sp}{sq}$. Then, $sq \neq 0$, since $s \neq 0$ and $q \neq 0$; rq, sp, and $(rq + sp)$ stand for integers; the quotient $\frac{rq + sp}{sq}$ stands for a quotient of integers, that is, a rational number.

Example 2. Prove each of these properties of 1:

$$\frac{b}{b} = 1 \text{ for any integer } b \neq 0;$$

$$\frac{r}{s} \times 1 = \frac{r}{s} \text{ for any rational number } \frac{r}{s}.$$

PROOF: We identify the rational number $\frac{1}{1}$ with the integer 1; for any integer $b \neq 0$, $\frac{b}{b}$ stands for a rational number and $\frac{b}{b} = \frac{1}{1}$, since $b \times 1 = b \times 1$ by the reflexive property of $=$. For any rational number $\frac{r}{s}$, we have

$$\frac{r}{s} \times 1 = \frac{r}{s} \times \frac{1}{1} = \frac{r \times 1}{s \times 1} = \frac{r}{s}.$$

Exercises

Prove:

1. The set of rational numbers is closed under multiplication.

2. The addition of rational numbers is commutative.

3. The addition of rational numbers is associative.

4. The multiplication of rational numbers is commutative.

5. The multiplication of rational numbers is associative.

6. Give a definition for division by a rational number different from zero and show that it is always possible.

7. Each rational number $\frac{a}{b}$ different from zero has a reciprocal; that is, a number which when multiplied by $\frac{a}{b}$ is 1.

8. If $k \neq 0$, then $\frac{ak}{bk} = \frac{a}{b}$.

9. Any quotient $\frac{a}{b}$ may be reduced so that a and b are not both even.

8–5 Real Numbers

We know that a scale of integers or rational numbers can be marked on a number line. We need to extend our concept of numbers to include real numbers, so that each point on the line will have a number as its *coordinate*. Then, on an ordinary line, each real number will have a point on the number line as its *graph*.

A real number is *rational* if it can be expressed as a quotient of two integers; it is *irrational* if it cannot be expressed as a quotient of two integers. In each case, note that the divisor cannot be zero.

We assume that equalities of real numbers have the usual properties (reflexive, symmetric, and transitive, as in §8–1); that any real number is positive, negative, or zero; that any two real numbers a and b satisfy exactly one of the relations $a < b, a = b, a > b$; and that $a < b$ if and only if $a + c = b$ for some real number $c > 0$.

Any sum, difference, product, or quotient (with divisor different from zero) of rational numbers is a rational number. Thus, we must consider another operation to show the need for irrational numbers. We need irrational numbers to obtain square roots of all positive numbers; that is, to solve equations such as $x^2 - 2 = 0$. To illustrate this need for irrational numbers, we now prove that $\sqrt{2}$ cannot be a rational number.

Suppose that $\sqrt{2}$ is a rational number. Then, $\sqrt{2} = \dfrac{a}{b}$, and we may select the integers a and b so that they are not both even (if at first both are even, reduce the fraction as in Ex. 8 of §8–4);

$$2 = \frac{a^2}{b^2}, \; 2b^2 = a^2, \text{ and } a \text{ is even by Ex. 4, §8–3.}$$

Let $\qquad a = 2k$ for some integer k, as in §8–3;

then $\qquad 2b^2 = (2k)^2, \; b^2 = 2k^2, \text{ and } b \text{ is even.}$

This is contrary to the assumption that a and b are not both even. Thus, our assumption that $\sqrt{2}$ is rational must be false, and $\sqrt{2}$ is irrational.

Exercises

1. Prove that $\sqrt{3}$ is irrational.
2. Prove that $\sqrt{5}$ is irrational.

Application and Additional Readings

The properties of numbers that we have considered in this chapter should be recognized by most students starting in the first course in algebra. The properties of addition and multiplication have provided a basis for the families of number facts considered in elementary grades; they are important as the student extends his work in arithmetic to work in algebra; the names of the properties should be recognized at least during the second course in algebra. The emphasis upon definitions should permeate courses at all levels.

The simpler proofs should be considered in the first course in algebra as an introduction to the formal proofs in geometry. Other proofs may be considered as the maturity of the student increases. The detailed proofs are primarily for the teacher and the better students in the senior high school.

Properties of $=$, $<$, and $>$ have been considered, since, if a and b stand for any two numbers,

(a) either $a = b$ or $a \neq b$;

(b) if $a \neq b$, then either $a < b$ or $a > b$.

As we have seen, for any two numbers a and b, exactly one of the relations

$$a = b, \qquad a < b, \qquad a > b$$

must hold. Thus, inequalities are important to complete our comparisons of numbers. Inequalities are also important because they arise very frequently in nature, indeed, more frequently than equalities.

Some use of proofs in algebra may be expected in secondary school textbooks in the near future; indeed they are already included in some textbooks. Proofs are already common in college freshman texts, such as [40] and [52]; they are also common in books on the foundations of algebra, such as [18] and [31].

Answers for Exercises

8–1 *Equations and Natural Numbers*

1. $6 + 7 = 13$.   **2.** $8 + 9 = 17$.   **3.** $4 + 497 = 501$.

4. $2 \times 5 = 10$.   **5.** $3 \times 32 = 96$.   **6.** $314 \times 4 = 1,256$.

7. Transitive but neither reflexive nor symmetric.

8. Reflexive and transitive but not symmetric.

9. Transitive but neither reflexive nor symmetric.

10. Symmetric but neither reflexive nor transitive.

11. Reflexive, symmetric, and transitive.

12. Transitive but neither reflexive nor symmetric.

13. Not reflexive, symmetric, or transitive.

14. Distributive law.

15. Commutative law for addition.

16. Associative law for addition.

17. Commutative law for multiplication.

18. Commutative law for addition.

19. Symmetric property of equality.

20. Associative law for multiplication.

21. Distributive law.

22. Transitive property of equality.

23. Reflexive property of equality.

24. Commutative law for multiplication.

25. Distributive law.

26. Associative law for multiplication.

27. Commutative law for multiplication.

28. Associative law for multiplication.

29. Distributive law.

30. Commutative law for addition.

31. From the definition of the order of natural numbers, $a < b$ means $a + d = b$ for some natural number b. Then, $c = c$ from the reflexive property of $=$; $(a + d) + c = b + c$, from Example 4 of this section; $a + (d + c) = b + c$ from the associative property of addition; $a + (c + d) = b + c$ from the commutative property of addition; $(a + c) + d = b + c$ from the associative property of addition; and $a + c < b + c$ from the definition of order.

32. If a and b stand for the same number, then ac and bc each stand for the product of that number and c. Since any two numbers have one and only one product, the expressions ac and bc must both stand for that product; that is, $ac = bc$.

33. From the definition of order, $a < b$ means $a + d = b$ for some natural number d. Then $(a + d)c = bc$ from Ex. 32; $ac + dc = bc$ from the distributive property of multiplication with respect to addition; dc stands for a natural number from the closure property under multiplication; $ac < bc$ from the definition of order.

34. If $a = b$, then $a^2 = ba$ and $ab = b^2$, from Ex. 32; $a^2 = ab$ from the commutative property of multiplication; and $a^2 = b^2$ from the transitive property of $=$.

35. If $a = b$ and $c = d$, then a and b each stand for one number and c and d each stand for another number. Then $a + c$ and $b + d$ each stand for the sum of those two numbers. Since any two numbers have one and only one sum, $a + c = b + d$.

36. If $a = b$ and $c = d$, then a and b each stand for one number and c and d each stand for another number. Then ac and bd each stand for the product of these two numbers. Since any two numbers have one and only one product, $ac = bd$.

37. If $a - c = b - c$, then, by Example 4, $(a - c) + c = (b - c) + c$. By an assumed property of subtraction $(a - c) + c = a$ and $(b - c) + c = b$. Then, $a = b$ by the transitive property of $=$.

38. If $a \div c = b \div c$, then, by Ex. 32, $(a \div c) \times c = (b \div c) \times c$. By an assumed property of division, $(a \div c) \times c = a$ and $(b \div c) \times c = b$. Then $a = b$ by the transitive property of $=$.

39. If $a + c = b + c$, then, by an assumed property of subtraction, $(a + c) - c = a$ and $(b + c) - c = b$; since $a + c$ and $b + c$ stand for the same number, there is one and only one difference, and $(a + c) - c = (b + c) - c$; then $a = b$ by the transitive property of $=$.

40. If $a + c = b + d$ and $a = b$, then, by substitution for b, we have $a + c = a + d$; by the commutative property of addition, $c + a = d + a$; and, by Ex. 39, $c = d$.

41. If $ac = bc$, then, by an assumed property of division, $ac \div c = a$ and $bc \div c = b$; since ac and bc stand for the same number, there is one and only one quotient, and $ac \div c = bc \div c$; then $a = b$ by the transitive property of $=$.

42. If $ac = bd$ and $a = b$, then, by substitution for b, we have $ac = ad$; by the commutative property of multiplication, $ca = da$; and, by Ex. 41, $c = d$.

8–2 *Integers*

1. Let $[a - b]$ and $[c - d]$ be any two integers; then $[a - b] \times [c - d] = [(ac + bd) - (ad + bc)]$ by definition; $ac + bd$ and $ad + bc$ are natural numbers, since products and sums of natural numbers are natural numbers; the product $[(ac + bd) - (ad + bc)]$ is a difference of natural numbers and, therefore, an integer.

2. Let $p = [a - b]$ and $q = [c - d]$ be any two integers. Then,

$$p + q = [a - b] + [c - d];$$
$$= [(a + c) - (b + d)],$$

      by the definition of a sum of integers;

$$= [(c + a) - (d + b)],$$

      by the commutative property of addition of natural numbers;

$$= [c - d] + [a - b] = q + p,$$

      by the definition of a sum of integers.

3. Let $p = [a - b]$, $q = [c - d]$, and $r = [e - f]$ be any three integers. Then,

$$(p + q) + r = \{[a - b] + [c - d]\} + [e - f];$$
$$= [(a + c) - (b + d)] + [e - f],$$

      by the definition of a sum of integers;

$$= [\overline{(a + c + e)} - \overline{(b + d + f)}],$$

      by the definition of a sum of integers;

$$= [(a + \overline{c + e}) - (b + \overline{d + f})],$$

      by the associative property of addition of natural numbers;

$$= [a - b] + [(c + e) - (d + f)],$$

      by the definition of a sum of integers;

$$= [a - b] + \{[c - d] + [e - f]\} = p + (q + r),$$

      by the definition of a sum of integers.

4. Let $p = [a - b]$, $q = [c - d]$, and $r = [e - f]$ be any three integers. Then,

$$(pq)r = \{[a - b] \times [c - d]\} \times [e - f];$$
$$= [(ac + bd) - (ad + bc)] \times [e - f],$$

      by the definition of a product of integers;

$$= [\{(ac + bd)e + (ad + bc)f\} - \{(ac + bd)f + (ad + bc)e\}],$$

      by the definition of a product of integers;

$$= [\{(ace + bde) + (adf + bcf)\} - \{(acf + bdf) + (ade + bce)\}],$$

      by the distributive property of multiplication of natural numbers with respect to addition;

$$= [\{ace + (bde + \overline{adf + bcf})\} - \{acf + (bdf + \overline{ade + bce})\}],$$
by the associative property of addition of natural numbers;

$$= [\{ace + (\overline{adf + bcf} + bde)\} - \{acf + (\overline{ade + bce} + bdf)\}],$$
by the commutative property of addition of natural numbers;

$$= [\{ace + (adf + \overline{bcf + bde})\} - \{acf + (ade + \overline{bce + bdf})\}],$$
by the associative property of addition of natural numbers;

$$= [\{(ace + adf) + (bcf + bde)\} - \{(acf + ade) + (bce + bdf)\}],$$
by the associative property of addition of natural numbers;

$$= [\{a(ce + df) + b(cf + de)\} - \{a(cf + de) + b(ce + df)\}],$$
by the distributive property of multiplication of natural numbers with respect to addition;

$$= [a - b] \times [(ce + df) - (cf + de)],$$
by the definition of a product of integers;

$$= [a - b] \times \{[c - d] \times [e - f]\} = p(qr),$$
by the definition of a product of integers.

5. Let $[a - b]$ represent any integer. Exactly one of the relations $a < b$, $a = b$, and $a > b$ must hold, §8–1. If $a < b$, then there exists a natural number c such that $a + c = b$; $[a - b] = [a - (a + c)]$ by substitution for b; $[a - (a + c)] = [0 - c]$, since $a + c = (a + c) + 0$ by a property of 0; $[a - b] = [0 - c]$ by the transitive property of $=$; $[a - b]$ is a negative integer by definition. If $a = b$, then $[a - b] = [b - b]$ by substitution for b and $[a - b] = 0$ by definition. If $a > b$, then $b < a$ and there exists a natural number c such that $b + c = a$; $[a - b] = [(b + c) - b]$ by substitution for a; $[(b + c) - b] = [c - 0]$, since $(b + c) + 0 = b + c$ by a property of 0; $[a - b] = [c - 0]$ by the transitive property of $=$; $[a - b]$ is a positive number by definition.

6. Let $p = [a - 0]$ and $q = [b - 0]$ be any two positive integers. Then,

$$pq = [a - 0] \times [b - 0],$$
$$= [(ab + 0 \times 0) - (0 \times b + a \times 0)],$$
by the definition of a product of integers;

$$= [ab - 0] \text{ and is a positive integer,}$$
by the properties of zero and the definition of a positive integer.

7. Let $p = [0 - a]$ and $q = [0 - b]$ be any two negative integers. Then,

$$pq = [0 - a] \times [0 - b],$$
$$= [(0 \times 0 + ab) - (0 \times b + a \times 0)],$$
  by the definition of a product of integers;
$$= [ab - 0] \text{ and is a positive integer,}$$
  by the properties of zero and the definition of a positive integer.

8. Let $m = [a - b]$ be any integer. Then,

$$m \times 0 = [a - b] \times [c - c],$$
$$= [(ac + bc) - (ac + bc)] = 0,$$
  by the definition of a product of integers and the definition of 0;
$$m + 0 = [a - b] + [c - c],$$
$$= [(a + c) - (b + c)],$$
  by the definition of a sum of integers;
$$= [a - b] = m,$$
  since, as is needed for $[(a + c) - (b + c)] = [a - b]$, $(a + c) + b = (b + c) + a$ from the commutative and associative properties of addition of natural numbers.

9. Let $p = [a - 0]$ be any positive integer and $q = [0 - b]$ be any negative integer. Then,

$$pq = [a - 0] \times [0 - b],$$
$$= [(a \times 0 + 0 \times b) - (ab + 0 \times 0)],$$
  by the definition of a product of integers;
$$= [0 - ab] \text{ and is a negative integer,}$$
  by the properties of zero and the definitions of a negative integer.

10. Let $p = [a - b]$ and $q = [c - d]$ be any two integers and define:

$$p - q = [a - b] - [c - d] = [a - b] + [d - c].$$

Subtraction is always possible, since each subtraction problem is expressed in terms of an addition problem, which is always possible.

11. Note that, to prove that a property does not hold, it is sufficient to find a single situation in which it does not hold. Consider $[0 - 0]$ and $[0 - b]$; $[0 - 0] - [0 - b] = [0 - 0] + [b - 0] = [b - 0]$; $[0 - b] - [0 - 0] = [0 - b] + [0 - 0] = [0 - b]$; but $[b - 0] \neq [0 - b]$ when $b \neq 0$. Thus, using the definitions of addition and subtraction of integers and the properties of 0, we find that subtraction is not commutative.

12. Consider $[0 - 0]$, $[0 - a]$, and $[0 - b]$; then,

$$([0 - 0] - [0 - a]) - [0 - b] = ([0 - 0] + [a - 0]) + [b - 0],$$
$$\text{by the definition of subtraction,}$$
$$\text{Ex. 10;}$$

$$= [a - 0] + [b - 0], \text{ by Ex. 8;}$$

$$= [(a + b) - 0],$$
$$\text{by definition of addition of}$$
$$\text{integers;}$$

$$[0 - 0] - ([0 - a] - [0 - b]) = [0 - 0] - ([0 - a] + [b - 0]),$$
$$\text{by the definition of subtraction,}$$
$$\text{Ex. 10;}$$

$$= [0 - 0] - [b - a],$$
$$\text{by the definition of addition and}$$
$$\text{properties of zero;}$$

$$= [0 - 0] + [a - b],$$
$$\text{by the definition of subtraction;}$$

$$= [a - b],$$
$$\text{by the definition of addition and}$$
$$\text{properties of zero.}$$

Then, $[(a + b) - 0] \neq [a - b]$, since $(a + b) + b \neq 0 + a$ when $b \neq 0$.

13. Let $p = [a - b]$; then $-p = [b - a]$ and

$$p + (-p) = [a - b] + [b - a] = [(a + b) - (b + a)],$$
$$\text{by the definition of addition;}$$

$$= [(a + b) - (a + b)] = 0,$$
$$\text{by the commutative property of}$$
$$\text{the addition of natural numbers}$$
$$\text{and the definition of zero.}$$

14. Let $a = [r - s]$ and $b = [w - v]$; then $a - b = [r - s] - [w - v] = [r - s] + [v - w]$,

by definition of subtraction, Ex. 10;

$$= a + (-b),$$
by definition of $-b$.

15. For any integers $[a - b]$, $[c - d]$, and $[e - f]$, we have:

$[a - b] = [a - b]$, since $a + b = b + a$, by the commutative property of the addition of natural numbers.

If $[a - b] = [c - d]$, then, by definition, $a + d = b + c$;

$d + a = c + b$, by the commutative property of addition of natural numbers;

$c + b = d + a$, by the symmetric property of $=$ for natural numbers, and $[c - d] = [a - b]$, by definition.

If $[a - b] = [c - d]$ and $[c - d] = [e - f]$, then by definition $a + d = b + c$ and $c + f = d + e$;

$(a + d) + (c + f) = (b + c) + (d + e)$, by Ex. 35, §8–1;

$(d + a) + (f + c) = (c + b) + (e + d)$,
by the commutative property of addition;

$d + \{a + (f + c)\} = \{(c + b) + e\} + d$,
by the associative property of addition;

$a + (f + c) = (c + b) + e$,
by the commutative property of addition and Ex. 39, §8–1;

$(a + f) + c = c + (b + e)$,
by the associative property of addition;

$a + f = b + e$,
by the commutative property of addition and Ex. 39, §8–1;

$[a - b] = [e - f]$,
by definition of equality of integers.

16. Let $p = [a - b]$, $q = [c - d]$, and $r = [e - f]$ be any three integers. Then,

$$p(q + r) = [a - b] \times \{[c - d] + [e - f]\},$$
$$= [a - b] \times \{[(c + e) - (d + f)]\},$$
by the definition of a sum of integers;
$$= [\{a(c + e) + b(d + f)\} - \{a(d + f) + b(c + e)\}],$$
by the definition of a product of integers;
$$= [\{(ac + ae) + (bd + bf)\} - \{(ad + af) + (bc + be)\}],$$
by the distributive property of multiplication of natural numbers with respect to addition;
$$= [\{ac + (ae + \overline{bd + bf})\} - \{ad + (af + \overline{bc + be})\}],$$
by the associative property of addition;
$$= [\{ac + (\overline{ae + bd} + bf)\} - \{ad + (\overline{af + bc} + be)\}],$$
by the associative property of addition;
$$= [\{ac + (\overline{bd + ae} + bf)\} - \{ad + (\overline{bc + af} + be)\}],$$
by the commutative property of addition;
$$= [\{ac + (bd + \overline{ae + bf})\} - \{ad + (bc + \overline{af + be})\}],$$
by the associative property of addition;
$$= [\{(ac + bd) + (ae + bf)\} - \{(ad + bc) + (af + be)\}],$$
by the associative property of addition;
$$= [(ac + bd) - (ad + bc)] + [(ae + bf) - (af + be)],$$
by the definition of a sum of integers;
$$= [a - b] \times [c - d] + [a - b] \times [e - f] = pq + pr,$$
by the definition of a product of integers.

8–3 *Even and Odd Integers*

1. Let p be any integer; then, by the assumption stated at the beginning of this section, either $p = 2k + 0$ or $p = 2k + 1$ for some integer k. If $p = 2k + 0$, then p is even; if $p = 2k + 1$, then p is odd.

2. Let p be any even integer; by definition, $p = 2m$ for some integer m; then $p^2 = (2m)(2m) = 2[m(2m)]$ by the associative property of multiplication; then p^2 is even, since $m(2m)$ is an integer by the closure property of integers under multiplication.

3. Let p be any odd integer; by definition, $p = 2k + 1$ for some integer k; then,

$$p^2 = (2k + 1)(2k + 1),$$
$$= (2k + 1)(2k) + (2k + 1)(1),$$
by the distributive property of multiplication with respect to addition;
$$= (2k)(2k + 1) + (2k + 1),$$
by the commutative property of multiplication and a property of 1;
$$= \{2[k(2k + 1)] + 2k\} + 1,$$
by the associative properties of multiplication and addition;
$$= 2[k(2k + 1) + k] + 1$$
by the distributive property of multiplication with respect to addition.

Then p^2 is odd by the closure of the set of integers under addition and multiplication and the definition of an odd integer, since p^2 is of the form $2m + 1$ for some integer m.

4. Any integer is either even or odd, Ex. 1. If an integer is even, its square is even, Ex. 2; if an integer is odd, its square is odd, Ex. 3. If the square of an integer is odd, the integer cannot be even and thus must be odd. If the square of an integer is even, the integer cannot be odd and thus must be even.

5. Let $2k$ and $2m$ be any two even integers. Then their sum $2k + 2m = 2(k + m)$, by the distributive property of multiplication, and their sum is even, by the closure of the set of integers under addition and the definition of an even integer.

Let $2k + 1$ and $2m + 1$ be any two odd integers. Then their sum:
$$(2k + 1) + (2m + 1) = \{(2k + 1) + 2m\} + 1,$$
by the associative property of addition;
$$= \{2k + (1 + 2m)\} + 1,$$
by the associative property of addition;
$$= \{2k + (2m + 1)\} + 1,$$
by the commutative property of addition;

$$= \{(2k + 2m) + 1\} + 1$$
by the associative property of addition;

$$= (2k + 2m) + (1 + 1)$$
by the associative property of addition;

$$= 2(k + m) + 2 \times 1,$$
by the distributive law and the definition of 2;

$$= 2\{(k + m) + 1\},$$
by the distributive law.

Then the product is even by the closure of the set of integers under addition and the definition of an even integer.

6. Let $2k$ be any even integer and $(2m + 1)$ be any odd integer. Then their sum $2k + (2m + 1) = (2k + 2m) + 1 = 2(k + m) + 1$ and is odd, by the associative property of addition, the distributive property of multiplication with respect to addition, the closure of the set of integers under addition, and the definition of an odd integer.

7. Let $(2k + 1)$ and $(2m + 1)$ be any two odd integers. Then their product:

$$(2k + 1)(2m + 1) = (2k + 1)(2m) + (2k + 1)(1),$$
by the distributive property of multiplication with respect to addition;

$$= (2m)(2k + 1) + (2k + 1),$$
by the commutative property of multiplication and a property of 1;

$$= \{2[m(2k + 1)] + 2k\} + 1,$$
by the associative property of addition and multiplication;

$$= 2[m(2k + 1) + k] + 1,$$
by the distributive property of multiplication with respect to addition.

Then the product is odd, by the closure of the set of integers under addition and multiplication and the definition of an odd integer.

8. Any integer is either even or odd, Ex. 1. If the product of two integers is even, they are not both odd, Ex. 7, and thus at least one of the integers must be even.

9. As in Ex. 4 for the factor 2, we now prove that if p has a factor 3, then p^2 has a factor 3; if p does not have a factor 3, then p^2 does not have a factor 3. By the assumption at the beginning of this section, $p = 3m + 0$, $p = 3m + 1$, or $p = 3m + 2$ for some integer m. If $p = 3m$, then $p^2 = (3m)(3m) = 3[m(3m)]$, by the associative property of multiplication, and 3 is a factor of p^2. If $p = 3m + 1$, then

$$p^2 = (3m + 1)(3m + 1),$$
$$= (3m + 1)(3m) + (3m + 1)(1),$$
by the distributive property of multiplication with respect to addition;
$$= (3m)(3m + 1) + (3m + 1),$$
by the commutative property of multiplication and a property of 1;
$$= \{3[m(3m + 1)] + 3m\} + 1,$$
by the associative properties of addition and multiplication;
$$= 3[m(3m + 1) + m] + 1,$$
by the distributive property of multiplication with respect to addition.

Thus, if $p = 3m + 1$, then p^2 does not have 3 as a factor.
Similarly, if $p = 3m + 2$, then,

$$p^2 = (3m + 2)(3m + 2)$$
$$= (3m + 2)(3m) + (3m + 2)(2)$$
$$= (3m)(3m + 2) + (6m + 4)$$
$$= \{3[m(3m + 2)] + 6m\} + 4$$
$$= 3[m(3m + 2) + 2m] + 4,$$

and p^2 does not have 3 as a factor.
Thus, if p^2 has 3 as a factor, then $p \neq 3m + 1$, $p \neq 3m + 2$, and $p = 3m$ with a factor 3.

10. By the assumption at the beginning of this section, $p = 5m$ or $p = 5m + k$ for $k = 1, 2, 3,$ or 4. If $p = 5m$, then $p^2 = (5m)(5m) = 5[m(5m)]$, by the associative property of multiplication, and p^2 has 5 as a factor. If $p = 5m + k$ for some $k = 1, 2, 3,$ or 4, then,

$$p^2 = (5m + k)(5m + k),$$

$= (5m + k)(5m) + (5m + k)(k),$

by the distributive property of multiplication with respect to addition;

$= (5m)(5m + k) + [(5m)k + k^2],$

by the commutative and distributive properties of multiplication;

$= [(5m)(5m + k) + (5m)k] + k^2,$

by the associative property of addition;

$= 5\{m[(5m + k) + k]\} + k^2,$

by the distributive and associative properties of multiplication.

Then, since k^2 does not have a factor 5 for any of the values 1, 2, 3, 4, p^2 does not have a factor of 5 if $p \neq 5m$. Thus, if p^2 has a factor of 5, then $p = 5m$ and p has a factor of 5.

8-4 Rational Numbers

1. Let $p = \dfrac{a}{b}$ and $q = \dfrac{c}{d}$ be any two rational numbers. Then $pq = \dfrac{a}{b} \times \dfrac{c}{d} = \dfrac{ac}{bd}$, by definition of a product of rational numbers; ac and bd are integers, Ex. 1, §8–2; pq is a quotient of integers with $bd \neq 0$ and thus is a rational number.

2. Let $p = \dfrac{a}{b}$ and $q = \dfrac{c}{d}$ be any two rational numbers. Then,

$$p + q = \frac{a}{b} + \frac{c}{d} = \frac{ad + bc}{bd},$$

by the definition of a sum of rational numbers;

$$= \frac{bc + ad}{bd},$$

by the commutative property of addition for integers;

$$= \frac{cb + da}{db},$$

by the commutative property of multiplication for integers;

$$= \frac{c}{d} + \frac{a}{b} = q + p,$$

by the definition of a sum of rational numbers.

3. Let $p = \frac{a}{b}$, $q = \frac{c}{d}$, and $r = \frac{e}{f}$ be any three rational numbers. Then,

$$(p + q) + r = \left(\frac{a}{b} + \frac{c}{d}\right) + \frac{e}{f},$$

$$= \frac{ad + bc}{bd} + \frac{e}{f} = \frac{(ad + bc)(f) + (bd)e}{(bd)f},$$

by the definition of sum of rational numbers;

$$= \frac{[(ad)f + (bc)f] + (bd)e}{(bd)f},$$

by the distributive property of multiplication with respect to addition;

$$= \frac{(ad)f + [(bc)f + (bd)e]}{(bd)f},$$

by the associative property of addition;

$$= \frac{a(df) + [b(cf) + b(de)]}{b(df)},$$

by the associative property of multiplication;

$$= \frac{a(df) + b(cf + de)}{b(df)},$$

by the distributive property of multiplication with respect to addition;

$$= \frac{a}{b} + \frac{cf + de}{df} = \frac{a}{b} + \left(\frac{c}{d} + \frac{e}{f}\right) = p + (q + r),$$

by the definition of a sum of rational numbers.

4. Let $p = \dfrac{a}{b}$ and $q = \dfrac{c}{d}$ be any two rational numbers. Then,

$$pq = \frac{a}{b} \times \frac{c}{d} = \frac{ac}{bd} = \frac{ca}{db} = \frac{c}{d} \times \frac{a}{b} = qp,$$

by the definition of a product of rational numbers and the commutative property of multiplication for integers.

5. Let $p = \dfrac{a}{b}$, $q = \dfrac{c}{d}$, and $r = \dfrac{e}{f}$ be any three rational numbers. Then

$$p(qr) = \frac{a}{b}\left(\frac{c}{d} \times \frac{e}{f}\right),$$

$$= \frac{a}{b} \times \frac{ce}{df} = \frac{a(ce)}{b(df)},$$

by the definition of a product of rational numbers;

$$= \frac{(ac)e}{(bd)f},$$

by the associative property of multiplication for integers;

$$= \frac{ac}{bd} \times \frac{e}{f} = \left(\frac{a}{b} \times \frac{c}{d}\right) \times \frac{e}{f} = (pq)r,$$

by the definition of a product of rational numbers.

6. Given any rational number $\dfrac{a}{b}$ and any rational number $\dfrac{c}{d} \neq 0$, we define $\dfrac{a}{b} \div \dfrac{c}{d} = \dfrac{a}{b} \times \dfrac{d}{c}$. Thus, division by a number different from zero is always possible, since it is defined in terms of multiplication, which is always possible.

7. If $\dfrac{a}{b} \neq 0$, then $\dfrac{b}{a}$ is the reciprocal of $\dfrac{a}{b}$, since $\dfrac{a}{b} \times \dfrac{b}{a} = \dfrac{ab}{ab} = 1$.

8. If $k \neq 0$ and $b \neq 0$, then $bk \neq 0$, $(ak)b = a(kb) = (kb)a = (bk)a$, by the associative and commutative properties of multiplication;

$\dfrac{ak}{bk} = \dfrac{a}{b}$, by definition of the equality of rational numbers, since $(ak)b = (bk)a$ by the transitive property of $=$ in the sequence of equalities just considered.

9. Whenever a and b are both even, $\dfrac{a}{b} = \dfrac{2k}{2m} = \dfrac{k}{m}$, by Ex. 8. Since a is finite, this process may be repeated until a and b are not both even.

8–5 *Real Numbers*

1. Suppose that $\sqrt{3} = \dfrac{a}{b}$, where a and b are integers that are not both divisible by 3; then, $3 = \dfrac{a^2}{b^2}$; $3b^2 = a^2$; $a = 3k$, by Ex. 9, §8–3; $3b^2 = 9k^2$; $b^2 = 3k^2$; b has a factor 3, contrary to the assumption that a and b do not both have a factor 3. Thus, our assumption that $\sqrt{3}$ is rational is false, and $\sqrt{3}$ is irrational.

2. Suppose that $\sqrt{5} = \dfrac{a}{b}$, where a and b are integers that are not both divisible by 5; then $5 = \dfrac{a^2}{b^2}$; $5b^2 = a^2$; $a = 5k$, by Ex. 10, §8–3; $5b^2 = 25k^2$; $b^2 = 5k^2$; b has a factor 5, contrary to the assumption that a and b do not both have a factor 5. Thus, our assumption that $\sqrt{5}$ is rational is false, and $\sqrt{5}$ is irrational.

CHAPTER

NINE

AN INTRODUCTION TO ABSTRACT ALGEBRA

Abstract algebra is concerned with sets of elements and operations upon these elements. The elements are usually numbers and variables. The most common operations are the four rational operations: addition, subtraction, multiplication, and division. We shall begin our discussion with the set of positive integers, and make several extensions of the set of numbers under consideration in order to be able to perform new operations.

9–1 The Set of Integers

The **positive integers** correspond to the natural numbers used in counting (§8–1). As in §8–1, any sum or product of two positive integers is a positive integer.

We introduce the number 0, and call the set of positive integers and zero the set of **non-negative integers.** The reasons for making this extension are:

1. To obtain a number 0 such that $a + 0 = a$ for any positive integer a;

2. To solve equations of the form $a + x = a$ for any positive integer a; and

3. To associate a number with the number of elements in the empty set.

Next, we define the negative of a positive integer b to be $(-b)$, such that $b + (-b) = 0$. This extension of the set of non-negative integers to the set of **integers** (positive, negative, and zero) enables us:

4. To subtract any integer a from any integer b;
5. To solve equations of the form $x + a = b$ for any integers a and b; and
6. To obtain the inverse $(-a)$ under addition for any integer a; that is, to obtain the additive inverse.

The importance of the inverse of a number under an operation will be clear after we consider "groups" of numbers.

We started with the set of positive integers. We needed zero and the negative integers in order to be able to have numbers to represent the results obtained by subtraction (for example, $5 - 5$ and $5 - 7$), as well as to solve simple equations (such as $x + 5 = 5$ and $x + 7 = 5$). Consider the addition of integers under the assumptions stated in §8–1. Then,

1. The set of integers is **closed** under addition; that is, the sum of any two integers is an integer.
2. The **associative** law for addition is satisfied; that is,

$$a + (b + c) = (a + b) + c$$

for any integers a, b, and c.
3. The set contains an **identity element,** 0, for addition; that is, an element 0 such that $a + 0 = a$ for every integer a.
4. The set contains the **inverse** under addition of each element; that is, for each integer a, there is an integer $(-a)$ in the set such that $a + (-a) = 0$.

We indicate that the set of integers has these four properties by saying that *the set of integers forms a* **group** *under addition.* Notice that these properties involve an identity element and the inverse of each element under addition.

Zero is the **identity element for addition,** because $b + 0 = b$ for any integer b; one is the **identity element for multiplication,** because $b \times 1 = b$ for any integer b.

The **inverse of a positive or negative number under addition** is the *negative* of the number: $2 + (-2) = 0$; $(-5) + [-(-5)] = 0$; $b + (-b) = 0$. The identity element, 0, is its own inverse under addition: $0 + 0 = 0$. The **inverse of a number under multiplication** is its *reciprocal*: $5(\frac{1}{5}) = 1$; $\frac{1}{2}\dfrac{1}{(\frac{1}{2})} = 1$; $b\left(\dfrac{1}{b}\right) = 1$ for any number $b \neq 0$.

Notice that the sum of any number and its inverse under addition is 0, the identity element for addition; the product of any number and its inverse under multiplication is 1, the identity element for multiplication.

Subtraction may be defined by

$$a - b = a + (-b); \qquad a - 0 = a + 0.$$

Thus, the presence of the negative of each number makes subtraction possible: To subtract a number, add its negative. This is a precise form of the saying, "Change the sign and add."

Division may be defined by

$$a \div b = a\left(\frac{1}{b}\right) \quad \text{for any } b \neq 0.$$

Notice that 1 and -1 are the only integers which have reciprocals that are integers. This implies that division is not, in general, possible as long as we are restricted to the set of integers. Indeed, this will provide our basis for extending the set of numbers under consideration to include all rational numbers.

Exercises

1. List each integer that is its own negative.
2. List each integer that is its own reciprocal.
3. List each integer that does not have a rational number as its reciprocal.

9–2 Groups and Rings

A set of elements forms a *group with respect to addition* if:

1. The set is closed under addition;
2. The associative law for addition holds;
3. The identity element for addition (0) is a member of the set; and
4. Each element of the set has its inverse under addition (its negative) in the set.

A set of elements forms a *group with respect to multiplication* if:

1. The set is closed under multiplication;
2. The associative law for multiplication holds;
3. The identity element for multiplication (1) is a member of the set; and
4. Each element of the set has its inverse under multiplication (its reciprocal) in the set.

In each case, a group is *commutative*, sometimes called **Abelian**, if the commutative law holds. Thus, since $a + b = b + a$ for any two integers, the set of integers forms a commutative group with respect to addition. The set of rational numbers different from zero forms a commutative group with respect to multiplication, since $a \times b = b \times a$.

A set of elements forms a **ring** if:

1. The elements of the set form a commutative group under addition;
2. The set is closed under multiplication;
3. The elements of the set satisfy the associative law for multiplication; and
4. The elements of the set satisfy the distributive law for multiplication with respect to addition.

Exercises

The properties that a set of elements must have in order to form a ring are identified at the left. Copy the array; use "+" to show that the set identified

	1.	2.	3.	4.	*5.
Property	Integers	Even Integers	Odd Integers	$3n$	nk
Closed +					
Associative +					
0, the + identity					
Negatives, the + inverses					
Group +					
Commutative group +					
Closed ✗					
Associative ✗					
Distributive law					
Ring					

at the top of the column has the property; use "—" to show that the set does not have the property.

Note: Definitions for "even integers" and "odd integers" may be found in §8–3. In Ex. 4 we have used $3n$ to stand for the set of integral multiples of 3; in Ex. 5, nk to stand for the set of integral multiples of any given constant k that is different from zero. Notice that 0 may be expressed in the form $3(0)$ and also in the form $(0)k$.

Show that:

6. The set of integers does not form a group under multiplication.

★7. The set consisting of the two elements $+1$ and -1 forms a commutative group under multiplication.

9–3 The Set of Rational Numbers

We have seen that the set of integers is not closed with respect to division; that is, division is not always possible. We extend the set of integers to include all rational numbers (fractions and integers) so that we may:

1. Divide any integer a by any integer b different from zero;
2. Solve equations of the form $bx = a$, where a and b are integers, b different from zero; and

3. Obtain the inverse $\left(\dfrac{1}{b}\right)$ for any integer b different from zero under

multiplication.

Let us pause and consider the extensions of the set of natural numbers that we have discussed. Each natural number n has been identified with a positive number $+n$ in the set of integers. Each positive integer $+n$ has been identified with a positive rational number $+\dfrac{n}{1}$ in the set of rational numbers. We write $n = +n = +\dfrac{n}{1}$.

These equalities show a matching of the elements as we expand the set of elements under consideration and, at each stage, identify the preceding set with a subset of the new set. We are "building" our number system.

The set of rational numbers forms a field. Any set of numbers forms a **field** if it forms a ring and:

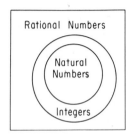

1. The identity element for multiplication, 1, is a member of the set;
2. The commutative law for multiplication is satisfied; and
3. Each element of the set except 0, the identity element for addition, has its inverse under multiplication in the set.

Responsible people have described the main goal of the first course in algebra as an understanding of the properties of a field. You may think of these as properties of the set of rational numbers. The above definitions describe them; the exercises will develop them further.

One other property of the set of rational numbers deserves consideration. The set of rational numbers is **dense**; that is, between any two elements of the set, there is another element of the set. Between any two rational numbers a and b, you can find many rational numbers, including, for example, $\dfrac{a+b}{2}$. It is this property of the rational numbers that makes them so useful for measurements; you can use a rational number to describe a measurement as precisely as you wish.

Exercises

Property	1. Positive Integers	2. Integers	3. Positive Rationals	4. Rationals	5. $n\sqrt{2}$	*6. $p\sqrt{2}$	*7. $p+q\sqrt{2}$
Closed **+**							
Associative **+**							
0, the **+** identity							
Negatives, the **+** inverses							
Group **+**							
Commutative group **+**							
Closed **×**							
Associative **×**							
Distributive law							
Ring							
1, the **×** identity							
Commutative **×**							
Reciprocals, the **×** inverses							
Field							

The properties that a set of elements must have in order to form a field are identified at the left. Copy the array shown at the bottom of page 160; use "+" to show that the set identified at the top of the column has the property; use "−" to show that the set does not have the property.

Note: In Ex. 5 we have used $n\sqrt{2}$ for the set of multiples of $\sqrt{2}$, where n stands for an integer (positive, negative, or zero); in Ex. 6, $p\sqrt{2}$ for the set of multiples of $\sqrt{2}$, where p stands for a rational number (positive, negative, or zero); in Ex. 7, $p + q\sqrt{2}$ for the set of numbers expressible in this form, where p and q stand for rational numbers (positive, negative, or zero).

9–4 The Set of Real Numbers

We have seen that the rational numbers are dense. Yet the rational points do not fill the number line; that is, the line of rational points is not **continuous** and the set of rational numbers is not **complete**. For example, a unit square has diagonal of length $\sqrt{2}$, and (as in §8–5) we know that $\sqrt{2}$ is not a rational number. There is a point on the number line with coordinate $\sqrt{2}$. If we are to have coordinates for all points on a number line, we must extend the set of numbers under consideration to include all real numbers. The line of real points is continuous and the set of real numbers is both dense and complete.

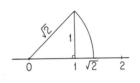

This need for extending the set of numbers under consideration can also be expressed in terms of roots of equations such as $x^2 - 2 = 0$. If x stands for any integer, the solution set of $x^2 - 2 = 0$ is the empty set; if x stands for a rational number, the solution set of $x^2 - 2 = 0$ is the empty set. We need to extend the set of numbers under consideration to include irrational numbers in order to have roots for equations such as $x^2 - 2 = 0$. We may do this by accepting all decimals as numbers.

We recognize three types of decimals:

terminating decimals, such as $\frac{1}{4} = 0.25$;
repeating decimals, such as $\frac{1}{3} = 0.333\overline{3} \ldots$ and
$$\tfrac{12}{7} = 1.71428\overline{5}714285 \ldots;$$

nonterminating, nonrepeating decimals, such as $\sqrt{2} = 1.4142 \ldots$ and
$\pi = 3.1415962 \ldots$.

Note the use of a bar over the repeated digits or digit and the assumption that such a pattern of repeated digits does not occur when the bar is missing. You may, if you wish, think of any terminating decimal as having repeated zeros; $\frac{1}{4} = 0.2500\bar{0}$ . . ... Each terminating or repeating decimal represents a rational number; each nonterminating, nonrepeating decimal represents an **irrational number**, that is, a real number that is not a rational number.

If a decimal is terminating, you can write it as a fraction with a power of 10 as the denominator. For example,

$$\text{if } n = 0.7500\bar{0} \ . \ . \ ., \text{ then } 100n = 75,$$
$$\text{and } n = \tfrac{75}{100}, \text{ which reduces to } \tfrac{3}{4}.$$

If a fraction can be expressed as a terminating decimal, its denominator must be a factor of a power of 10; that is, its denominator must be of the form $2^p 5^q$ for some non-negative integers p and q. Any divisor of a power of 10 must be expressible as a product of 2's and 5's.

If a decimal n repeats one digit, we can find $10n - n$. For example, suppose $n = 3.244\bar{4}$. . . . Then,

$$
\begin{aligned}
10n &= 32.444\bar{4} \ldots \\
n &= \ \ 3.244\bar{4} \ldots \\
\hline
9n &= 29.200\bar{0} \ldots \\
n &= \frac{29.2}{9} = \frac{292}{90} = \frac{146}{45}.
\end{aligned}
$$

We can also avoid the use of decimals in common fractions:

$$
\begin{aligned}
100n &= 324.44\bar{4} \\
10n &= \ \ 32.44\bar{4} \\
\hline
90n &= 292 \\
n &= \frac{292}{90} = \frac{146}{45}.
\end{aligned}
$$

If a decimal n repeats two digits, we find $10^2 n - n$; if it repeats three digits, we find $10^3 n - n$; and so forth.

We have seen how any repeating decimal can be written as a rational number. Now consider any rational number such as $\frac{12}{7}$. When we divide by 7, the possible remainders are 0, 1, 2, 3, 4, 5, 6. If the remainder is 0, the division is exact; if any remainder occurs a second time, the terms after it will repeat also. Since there are only 7 possible remainders when you divide by 7, the remainders must repeat or be exact by the 7th decimal place. Similarly, any rational number $\frac{p}{q}$ can be expressed as a terminating or repeating decimal, and at most q decimal places will be needed to identify it.

We assume that all real numbers may be added, subtracted, multiplied, and divided according to the same rules as the rational numbers. Then the set of real numbers forms a field. We may distinguish the set of real numbers from the set of rational numbers by the fact that the inclusion of the irrational numbers enables us to assign a number as a coordinate to each point on a number line. In particular, each positive number has roots of all orders ($\sqrt{}$, $\sqrt[3]{}$, $\sqrt[4]{}$, and, indeed, $\sqrt[n]{}$ for any real number n).

The real numbers may be classified in several ways. Any real number is:

1. Positive, negative, or zero;
2. A rational number or an irrational number;
3. Expressible as a terminating, a repeating, or nonterminating, nonrepeating decimal;
4. Expressible in terms of 1 and the operations $+$, $-$, $\times$, $\div$, and $\sqrt{}$ (that is, **constructible**) or not so expressible. For example,

$$\sqrt{\tfrac{3}{2}} = \sqrt{(1 + 1 + 1) \div (1 + 1)};$$

$\sqrt[3]{3}$ cannot be so expressed since the cube root cannot be expressed in terms of square roots.

Many real numbers may be expressed in terms of rational operations $(+, -, \times, \div)$ and radicals. Given any such number, we can find an equation which it satisfies.

Example. Find an equation with integral coefficients satisfied by $\sqrt[3]{2 - 3\sqrt{5}}$.

SOLUTION: Let $x = \sqrt[3]{2 - 3\sqrt{5}}$. Then,

$$x^3 = 2 - 3\sqrt{5}$$
$$x^3 - 2 = -3\sqrt{5}$$
$$x^6 - 4x^3 + 4 = 45$$
$$x^6 - 4x^3 - 41 = 0.$$

The example may be checked by substitution:

$$(\sqrt[3]{2 - 3\sqrt{5}})^6 - 4(\sqrt[3]{2 - 3\sqrt{5}})^3 - 41$$
$$= 4 - 12\sqrt{5} + 45 - 8 + 12\sqrt{5} - 41 = 0.$$

Notice that the set of constructible numbers includes all rational numbers and a few irrational numbers; the set of numbers expressible in terms of rational operations and radicals includes all constructible numbers and some others besides. Some of these numbers satisfy equations with integral coefficients. However, these numbers do not include all roots of equations with integral coefficients, since it is not possible to solve general equations of degree greater than 4 in terms of rational operations and radicals.

Exercises

Factor each denominator and tell whether or not each rational number can be expressed by a terminating decimal:

1. $\frac{3}{8}$ **2.** $\frac{5}{12}$ **3.** $\frac{13}{32}$ **4.** $\frac{17}{20}$ **5.** $\frac{119}{256}$

Express each number in terms of 1's and the rational operations and $\sqrt{}$:

6. 3   **7.** $\frac{2}{3}$ **8.** $\sqrt{5}$ **9.** $\sqrt{\frac{1}{2}}$ **10.** $\frac{1}{2}\sqrt{3}$

Find an equation with integral coefficients satisfied by each number:

11. $2 - \sqrt{3}$ **12.** $3 + 2\sqrt{5}$

13. $\sqrt{5 - \sqrt{3}}$ **14.** $\sqrt{3 - 2\sqrt[3]{2}}$

15. Use an indirect method of proof and the fact that $\sqrt{2}$ is irrational to prove that $b\sqrt{2}$ is irrational for any rational number b different from zero.

Hint: Suppose that $b\sqrt{2} = q$, where q is a rational number. Does $\sqrt{2} = \frac{q}{b}$?

Is $\frac{q}{b}$ a rational number?

16. Repeat Ex. 15 for $a + b\sqrt{2}$ for any rational numbers a and b.

As in the exercises for §9–3, copy the array on page 165; use "+" to show that the set has the property; use "−" to show that the set does not have the property.

Note: The term "fractional" is used to mean rational but not equivalent to an integer.

Property	17. Real	18. Irrational	19. Fractional	20. Positive Real
Closed **+**				
Associative **+**				
0, the **+** identity				
Negatives, the **+** inverses				
Group **+**				
Commutative group **+**				
Closed **✗**				
Associative **✗**				
Distributive law				
Ring				
1, the **✗** identity				
Commutative **✗**				
Reciprocals, the **✗** inverses				
Field				

9–5 The Set of Complex Numbers

We make one final extension of our number system in order to be able to solve equations such as $x^2 + 1 = 0$. When our domain is the set of real numbers, the solution set for the preceding equation is the empty set. In order to offer a solution for this type of equation, we introduce the set of imaginary numbers with the definition $i = \sqrt{-1}$.

Any **complex number** may be expressed in the form $a + bi$ where a and b stand for real numbers and $i^2 = -1$. We also define:

$a + bi = c + di$ if and only if $a = c$ and $b = d$;
$(a + bi) + (c + di) = (a + c) + (b + d)i$;
$(a + bi)(c + di) = (ac - bd) + (ad + bc)i$.

We do not define order relations for complex numbers.

Complex numbers, like integers (§8–2), may be introduced as ordered pairs of numbers. Compare these definitions for ordered pairs (a, b) of real numbers with the previous definitions:

$(a, b) = (c, d)$ if and only if $a = c$ and $b = d$;

$(a, b) + (c, d) = (a + c, b + d)$;

$(a, b) \times (c, d) = (ac - bd, ad + bc)$.

The importance of recognizing the domain in which one is working is shown by the solution sets of the equations in the following array:

Domain	$x^2 - 1 = 0$	$4x^2 - 1 = 0$	$x^2 - 2 = 0$	$x^2 + 1 = 0$
Positive Integers	$\{1\}$	$\emptyset$	$\emptyset$	$\emptyset$
Integers	$\{1, -1\}$	$\emptyset$	$\emptyset$	$\emptyset$
Rational Numbers	$\{1, -1\}$	$\{\frac{1}{2}, -\frac{1}{2}\}$	$\emptyset$	$\emptyset$
Real Numbers	$\{1, -1\}$	$\{\frac{1}{2}, -\frac{1}{2}\}$	$\{\sqrt{2}, -\sqrt{2}\}$	$\emptyset$
Complex Numbers	$\{1, -1\}$	$\{\frac{1}{2}, -\frac{1}{2}\}$	$\{\sqrt{2}, -\sqrt{2}\}$	$\{i, -i\}$

The following chart shows the structure of our complex number system:

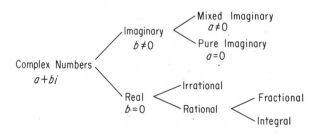

Notice that we have arrived at the set of complex numbers by several steps of broadening our concept of numbers. For example, we have considered:

the natural number 5

the positive integer $+5$

the positive rational number $+\frac{5}{1}$
the positive real number $+5.00\bar{0}\ldots$
the complex number $5 + 0i$.

These have been identified with each other as we extended our concept of numbers.

Students often ask how we might continue to expand our number system. Such students usually recognize that signed numbers (such as $+3$ and -2) may be represented by vectors on a line; complex numbers may be represented by vectors on a plane. We may continue our process in terms of three-dimensional vectors and, in general, linear vector spaces. The study of quaternions [26] may also be considered an extension, but the popular emphasis now is on vector spaces.

Exercises

Complete the array as on page 166 *to show the dependence of the solution set of each equation upon the domain of possible values for the variable.*

Domain	1. $x^2-4=0$	2. $9x^2-4=0$	3. $x^2-3=0$	4. $x^2+3=0$
Positive Integers				
Integers				
Rational Numbers				
Real Numbers				
Complex Numbers				

The above exercises depend upon these definitions:
Any complex number can be written in the form $a + bi$, where a and b stand for real numbers; each number that we consider is equivalent to a complex number. In other words, we usually study only complex numbers. A complex number $a + bi$ is real if $b = 0$; it is imaginary if $b \neq 0$. Thus, the numbers $3 = 3 + 0i$ and $0 = 0 + 0i$ are real and not imaginary. A complex number is **pure imaginary** if $b \neq 0$ and $a = 0$; it is **mixed imaginary** if $b \neq 0$ and $a \neq 0$.

As before, copy the array; use "+" to show that the set has the property; use "−" to show that the set does not have the property.

	5. Complex	6. Imaginary	7. Pure Imaginary	8. Mixed Imaginary
Property				
Closed +				
Associative +				
0, the + identity				
Negatives, the + inverses				
Group +				
Commutative group +				
Closed ×				
Associative ×				
Distributive law				
Ring				
1, the × identity				
Commutative ×				
Reciprocals, the × inverses				
Field				

Application and Additional Readings

The concepts considered in this chapter provide a basis for the use of numbers at all levels. All secondary school mathematics teachers should understand these properties of numbers. All students who study signed numbers should recognize (not necessarily by name) the properties of the integers and rational numbers. Properties of real numbers should be included in any four-year high school program. Indeed, the better students should consider all of the material discussed in this chapter. The study of groups, rings, and fields is found in nearly all abstract algebra textbooks; [4] and [6] are recommended. Their use in developing the complex number system will be found in greater detail in [18] and [31].

Answers for Exercises

9-1 *The Set of Integers*

1. 0.

2. 1, -1.

3. 0, since $\dfrac{1}{0}$ is undefined and thus is not a rational number.

9-2 *Groups and Rings*

Property	1. Integers	2. Even Integers	3. Odd Integers	4. $3n$	5. nk
Closed **+**	+	+	−	+	+
Associative **+**	+	+	+	+	+
0, the **+** identity	+	+	−	+	+
Negatives, the **+** inverses	+	+	+	+	+
Group **+**	+	+	−	+	+
Commutative group **+**	+	+	−	+	+
Closed **×**	+	+	+	+	+
Associative **×**	+	+	+	+	+
Distributive law	+	+	+	+	+
Ring	+	+	−	+	+

6. The set of integers cannot form a group under multiplication, since each integer different from 1 and -1 fails to have an inverse element (reciprocal) under multiplication in the set of integers.

7. We make a multiplication table for the given set of elements. The set is closed under multiplication, since its elements suffice to complete the table. The associative and commutative laws for multiplication hold for all integers and in particular for this subset of the set of integers. The multiplicative identity $+1$ is a member of

×	+1	−1
+1	+1	−1
−1	−1	+1

the set. Each element has a reciprocal in the set, since $+1$ occurs on each row of the table. Thus, the set forms a commutative group under multiplication. The symmetry of the table with respect to the main diagonal could have been used to show that the commutative law was satisfied.

9–3 *The Set of Rational Numbers*

Property	1. Positive Integers	2. Integers	3. Positive Rationals	4. Rationals	5. $n\sqrt{2}$	6. $p\sqrt{2}$	7. $p+q\sqrt{2}$
Closed **+**	+	+	+	+	+	+	+
Associative **+**	+	+	+	+	+	+	+
0, the **+** identity	−	+	−	+	+	+	+
Negatives, the **+** inverses	−	+	−	+	+	+	+
Group **+**	−	+	−	+	+	+	+
Commutative group **+**	−	+	−	+	+	+	+
Closed **×**	+	+	+	+	−	−	+
Associative **×**	+	+	+	+	+	+	+
Distributive law	+	+	+	+	+	+	+
Ring	−	+	−	+	−	−	+
1, the **×** identity	+	+	+	+	−	−	+
Commutative **×**	+	+	+	+	+	+	+
Reciprocals, the **×** inverses	−	−	+	+	−	+	+
Field	−	−	−	+	−	−	+

9–4 *The Set of Real Numbers*

1. Yes, $8 = 2^3$.

2. No; $12 = 2^2 \times 3$ and thus cannot be expressed in the form $2^p 5^q$ for non-negative integers p and q.

3. Yes; $32 = 2^5$.

4. Yes; $20 = 2^2 \times 5$.

5. Yes; $256 = 2^8$.

Note: There are many correct answers for Exercises 6 through 12. Here are some acceptable ones.

6. $1 + 1 + 1$.

7. $(1 + 1) \div (1 + 1 + 1)$.

8. $\sqrt{1 + 1 + 1 + 1 + 1}$

9. $\sqrt{1 \div (1 + 1)}$

10. $[1 \div (1 + 1)]\sqrt{1 + 1 + 1}$

Note: There are many correct answers for Exs. 11 through 14. Each may be obtained by multiplying both members of the equation given here by an integer different from zero or by rewriting the equation in an equivalent form. In Exs. 11, 13, and 14, note that the root used to obtain the equation is not the "principal" root of the equation.

11. $x^2 - 4x + 1 = 0$.

12. $x^2 - 6x - 11 = 0$.

13. $x^4 - 10x^2 + 22 = 0$.

14. $x^6 - 9x^4 + 27x^2 - 11 = 0$.

15. Suppose $b\sqrt{2} = p$ for some rational number p; then $\sqrt{2} = p \div b$ and $\sqrt{2}$ would be rational. Since $\sqrt{2}$ is irrational, our assumption that $b\sqrt{2}$ is rational must be false.

16. If $a + b\sqrt{2} = p$ for some rational number p, then $b\sqrt{2} = p - a$, a rational number, and $\sqrt{2}$ would be rational, as in Ex. 15. Since $\sqrt{2}$ is irrational, our assumption that $b\sqrt{2}$ is rational must be false.

Property	17. Real	18. Irrational	19. Fractional	20. Positive Real
Closed **+**	+	−	−	+
Associative **+**	+	+	+	+
0, the **+** identity	+	−	−	−
Negatives, the **+** inverses	+	+	+	−
Group **+**	+	−	−	−
Commutative group **+**	+	−	−	−
Closed **×**	+	−	−	+
Associative **×**	+	+	+	+
Distributive law	+	+	+	+
Ring	+	−	−	−
1, the **×** identity	+	−	−	+
Commutative **×**	+	+	+	+
Reciprocals, the **×** inverses	+.	+	−	+
Field	+	−	−	−

9–5. *The Set of Complex Numbers*

Domain	1.	2.	3.	4.
Positive Integers	$\{2\}$	$\emptyset$	$\emptyset$	$\emptyset$
Integers	$\{2,-2\}$	$\emptyset$	$\emptyset$	$\emptyset$
Rational Numbers	$\{2,-2\}$	$\left\{\frac{2}{3},-\frac{2}{3}\right\}$	$\emptyset$	$\emptyset$
Real Numbers	$\{2,-2\}$	$\left\{\frac{2}{3},-\frac{2}{3}\right\}$	$\{\sqrt{3},-\sqrt{3}\}$	$\emptyset$
Complex Numbers	$\{2,-2\}$	$\left\{\frac{2}{3},-\frac{2}{3}\right\}$	$\{\sqrt{3},-\sqrt{3}\}$	$\{i\sqrt{3},-i\sqrt{3}\}$

Property	5. Complex	6. Imaginary	7. Pure Imaginary	8. Mixed Imaginary
Closed **+**	+	−	−	−
Associative **+**	+	+	+	+
0, the **+** identity	+	−	−	−
Negatives, the **+** inverses	+	+	+	+
Group **+**	+	−	−	−
Commutative group **+**	+	−	−	−
Closed **✕**	+	−	−	−
Associative **✕**	+	+	+	+
Distributive law	+	+	+	+
Ring	+	−	−	−
1, the **✕** identity	+	−	−	−
Commutative **✕**	+	+	+	+
Reciprocals, the **✕** inverses	+	+	+	+
Field	+	−	−	−

PART
THREE

GEOMETRY

The teaching of geometry is undergoing relatively rapid evolution. Changes can be found in grades 7 and 8 and often earlier. The point of view of the first formal course in geometry is being broadened to include coordinate as well as synthetic methods. The geometry of three-space is being considered throughout the secondary school grades, especially in conjunction with plane geometry, instead of being treated as a separate course.

Geometry, as well as algebra, is increasingly being studied throughout the student's secondary school mathematics program. Geometry is an important phase of mathematics. The next few chapters are concerned with the scope and structure recommended for secondary school geometry.

Chapter 10. Geometry for Junior High School.
Chapter 11. Statements in Geometry.
Chapter 12. Structure of a First Course in Geometry.
Chapter 13. Coordinate Geometry for a First Course.
Chapter 14. Number Scales and Perspectivity.
Chapter 15. The Place of Solid and Other Geometries in the Secondary Schools.
Chapter 16. Topology.

CHAPTER

TEN

GEOMETRY FOR JUNIOR HIGH SCHOOL

There is a certain body of subject matter in the area of geometry which should be regarded as essential for the college-capable student in grades 7 and 8. All too often this work in geometry is slighted for increased emphasis on arithmetic. However, the emerging program of secondary school geometry, to be discussed in later chapters, dictates the necessity for giving special attention to the geometry program in the junior high school.

Among the primary aims for a unit on geometry in grades 7 and 8 are the following:

1. Recognition of certain basic figures;
2. Development of such basic skills and techniques as the construction of geometric figures and the proper use of a drawing compass and protractor;
3. Acquisition of basic vocabulary and certain facts, such as the sum of the angles of a triangle and the Pythagorean Theorem;
4. Development of an appreciation of the beauty of geometric form; and
5. Elementary training in space perception.

The emphasis in teaching techniques at these grade levels should be on an experimental, informal, investigative approach, with the laboratory method of teaching as the predominant procedure to be followed.

Much of the material being recommended for the junior high school geometry program is quite traditional. Thus, we expect youngsters to be able to recognize and classify such plane figures as triangles and quadrilaterals, and such solids as prisms, pyramids, cylinders, and cones. They should become acquainted with the various formulas for the perimeters, areas, and volumes of such figures. They should learn how to do such basic constructions as bisecting an angle, constructing a perpendicular to a line, and copying a triangle. They should understand such relationships as those dealing with the angles formed by parallel lines, as well as those concerning similarity and congruency of triangles. Only by developing such material in the junior high school can we expect to have time for a modern course in geometry in the senior high school.

There are, however, some new concepts to be considered that are non-metric. **Non-metric geometry** is concerned with a study of geometric properties which are unrelated to the concept of distance or measurement. Basic to such a unit is an emphasis upon precise language as well as upon the use and application of the language and concepts of sets. It is to this area that we turn our attention in this chapter.

10–1 Sets of Points on a Line

We make no attempt to define a point, but rather describe it in terms of its properties. We consider space as a set of points. A line is then taken as a set of points in space and is normally understood to be a straight line. A line extends indefinitely in each of two directions. We designate this by means of naming any pair of points on the line and by placing a double arrow over this notation. Thus, we may speak of the line in the accompanying figure as $\overleftrightarrow{AB}$, $\overleftrightarrow{AC}$, $\overleftrightarrow{BC}$, and so forth.

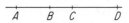

We shall understand that a line extends indefinitely in each of two directions whenever a line is drawn. This may be, but need not be, emphasized by placing arrows on the drawing as follows:

A **line segment**, often called simply a **segment**, is taken to mean two specific points on a line, together with all of the points between them. We designate a segment by naming the two end points and by placing a bar over this notation. Thus, consider segments AB and RS in the following diagrams:

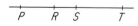

$$A \underline{\hspace{2em}} B \qquad R \underline{\hspace{2em}} S$$
$$(\overline{AB}) \qquad\qquad (\overline{RS})$$

We may now consider the union and intersection of sets of points on a line. Each of the following examples refers to this diagram:

$$P \qquad R \quad S \qquad\quad T$$

Example 1. Find $\overline{PR} \cup \overline{RS}$.

SOLUTION: The union of the set of points on segments PR and RS consists of the points P, S, and all the points between P and S. Thus, we have $\overline{PR} \cup \overline{RS} = \overline{PS}$.

Example 2. Find $\overline{PR} \cap \overline{RS}$.

SOLUTION. The point R is the only point common to both segments. Therefore, $\overline{PR} \cap \overline{RS}$ is the point R.

Example 3. Find $\overline{PR} \cap \overline{ST}$.

SOLUTION: There are no points common to these two segments; their intersection is the empty set, $\emptyset$.

Any point on a line separates the line into two **half-lines**. Thus, we may select any point A on a line and consider the half-line on one side of A and the half-line on the other side of A. Note that neither half-line includes the point A and that, since the line may be extended indefinitely in either sense, each point on the line divides it into two half-lines. Now, if we take the point A and all the points on the line which are on one side of A, we have a ray. Thus, a **ray** is the union of a half-line and the point determining it, that is, the **end point** of the ray.

In the following figure, we may speak of ray AR, written $\overrightarrow{AR}$, as the set of points on the line consisting of A and all the points on the R side of A. We may also speak of ray AS, $(\overrightarrow{AS})$, which consists of point A and all the points on the line on the S side of A. Note that a ray has an end point, whereas a half-line does not.

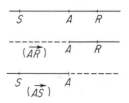

In the given figure, ray AR is not the same set of points as ray RA. Note that $\overrightarrow{AR}$ consists of point A and all the points on a line to the right of A; $\overrightarrow{RA}$ consists of R and all the points on a line to the left of R. The union of these two rays is the line AR; their intersection is the segment AR.

Exercises

Describe the following sets of points, each referring to the accompanying figure.

1. $\overline{AB} \cup \overline{BD}$

2. $\overline{AB} \cap \overline{CD}$

3. $\overline{AC} \cap \overline{BD}$

4. $\overline{AB} \cap \overline{BC}$

5. $\overline{AD} \cap \overline{BC}$

6. $\overline{AD} \cup \overline{BC}$

7. $\overleftrightarrow{AB} \cap \overline{BC}$

8. $\overleftrightarrow{AB} \cap \overrightarrow{BC}$

9. $\overrightarrow{BC} \cup \overrightarrow{CD}$

10. $\overrightarrow{BC} \cap \overrightarrow{CD}$

11. $\overrightarrow{BC} \cap \overrightarrow{BA}$

12. $\overrightarrow{DC} \cup \overrightarrow{CA}$

10–2 Sets of Points on a Plane

We may now use the concepts previously developed to define an **angle** as the geometric figure formed by two rays having a common end-point. Thus, an angle is a set of points on a plane.

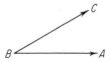

In the figure above, angle ABC, written $\angle ABC$, is the union of two rays, $\overrightarrow{BA}$ and $\overrightarrow{BC}$. Their intersection, $(\overrightarrow{BA} \cap \overrightarrow{BC})$, is the point B, called the **vertex** of the angle. The rays are also called the **sides** of the angle.

The **interior** of $\angle ABC$ is the intersection of the set of points on the A side of line BC and the set of points on the C side of line AB. The **exterior** of $\angle ABC$ is the complement of the union of $\angle ABC$ and the set of points in the interior of $\angle ABC$. The angle is the common boundary of its interior and exterior; it does not belong to either. Note that, if A, B, and C are collinear the interior and the exterior are not defined.

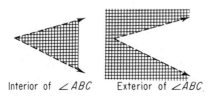

Interior of $\angle ABC$ Exterior of $\angle ABC$.

The definition of an angle on a plane can be very easily extended to define a **dihedral angle** in space. A point on a line separates the line into two rays, of which it is the common end point. A line on a plane separates the plane into two half-planes, of which it is the common edge. Two rays with a common end point form a plane angle. Two half-planes with a common edge form a dihedral angle.

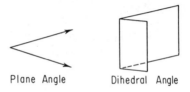

Plane Angle   Dihedral Angle

Note the analogy between a point on a line separating the line into two half-lines, and a line on a plane separating the plane into two half-planes. In a similar manner, we may consider any plane in space separating space into two half-spaces.

The concept of intersection of sets is useful in describing various relationships between lines and planes, as well as between two planes. Thus, two different planes in space may have the empty set as their intersection if they are parallel. If their intersection is not empty, then they intersect in a straight line. In the following figures, we let α and β denote two planes.

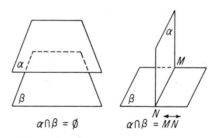

$\alpha \cap \beta = \emptyset$ $\alpha \cap \beta = \overleftrightarrow{MN}$

A line, AB, and a plane, α, may have the empty set as their intersection, may intersect in a point, or may intersect in many points if the line is on the plane.

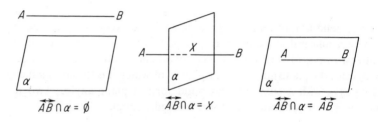

$\overleftrightarrow{AB} \cap \alpha = \emptyset$ $\overleftrightarrow{AB} \cap \alpha = X$ $\overleftrightarrow{AB} \cap \alpha = \overleftrightarrow{AB}$

Exercises

Describe the following sets of points, each referring to the accompanying figure.

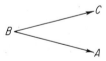

1. (Exterior $\angle ABC$) $\cap$ $\overrightarrow{BA}$

2. (Interior $\angle ABC$) $\cap$ $\overrightarrow{BC}$

3. (Interior $\angle ABC$) $\cap$ (exterior $\angle ABC$)

4. (Interior $\angle ABC$) $\cup$ (exterior $\angle ABC$) $\cup$ $\angle ABC$

5. (Exterior $\angle ABC$) $\cap$ $\overrightarrow{AB}$

6. (Exterior $\angle ABC$) $\cap$ $\overline{AB}$

10–3 Simple Closed-Plane Curves

The definition of a polygon is usually based upon the recognition of a single interior region. This intuitive concept may be avoided by defining a **polygon** as a simple, closed, broken line. A broken line is

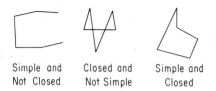

Simple and   Closed and   Simple and
Not Closed   Not Simple   Closed

simple if it does not intersect itself. A simple broken line is **closed** if, as one draws it without lifting the pencil from the paper, one returns to the starting point. The notions of simple and closed figures are basically topological concepts to be explored in greater detail in §16–3.

The interior of a simple closed curve is called a **region**. The curve is the boundary between its interior and exterior. Thus, we may speak of the interior of a circle as the shaded portion in the accompanying figure.

(Note that when we speak of the area of a circle, we really mean the area of its interior. A circle is a simple closed curve which has no area.)

A polygon may be considered as a simple closed curve made up of line segments. For example, triangle ABC may be thought of as $\overline{AB} \cup \overline{BC} \cup \overline{AC}$; the interior of $\triangle ABC$ may be thought of as the intersection of the interiors of its three angles. The following examples are based on the figure for triangle ABC.

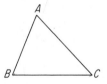

Example 1. Find $\triangle ABC \cap \overrightarrow{BC}$.

SOLUTION: This intersection consists of the set of points on ray BC which are also on the triangle, namely, segment BC.

Example 2. Find $\angle ABC \cap \overline{AC}$.

SOLUTION: Angle ABC consists of the union of the rays BA and BC. The intersection of these rays with the segment AC consists of a set of two points, A and C.

Example 3. Find $\overline{AB} \cap \overrightarrow{CB}$.

SOLUTION: B is the only point which is a member of each of these sets of points. We write: $\overline{AB} \cap \overrightarrow{CB} = B$.

Example 4. Find (interior $\triangle ABC$) $\cap$ (exterior $\triangle ABC$).

SOLUTION: There is no point which is both in the interior as well as in the exterior of the triangle. Therefore, the intersection is the empty set.

We may also wish to distinguish between a convex polygon and a concave polygon:

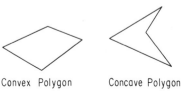

Convex Polygon   Concave Polygon

Think of a point as dividing a line into two rays, of which it is the common end point; think of a line as dividing a plane into two half-planes, of which it is the common edge. Then consider the half-planes determined by the lines along the sides of the polygon. The polygon is **convex** if and only if, in each of these cases, it lies entirely in or on the edge of one half-plane. For the convex polygon *ABCD*, we have:

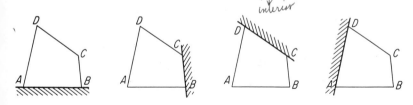

For the polygon *RSTU*, we have:

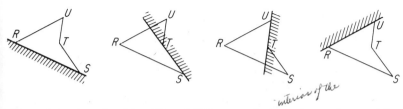

Note that when the sides *ST* and *TU* are used, the polygon does not lie entirely in or on the edge of one of the half-planes determined by the sides. Therefore, polygon *RSTU* is not convex and thus is **concave.**

Exercises

Describe the following sets of points, each referring to the accompanying figure.

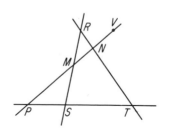

1. $\overrightarrow{MN} \cap \overrightarrow{TS}$

2. $\overrightarrow{SR} \cap \overrightarrow{ST}$

3. $\triangle RST \cap \overline{PM}$

4. (Exterior $\triangle RST$) $\cap \overline{MN}$

5. $\overrightarrow{TS} \cap \overline{PM}$

6. $\overline{PV} \cap \triangle RST$

7. (Interior $\triangle RST$) $\cap \overline{MN}$

8. $\overline{RS} \cap \overline{ST}$

9. $\overline{RM} \cup \overline{MN} \cup \overline{RN}$

10. (Exterior $\triangle RST$) $\cap \overrightarrow{NM}$

11. (Exterior $\triangle RST$) $\cap \overleftrightarrow{MN}$

12. $\overrightarrow{PM} \cup \overrightarrow{PS}$

13. $\overline{PV} \cap \triangle MRN$

14. (Interior $\triangle RST$) $\cap$ (interior $\triangle MRN$)

10–4 Explorations

It was suggested in the introductory remarks to this chapter that the work in geometry in the junior high school should emphasize the investigative, laboratory-type approach. There are a number of ways in which this can be done. One worthwhile procedure is to provide students with laboratory sheets with instructions to be followed which lead to some discovery. An example of one such experiment follows. The assumption is made that the class has previously discussed such topics as perpendicular lines, right triangles, and bisection of line segments.

Sample Classroom Experiment*

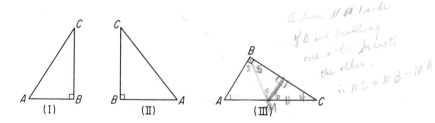

1. Each of the triangles above appears to be a *right* triangle. Why?
2. In each triangle, the *hypotenuse* is labeled as _____ .
3. Bisect each hypotenuse and label the mid-point *M*.
4. Draw *BM* in each triangle. (*Note:* A line drawn from the vertex of a triangle to the mid-point of the opposite side is called a *median* of the triangle. How many medians does a triangle have?)
5. Measure the length of the hypotenuse ($\overline{AC}$) for each triangle, as well as the length of the median to the hypotenuse ($\overline{BM}$) for each triangle. Complete the following chart:

Triangle	Length of Hypotenuse	Length of Median
I		
II		
III		

6. Examine the results of your measurements and try to draw some conclusion concerning the ratio of the length of the hypotenuse to the length of the median to the hypotenuse of a right triangle.
7. Construct a right triangle. Bisect the hypotenuse and draw the median from the vertex of the right angle. Take the necessary measurements and attempt to support the conclusion which you made in step 6.

---

* Anyone wishing to reproduce this experiment for classroom use, giving due credit for its source, is hereby authorized to do so.

10–5 Space Figures

Another item worthy of major concern in the junior high school deals with space figures. Thus, we should encourage drawings of two-dimensional representations of three-dimensional figures such as prisms, cones, cylinders, and pyramids. In addition, students may make patterns for various polyhedra and construct models for these. For example, consider the following patterns for a cube and a tetrahedron:

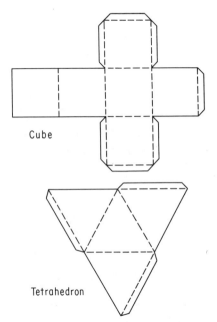

Cube

Tetrahedron

An interesting exploration is to have youngsters examine a number of solids and count their vertices, edges, and faces. In so doing we lead them to the "discovery" of the famous **Euler Formula**, which states that the sum of the numbers of vertices and faces is two more than the number of edges: $V + F = E + 2$.

10–6 Paper Folding

Still another approach to the informal development of basic facts and perceptions may be obtained through the medium of paper folding.

As a typical example of what might be done, consider the following
project, which attempts to show that the sum of the angles of a triangle
is 180°. (Wax paper works very well in projects of this sort.)

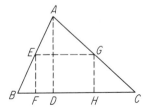

1. Cut the interior of △*ABC* out of a piece of paper.
2. Fold *B* over the segment *BC* so that the crease passes through *A*.
   This determines the point *D* on $\overline{BC}$.
3. Fold *B* over to *D*, forming the crease *EF*.
4. Fold *C* over to *D*, forming the crease *GH*.
5. Fold *A* down to *D*, forming the crease *EG*.
6. Note that, when all three angles, *A*, *B*, and *C*, are folded over to
   point *D*, they appear to form an angle of 180°.

Other examples of what might be accomplished by paper folding are
developed in the following set of exploration exercises and in §13–6.

Exploration Exercises on Paper Folding

1. Use a strip of wax paper about 3 inches wide:

(a) Fold to form a straight edge.

(b) Make a scale on this straight fold by estimating an inch, folding
to copy it for a scale of at least 10 inches.

(c) Check your estimate of 1 inch by comparing your 10 "inches"
with a ruler.

(d) Bisect a given line segment.

(e) Find the perpendicular bisector of a given line segment.

(f) Find a line segment equal to the sum of two given line segments.

(g) Find a line segment equal to the difference of two given line
segments.

(h) Find a line segment whose length is the average of the lengths of
two given line segments.

2. Use a piece of wax paper about 3 inches square:

    (a) Form a right angle.

    (b) Bisect the right angle.

    (c) Find an angle of $11\frac{1}{4}°$.

    (d) Tell how to bisect any angle.

3. Use a piece of wax paper about 3 inches square:

    (a) Form a right angle.

    (b) Form an angle of 30°.

    (c) Form an angle of 120°.

4. Use a piece of wax paper about 3 inches square:

    (a) Form an angle of about 70°.

    (b) Bisect the angle.

5. Tell how to do each of these on wax paper:

    (a) Find a line through two given points.

    (b) Find a line perpendicular to a given line at a given point on that line.

    (c) Find a line perpendicular to a given line and through a given external point.

    (d) Find a line parallel to a given line and through a given point.

    (e) Find a line parallel to a given line and at a given distance from it.

    (f) Find a line intersecting a given line at a given point and at a given angle.

Application and Additional Readings

This entire chapter has been concerned with the subject matter of geometry which is appropriate for instruction in the junior high school. The traditional aspects of geometry have been suggested in the introductory paragraphs but not developed. The new language and ideas now finding their way into the program for grades 7 and 8 have been explored. Even a short unit on non-metric geometry will serve as an excellent means of demonstrating some of the uses and definitions of sets developed earlier, and indicates the power of the concept of sets as a unifying concept. The teacher who wishes to pursue the subject further may consult the publications of experimental groups, such as [42] and [49]. The National Council of Teachers of Mathematics has an excellent publication on paper folding, [21]. The book *Flatland* provides interesting recreational reading, [1]. For a full treatment of the concepts of informal geometry suitable for the junior high school, see [5].

Answers for Exercises

10–1 *Sets of Points on a Line*

1. $\overline{AD}$ 2. $\emptyset$ 3. $\overline{BC}$ 4. B 5. $\overline{BC}$ 6. $\overline{AD}$

7. $\overline{BC}$ 8. $\overrightarrow{BC}$ 9. $\overrightarrow{BC}$ 10. $\overrightarrow{CD}$ 11. B 12. $\overrightarrow{DC}$

10–2 *Sets of Points on a Plane*

1. $\emptyset$ 2. $\emptyset$ 3. $\emptyset$ 4. The entire plane of $\angle ABC$.

5. The half-line which is determined on $\overleftrightarrow{AB}$ by B and does not contain A.

6. $\emptyset$

10–3 *Simple Closed-Plane Curves*

1. $\emptyset$ 2. S 3. M 4. $\emptyset$ 5. P 6. M, N

7. The set of points on $\overline{MN}$ between M and N; that is, the points of $\overline{MN}$ except that M and N are not included.

8. S 9. $\triangle RMN$ 10. The half-line MP without the end point M.

11. The union of the two half-lines MP and NV; that is, all of line MN except the points on segment MN.

12. $\angle MPS$ 13. $\overline{MN}$ 14. The interior of $\triangle MRN$.

CHAPTER
ELEVEN

STATEMENTS IN
GEOMETRY

Statements in arithmetic and statements in algebra were considered in §7–1 and §7–2. Any arithmetic statement may be identified as true or false. Statements in algebra may be considered as arithmetic statements for particular values of the variables: they are true for the elements of their solution sets. The truth of statements in geometry cannot be based simply upon counting, as in arithmetic or algebra. Also, it cannot be based solely upon appearances.

The use of deductions in algebra, which was considered in Chapter 8, is extended in this chapter to a systematic consideration of elementary logic, with special applications to geometry.

11–1 Statements

We assume that any simple statement is either true or false; that no simple statement can be both true and false. Note that there is a distinction between the truth of a statement and the validity of an argument:

A statement is **true** if it is postulated or if it appears to be correct in the physical universe. *agrees with observable reality*

An argument is **valid** if its conclusion is a necessary logical consequence of its premises (assumptions).

192

For example, if we assume that all pieces of fruit are red and that all lemons are pieces of fruit, then the conclusion, "All lemons are red" is a *valid* consequence of our assumptions. However, it is not a *true* statement according to our experience in the physical universe.

The study of forms of statements is most meaningful when we are able to consider the form of the statement without reference to its being true or false. We do this by using symbols for statements. For example, we may use p and q to represent these simple statements:

> *p:* It is a lemon.
> *q:* It is a piece of fruit.

This use of symbols is particularly convenient when two or more statements are used to form a new statement. For example, the statement,

> If it is a lemon, then it is a piece of fruit

can be expressed in the **if—then** form:

> If p, then q

which can be expressed in symbols as

> $p \to q$ (read as, "p implies q").

The symbol "$\to$" is called the **implication symbol**. Any statement in *if—then* form can be expressed as an implication.

Notice that the statements "$p \to q$" and "$q \to p$" are both implications. The statement "$q \to p$" can also be made in the form:

> If q, then p.

It can be expressed in words without employing symbols, as,

> If it is a piece of fruit, then it is a lemon.

Notice that for these particular statements p and q, the implication "$p \to q$" is true, whereas the implication "$q \to p$" is not always true.

We next introduce a symbol for asserting that a statement is false. We write:

> *p:* It is a lemon.
> $\sim$*p:* It is not a lemon.

We read the **negation symbol**, "$\sim$" as "not," thus "$\sim p$" is read as "not p." Notice that "$\sim p$" is a statement that p is false. However, it is more than a statement contrary to p. For example, consider this statement:

s: It is an orange.

The statements p and s are called **contrary statements**, since they cannot both be true of the same object. The statements p and $\sim p$ are also contrary statements, but they have the additional property that they cannot both be false; either it is a lemon or it is not a lemon. Consider these statements:

p: It is a lemon.

$\sim p$: It is not a lemon.

Exactly one of the statements must be true; exactly one of the statements must be false. If either statement is true, the other is false. If either statement is false, the other is true. This special relationship between "p" and "$\sim p$" is indicated by calling them contradictory statements. Two statements are **contradictory** if they cannot both be true and they cannot both be false. Notice that any two contradictory statements are also contrary; two contrary statements may or may not be contradictory, since in some cases contrary statements may both be false.

We use the symbol "$\leftrightarrow$" to show that two statements are equivalent. Consider these statements:

p: I cut the grass this afternoon.

q: The sun is shining.

Then the statement "$p \leftrightarrow q$", that is, p if and only if q, is true

(a) if I cut the grass and the sun is shining, or
(b) if I do not cut the grass and the sun is not shining.

In all other cases, the statement "$p \leftrightarrow q$" is false. Briefly, two statements "p" and "q" are **equivalent** if each implies the other; in other words, we may write "$p \leftrightarrow q$" if it is true that $p \rightarrow q$ and also that $q \rightarrow p$.

The words "and" and "or" are used so often in forming statements that we introduce symbols for each of them. The symbol for **conjunction** "$\wedge$" is read as "and"; the symbol for **disjunction** "$\vee$" is read as "or". Then for any statements p and q, we write these symbols:

"p" means "p is true,"
"$\sim p$" means "p is false,"

"$p \wedge q$" means "Both p and q are true,"

"$p \vee q$" means "At least one of the statements p, q is true; that is, either p is true, or q is true, or both p and q are true."

We shall not attempt to give a complete development of the logical processes used in making formal proofs. Instead, we shall assume the following laws of logic:

Aristotle's Laws of Logic

(i) $p \leftrightarrow p$, law of identity,

(ii) $\sim[p \wedge (\sim p)]$, law of noncontradiction—a statement and its contradictory statement cannot both be valid,

(iii) $p \vee (\sim p)$, law of the excluded middle—at least one of any two contradictory statements must be valid.

Notice that these laws imply that $\sim(\sim p) \leftrightarrow p$.

The symbols $\wedge$, $\vee$, $\rightarrow$, and $\leftrightarrow$ are called **connectives**. Any statement involving one or more of these connectives is called a **compound statement**.

Exercises

1. Indicate which of the following pairs of statements are contrary:

(a) That is John Smith. That is Henry Jones.
(b) It is a citrus fruit. It is an orange.
(c) The car is a Buick. The car is not a Cadillac.
(d) x is positive. x is negative.
(e) $x < 3$. $x \geq 3$.
(f) $x < 6$. $x = 7$.
(g) $x^2 = 9$. $x \neq 3$.

2. Indicate which of the pairs of statements in Exercise 1 are contradictory.

3. What name is used to describe the relationship between statements p and q given by $\sim(p \wedge q)$?

4. What name is used to describe the relationship between statements p and q given by
$$[p \rightarrow (\sim q)] \wedge [(\sim p) \rightarrow q]?$$

Write each statement in if—then *form:*

5. The boy is a Johnson, if he has red hair.

6. All ducks are birds.

7. Vertical angles are equal.

8. Complements of the same angle are equal.

9. Supplements of equal angles are equal.

10. Any two parallel lines are coplanar.

11–2 The Nature of Proof—Modus Ponens

Any proof must be based upon assumptions. With a little guidance, most pupils can be led to recognize:

(a) That all decisions are based upon assumptions, even though the person making the decision may not recognize his assumptions;

(b) That nearly all of our family, national, and international disagreements arise from the use of different assumptions;

(c) That agreements can best be reached after the assumptions have been agreed upon; and

(d) That in geometry we try to state our assumptions clearly and precisely so that each person following these assumptions must arrive at the same conclusion.

The outline of the New York integrated sequence for tenth-year mathematics suggests that such non-mathematical situations as eligibility for membership on a school team, the desirability of high school fraternities, the effectiveness of the United States protective tariffs, and the benefits of isolationism in the United States be used to stress the importance of recognizing assumptions and the importance of using (assuming) the same definitions.

Proofs can best be introduced in terms of *if—then* statements (§11–1). Syllogisms (§11–3) and truth tables (§11–5) may be considered later.

The Commission on Mathematics recommends that a discussion of rules of inference be included in the unit on deductive reasoning. One such rule, the **law of detachment** or **modus ponens**, states:

If a statement of the form "If p, then q" is assumed to be true, and if p is known to be true, then q *must* be true.

Symbolically, we may write this rule as

$$\begin{array}{ll} p \to q & \text{If } p, \text{ then } q; \text{ and} \\ \underline{p} & p \\ \therefore q & \text{imply } q. \end{array}$$

We may also write the rule in the form

$$[(p \rightarrow q) \wedge p] \rightarrow q.$$

Consider these specific examples of this valid form of reasoning:

(a) Use p: Mary is a junior.
    q: Mary is taking algebra.

and apply the rule of modus ponens:

> If Mary is a junior, then she is taking algebra. $p \rightarrow q$
> Given: Mary is a Junior. p
> Therefore, she is taking algebra. $\therefore q$

(b) Use p: $3x - 1 = 8.$
    q: $3x = 9.$

and apply the rule of modus ponens:

> If $3x - 1 = 8$, then $3x = 9$. $p \rightarrow q$
> Given: $3x - 1 = 8$. p
> Therefore, $3x = 9$. $\therefore q$

(c) Use p: $KLMN$ is a parallelogram.
    q: Its opposite sides are equal.

and apply the rule of modus ponens:

> If $KLMN$ is a parallelogram, then its opposite
>   sides are equal. $p \rightarrow q$
> Given: $KLMN$ is a parallelogram. p
> Therefore, its opposite sides are equal. $\therefore q$

(d) Use p: $n = 2k + 1.$
    q: n is an odd number.

and apply the rule of modus ponens:

> If $n = 2k + 1$, then n is an odd number. $p \rightarrow q$
> Given: $n = 2k + 1$. p
> Therefore, n is an odd number. $\therefore q$

Exercises

1. Let p represent the statement "You will study hard." Let q represent the statement "You will get an A." Translate each of the following symbolic statements into an English sentence.

(a) $p \rightarrow q$
$$\underline{p}$$
$$\therefore q$$

(b) $p \rightarrow q$
$$\underline{\sim q}$$
$$\therefore \sim p$$

(c) $p \rightarrow q$
$$\underline{q}$$
$$\therefore p$$

(d) $p \rightarrow q$
$$\underline{\sim p}$$
$$\therefore \sim q$$

2. Repeat Ex. 1 for the statements:

p: The triangle is equilateral.
q: The triangle is isosceles.

11-3 Syllogisms

Formal proofs are based upon deductions such as those used in the law of modus ponens (§11-2). A **syllogism** is a more general form of an ordinary deduction. Each syllogism consists of three parts:

G: a general statement (This may be a definition, an assumption, or an implication);

S: a specific statement or hypothesis (This is a particular example of the situation under consideration in the general statement; for example, if the general statement is of the form $p \rightarrow q$, then the specific statement provides a specific instance of p); and

C: a conclusion (This is the logical consequence of the general and specific statements; for example, in the case of an implication $p \rightarrow q$, the conclusion is a specific statement of q which is true because of the truth of the previous statements).

Consider these examples:

(a) G: All right angles are equal.
    S: $\angle A$ and $\angle B$ are right angles.
    C: $\angle A = \angle B$.
(b) G: If two triangles are congruent, then they are similar.
    S: $\triangle ABC \cong \triangle DEF$.
    C: $\triangle ABC \sim \triangle DEF$.

Syllogisms are often considered the "building blocks" of proofs. Any formal proof may be expressed as a sequence of syllogisms. Although we shall not attempt such a formal approach, it is worth while to recognize the patterns used in syllogisms. Additional examples will be found in the exercises.

Exercises

In each of the following syllogisms, one part of the pattern is missing. Supply a suitable statement for the missing part.

1. G: Vertical angles are equal.
   S: $\angle r$ and $\angle s$ are vertical angles.
   C:

2. G: No person less than 21 years old may vote.
   S: Jane is 19 years old.
   C:

3. G: No person less than 21 years old may vote.
   S:
   C: Jack voted.

4. G: If equal expressions are added to equal expressions, their sums are equal.
   S: $x + y = 7$ is added to $x - y = 12$.
   C:

5. G:
   S: $y = 3$ is subtracted from $x + y = 7$.
   C: $x = 4$.

11–4 Converse, Inverse, Contrapositive

Any simple statement of implication may be written in the form $p \rightarrow q$ and also in *if—then* form:

If p, then q.

Given any simple statement of implication, three other related statements may be identified:

Statement: $p \rightarrow q$	If p, then q.
Converse: $q \rightarrow p$	If q, then p.
Inverse: $(\sim p) \rightarrow (\sim q)$	If not p, then not q.
Contrapositive: $(\sim q) \rightarrow (\sim p)$	If not q, then not p.

In §11–5, we use truth tables to prove that any simple statement of implication and its contrapositive are equivalent; also, that the inverse and the converse of any simple statement of implication are equivalent.

Statement: $p \rightarrow q$ Converse: $q \rightarrow p$
Inverse: $(\sim p) \rightarrow (\sim q)$ Contrapositive: $(\sim q) \rightarrow (\sim p)$

Consider these examples:

(a) Statement: If it is snowing, I leave my car in the garage.
    Converse: If I leave my car in the garage, it is snowing.
    Inverse: If it is not snowing, I do not leave my car in the garage.
    Contrapositive: If I do not leave my car in the garage, it is not snowing.

(b) Statement: If $\triangle ABC \cong \triangle XYZ$, then $\triangle ABC \sim \triangle XYZ$.
    Converse: If $\triangle ABC \sim \triangle XYZ$, then $\triangle ABC \cong \triangle XYZ$.
    Inverse: If $\triangle ABC$ is not congruent to $\triangle XYZ$, then $\triangle ABC$ is not similar to $\triangle XYZ$.
    Contrapositive: If $\triangle ABC$ is not similar to $\triangle XYZ$, then $\triangle ABC$ is not congruent to $\triangle XYZ$.

(c) Statement: If x is negative, then $x \neq 0$.
    Converse: If $x \neq 0$, then x is negative.
    Inverse: If x is not negative, then $x = 0$.
    Contrapositive: If $x = 0$, then x is not negative.

(d) Statement: If $x + 2 = 5$, then $x = 3$.
    Converse: If $x = 3$, then $x + 2 = 5$.
    Inverse: If $x + 2 \neq 5$, then $x \neq 3$.
    Contrapositive: If $x \neq 3$, then $x + 2 \neq 5$.

A statement may or may not be equivalent to its converse and its inverse. Thus, many common fallacies, or *invalid* examples of reasoning, stem from the assumption that the *converse* and the *inverse* of a true statement are necessarily true. Here is an example of false reasoning based upon the assumption that the converse is equivalent to the statement.

G: If two triangles are congruent, then they are similar.
S: Triangles ABC and DEF are similar.
C: Therefore, triangles ABC and DEF are congruent. (*Not valid.*)

This illustrates the fact that the following pattern of reasoning is not valid:

$$p \rightarrow q$$
$$\underline{q\qquad}$$
$$\therefore p$$

Here is an example of false reasoning based upon the assumption that the inverse is equivalent to the statement.

G: If two triangles are congruent, then they are similar.
S: Triangles STU and PQR are not congruent.
C: Therefore, triangles STU and PQR are not similar. (*Not valid.*)

This illustrates the fact that the following pattern of reasoning is not valid:

$$p \rightarrow q$$
$$\underline{\sim p\qquad}$$
$$\therefore \sim q$$

If the truth of a particular statement implies the truth of its converse, the statement is said to be **reversible.** Any definition should be reversible.

There is a valid form of reasoning similar to that considered in §11–2 and based upon the equivalence of any given statement and its contrapositive. As stated previously, any statement and its contrapositive are equivalent. Thus, if the contrapositive of a statement is true, the statement also must be true. We use this fact to obtain the following pattern of reasoning:

$$p \rightarrow q \qquad \text{If } p, \text{ then } q; \text{ and}$$
$$\underline{\sim q\qquad} \qquad \sim q$$
$$\therefore \sim p \qquad \text{imply } \sim p.$$

Here is another form in which the same idea may be expressed:

$$[(p \rightarrow q) \wedge (\sim q)] \rightarrow (\sim p).$$

Consider these specific examples of this valid form of reasoning:

(a) Use p: Mary is a junior.
       q: Mary is taking algebra.

and follow the pattern of reasoning:

    If Mary is a junior, then she is taking algebra. $p \rightarrow q$
    Mary is not taking algebra. $\sim q$
    Therefore, Mary is not a junior. $\therefore \sim p$

  (b) Use p: Two triangles are congruent.
         q: Two triangles are similar.

and as in syllogisms (§11–3), use the pattern of reasoning:

    If two triangles are congruent, then they are
      similar. $p \rightarrow q$
    Triangles PQR and XYZ are not similar. $\sim q$
    Therefore, triangles PQR and XYZ are not $\therefore \sim p$
    congruent.

In each of these cases, the reasoning, and thus the conclusion, is valid. This form of reasoning is a special case of the **indirect method of proof** of the given statement.

Exercises

Write the converse, inverse, and contrapositive of each statement:

1. If we can afford it, then we buy a new car.

2. If we play pingpong, then you win the game.

3. If two sides and the included angle of one triangle are equal to two sides and the included angle of another triangle, then the triangles are congruent.

4. If the square of the longest side of a triangle is equal to the sum of the squares of the other two sides, then the triangle is a right triangle.

5. If $x > 2$, then $x \neq 0$.

6. If $|x| \neq 3$, then $x^2 \neq 9$.

7. If $x(x - 1) = 0$, then $x = 1$.

For each of Exs. 3 through 7, tell whether or not you accept as always true:

8. The converse statement.

9. The inverse statement.

Note: Compare your answers for Exercises 8 and 9.

10. The contrapositive statement.

Discuss:

11. Any statement is the contrapositive of its contrapositive statement.

12. The contrapositive of the converse of a statement is the inverse of the statement.

Identify each of the following arguments as valid or not valid:

13. If the sun shines, then I will cut the grass.
    I am cutting the grass.
  ∴ The sun is shining.

14. If Jane is being married, then she will wear a white dress.
    Jane is not being married.
  ∴ Jane is wearing a dress that is not white.

15. If $x > 3$, then $x = 7$.
    $x \neq 7$.
  ∴ $x \not> 3$.

16. If $x^2 + y^2 < 9$, then $x = 2$.
    $x^2 + y^2 \not< 9$.
  ∴ $x \neq 2$.

17. If a chicken wants to get to the other side of the road, then the chicken crosses the road.
The chicken crosses the road.
The chicken wants to get to the other side of the road.

18. If $a + b = c$, then $a + b = d$.
    $a + b \neq d$.
  ∴ $a + b \neq c$.

11–5 Truth Tables

We may use truth tables to *define* the meaning of several of our symbols and forms of statements. For example, the table shows that $\sim p$ is false when p is true and that $\sim p$ is true when p is false. We may also observe, as specified in Aristotle's third law of logic (§11–1), that

p	$\sim p$
T	F
F	T

exactly one of the statements p and $\sim p$ must be true and exactly one of the statements must be false.

When two statements p, q are involved, four lines are required to specify each possible situation. We do this now to provide a definition for $p \rightarrow q$.

p	q	$p \rightarrow q$
T	T	T
T	F	F
F	T	T
F	F	T

Notice that, if p is false, the implication is considered to be true whether q is true or false. For example, each of these statements is true:

If $2 \times 2 = 5$, then you are now on the moon. (The statement "$p \rightarrow q$" is true when p is false and q is false.)

If $2 \times 2 = 5$, then Washington, D.C., is the capital of the United States of America. (The statement "$p \rightarrow q$" is true when p is false and q is true.)

This interpretation of the truth of implications is a matter of definition and must be accepted whenever the symbol "$\rightarrow$" is used.

These definitions may now be used to prove that any statement $p \rightarrow q$ is equivalent to its contrapositive $(\sim q) \rightarrow (\sim p)$. The statements are *equivalent* because their truth tables are identical.

p	q	Statement $p \rightarrow q$	$\sim q$	$\sim p$	Contrapositive $(\sim q) \rightarrow (\sim p)$
T	T	T	F	F	T
T	F	F	T	F	F
F	T	T	F	T	T
F	F	T	T	T	T

The compound statements "$p \wedge q$" and "$p \vee q$" were considered in §11–1:

"$p \wedge q$" means "Both p and q are true."
"$p \vee q$" means "At least one of the statements p, q is true."

When "$p \vee q$" is read as "p or q," we must recognize that this is the *inclusive* (at least one, possibly both) use of "or" rather than the *exclusive* (exactly one) use of "or". The exclusive "or" may also be indicated symbolically:

"$p \veebar q$" means "Exactly one of the statements p, q is true."

The symbols $\sim$, $\rightarrow$, $\leftrightarrow$, $\wedge$, $\vee$, and $\veebar$ are used to form compound statements and are called connectives. Truth tables for $\sim$, $\rightarrow$, and $\leftrightarrow$ have already been considered. Here are truth tables for the connectives $\wedge$, $\vee$, and $\veebar$.

p	q	$p \wedge q$	$p \vee q$	$p \veebar q$
T	T	T	T	F
T	F	F	T	T
F	T	F	T	T
F	F	F	F	F

Any simple statement $(p, q, \ldots)$ is true or false. Any argument is valid or invalid according as its conclusion is or is not a necessary logical consequence of its premises. Compound statements are formed by using simple statements and connectives. As shown in the array, there are compound statements involving p and q which are true for some truth values of p and q and false for other truth values of p and q. If a compound statement is true for all possible truth values of p and q, the statement is called a **tautology**. We may use truth tables to show whether or not a statement is a tautology. We may also use truth tables to determine the truth values of any compound statement: that is, when it is true and when it is false. The following truth table shows that $(p \vee q) \vee (\sim p)$ is a tautology.

p	q	p∨q	~p	(p∨q)∨(~p)
T	T	T	F	T
T	F	T	F	T
F	T	T	T	T
F	F	F	T	T

Exercises

1. Complete this array to show the truth values of a statement, its converse, and its inverse.

p	q	p→q	q→p	~p	~q	(~p)→(~q)
T	T	T	T	F	F	T
T	F	F	T	F	T	T
F	T	T	F	T	F	F
F	F	T	T	T	T	T

2. The symbol "↔" was defined in §11–1 to mean that $p \leftrightarrow q$ if it is true that $p \rightarrow q$ and also that $q \rightarrow p$. Complete the truth table to show that

$$[(p \rightarrow q) \wedge (q \rightarrow p)] \text{ is the same as } (p \leftrightarrow q).$$

p	q	p→q	q→p	(p→q)∧(q→p)	p↔q
T	T	T	T	T	T
T	F	F	T	F	F
F	T	T	F	F	F
F	F	T	T	T	T

Use truth tables to show each of the following equivalences:

3. $(p \wedge p) \leftrightarrow p.$

4. $(p \vee p) \leftrightarrow p.$

5. $(p \rightarrow q) \leftrightarrow [(\sim p) \vee q]$.

6. $(p \rightarrow q) \leftrightarrow \sim[p \wedge (\sim q)]$.

7. $(p \vee q) \leftrightarrow \sim[(\sim p) \wedge (\sim q)]$.

8. $\sim(p \vee q) \leftrightarrow [(\sim p) \wedge (\sim q)]$.

9. $\sim(p \wedge q) \leftrightarrow [(\sim p) \vee (\sim q)]$.

Use a truth table to test each of these compound statements, and tell whether or not the statement is a tautology:

10. $(p \wedge q) \rightarrow [q \rightarrow (\sim p)]$.

11. $(p \wedge q) \leftrightarrow (q \wedge p)$.

12. $(p \wedge q) \rightarrow p$.

13. $(p \wedge q) \rightarrow (p \vee q)$.

14. $[p \wedge (\sim p)] \rightarrow q$.

Simplify each of the following statements; use the results obtained in Exercises 3 through 9 whenever applicable:

15. $\sim[p \wedge (\sim q)]$.

16. $\sim[(\sim p) \vee q]$.

17. $\sim[(\sim p) \vee q] \wedge p$.

18. $[p \vee (\sim q)] \wedge (p \vee q)$.

19. $p \rightarrow (q \rightarrow p)$.

20. $(p \wedge q) \wedge \sim[(\sim p) \vee (\sim q)]$.

11–6 Symbolic Representation of Statements

We have already considered the symbolic representation of simple statements of the form p, $\sim p$, $p \rightarrow q$, $p \leftrightarrow q$, $p \wedge q$, $p \vee q$, and $p \underline{\vee} q$. More detailed statements may also be expressed in terms of their symbolic representation. For example, consider:

p: It is cold.
q: It is snowing.
$p \wedge (\sim q)$: It is cold and not snowing.
$\sim(p \vee q)$: It is neither cold nor snowing.
$(\sim p) \vee (\sim q)$: Either it is not cold or it is not snowing.
$\sim[(\sim p) \vee q)]$: It is not true that it is either not cold or snowing.

Additional examples may be found in the exercises. Look for examples of these statements:

$\sim(\sim p) \leftrightarrow p.$
$\sim(p \wedge q) \leftrightarrow [(\sim p) \vee (\sim q)].$
$\sim(p \vee q) \leftrightarrow [(\sim p) \wedge (\sim q)].$

The symbolic statement $p \rightarrow q$ may be used for each of these statements:

If p, then q.
p is a sufficient condition for q.
q, if p.
p, only if q.
If not q, then not p. (Contrapositive.)
q is a necessary condition for p.

Statements are often confusing because there exist many possible ways of making the same statement. The symbolic statement $p \leftrightarrow q$ may be used for each of these statements:

p is equivalent to q.
p if and only if q.
p is a necessary and sufficient condition for q.
The statement $(p \rightarrow q)$ implies its converse.
The statement $(p \rightarrow q)$ implies its inverse.
The statement $(p \rightarrow q)$ is reversible.

The equivalence of statements can be proved by means of truth tables.

Exercises

1. Use p: Jim is tall.
　　　　q: Bill is short.

Think of "short" as "not tall," and write each of these statements in symbolic form:

  (a) Jim is short and Bill is tall.
  (b) Bill and Jim are both tall.
  (c) Neither Jim nor Bill is tall.
  (d) Jim is not tall and Bill is short.
  (e) It is not true that Jim and Bill are both tall.
  (f) Either Jim is short or Bill is short.
  (g) Either Jim or Bill is tall.

2. Assume that Bill and Jim are both tall. Which of the statements in Ex. 1 are true?

3. Use *p*: The sun shines.
  q: I cut the grass.

Write each of these statements in symbolic form:

  (a) If the sun shines, then I cut the grass.
  (b) I will cut the grass only if the sun shines.
  (c) If the sun does not shine, then I do not cut the grass.
  (d) The sun shining is a necessary condition for me to cut the grass.
  (e) I cut the grass if and only if the sun shines.

4. Use *p*: I like this book.
  q: I like mathematics.

Give each of these statements in words:

  (a) $p \wedge q$ (b) $\sim p \wedge \sim q$
  (c) $p \rightarrow q$ (d) $\sim q \rightarrow \sim p$
  (e) $p \leftrightarrow q$ (f) $\sim [p \vee (\sim q)]$

5. Give an example of at least one statement in each of the following forms:

  (a) $p \rightarrow q$ (b) $(\sim p) \rightarrow q$
  (c) $p \rightarrow (\sim q)$ (d) $(p \wedge q) \rightarrow r$
  (e) $p \rightarrow (r \vee q)$ (f) $(p \wedge q) \rightarrow (r \vee s)$

11–7 Venn Diagrams

Statements are often represented geometrically. Think of a circle on a plane. Each point of the plane is either outside the circle or a point

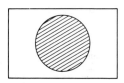

of the disk consisting of the points on the circle and in its interior. As in the figure, it is customary to use a rectangle and its interior to represent the plane, that is, the universe under consideration.

Circles, ellipses, squares, rectangles, and other simple closed-plane curves are often used as in the following figures in classifying:

(a) Lines on a plane as parallel or intersecting;
(b) People as living or dead;
(c) Real numbers as rational or irrational.

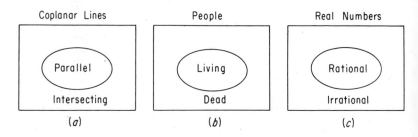

In these classifications, we have assumed that:

(a) Coplanar lines are either parallel or intersecting;
(b) People are either living or dead;
(c) Real numbers are either rational or irrational.

Since statements are assumed to be either true or false (§11–1), we may use similar figures for statements. These geometric representations are usually called Venn diagrams.

Venn diagrams were considered in Chapter 6 for sets A, B, U, $\emptyset$, $A \cap B$, $A \cup B$, and $\bar{A}$. The relations $A \subseteq B$, $A = B$, and $A \subset B$ were also considered. Now suppose that statements p and q are concerned with elements which we represent by the points of a universe U. Let A be the subset of U for which p is true; let B be the subset of U for which q is true. In other words, A represents the solution set of p, and B represents the solution set of q. The sets corresponding to various statements are shown in the following array.

Statement	Set
$\sim p$	$\bar{A}$
$p \wedge q$	$A \cap B$
$p \vee q$	$A \cup B$
$p \rightarrow q$	$\overline{A \cap \bar{B}}$
$p \leftrightarrow q$	$\overline{A \cap \bar{B} \cap B \cap \bar{A}}$

This correspondence may be used to obtain geometric representations for compound statements. If the representation is *U*, the statement is always true; if the representation is ∅, the statement is always false. Two statements are equivalent if they may be represented by the same Venn diagram.

Example 1. Represent ∼[*p* ∨ (∼*q*)] by a Venn diagram.

SOLUTION: Consider the following sequence of diagrams, where *A* represents the solution set of *p* and *B* represents the solution set of *q*.

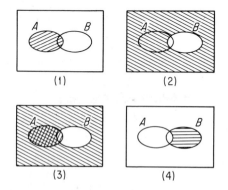

Notice that:

> the set for *p* is shaded in (1),
> the set for (∼*q*) is shaded in (2),
> the set for [*p* ∨ (∼*q*)] is shaded in (3), and
> the set for ∼[*p* ∨ (∼*q*)] is shaded in (4).

Example 2. Represent (*p* ∧ *q*) → *r* by a Venn diagram.

SOLUTION: Let, *A*, *B*, and *C* represent the solution sets of *p*, *q*, and *r*, respectively. A figure is needed in which the intersection of *p* and *q* is a subset of *r*. There are many such figures possible:

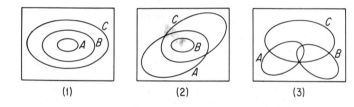

We select (3) as the best solution, since it does not show any unstated assumptions, such as $A \subset B$ and $B \subset A$.

Exercises

Use A, B, *and* C *to represent the solution sets of* p, q, *and* r, *respectively; write each statement in terms of* A, B, *and* C *and represent each statement by a Venn diagram:*

1. $q \rightarrow (\sim p)$.   **2.** $(\sim p) \lor q$.

3. $p \lor (\sim p)$.   **4.** $p \lor [(\sim p) \land q]$.

5. $\sim[p \land (\sim q)]$.   **6.** $(\sim q) \rightarrow p$.

7. $(\sim p) \rightarrow q$.   **8.** $p \rightarrow (q \lor r)$.

9. Tell which of the statements in Exercises 1 through 8 are equivalent.

Application and Additional Readings

All of the topics considered in this chapter are appropriate for capable students taking their first formal course in geometry. Several topics are appropriate for all geometry students. For example, all students should recognize statements (§11–1); should understand the type of reasoning used in §11–2 and §11–3; and should recognize the converse, inverse, and contrapositive of a simple statement of implication (§11–4). However, the average students may consider these topics without using their special notation and vocabulary.

Additional reading may be found in high school geometry textbooks; further details are found in [16] and [27].

Answers for Exercises

11–1 *Statements*

1. (a), (d), (e), and (f). **2.** (e). **3.** Contrary. **4.** Contradictory.

5. If he has red hair, then the boy is a Johnson.

6. If the creature is a duck, then it is a bird.

7. If two angles are vertical angles, then they are equal.

8. If the angles are complements of a given angle, then they are equal.

9. If the angles are supplements of equal angles, then they are equal.

10. If two lines are parallel, then they are coplanar.

11-2 *The Nature of Proof—Modus Ponens*

1. (a) If you will study hard, then you will get an A; and you will study hard, therefore you will get an A.
  (b) If you will study hard, then you will get an A; and you will not get an A, therefore you will not study hard.
  (c) If you will study hard, then you will get an A; and you will get an A, therefore you will study hard.
  (d) If you will study hard, then you will get an A; and you will not study hard, therefore you will not get an A.

2. (a) If the triangle is equilateral, then the triangle is isosceles; and the triangle is equilateral, therefore the triangle is isosceles.
  (b) If the triangle is equilateral, then the triangle is isosceles; and the triangle is not isosceles, therefore the triangle is not equilateral.
  (c) If the triangle is equilateral, then the triangle is isosceles; and the triangle is isosceles, therefore the triangle is equilateral.
  (d) If the triangle is equilateral, then the triangle is isosceles; and the triangle is not equilateral, therefore the triangle is not isosceles.

Note: The arguments in (a) and (b) are valid; the arguments in (c) and (d) are not valid.

11-3 *Syllogisms*

1. $\angle r = \angle s$. **2.** Jane may not vote. **3.** Jack is at least 21 years old. **4.** $2x = 19$. **5.** If equal expressions are subtracted from equal expressions, then the remainders are equal.

11-4 *Converse, Inverse, Contrapositive*

1. Converse: If we buy a new car, then we can afford it. Inverse: If we cannot afford it, then we do not buy a new car. Contrapositive: If we do not buy a new car, then we cannot afford it.

2. Converse: If you win the game, then we play pingpong. Inverse: If we do not play pingpong, then you do not win the game. Contrapositive: If you do not win the game, then we do not play pingpong.

3. Converse: If the triangles are congruent, then two sides and the included angle of one are equal to two sides and the included angle of the other. Inverse: If two sides and the included angle of one triangle are not equal to two sides and the included angle of another triangle, then the triangles are not congruent. Contrapositive: If two triangles are not congruent, then two sides and the included angle of one are not equal to two sides and the included angle of the other.

4. Converse: If a triangle is a right triangle, then the square of the longest side is equal to the sum of the squares of the other two sides. Inverse: If the square of the longest side of a triangle is not equal to the sum of the squares of the other two sides, then the triangle is not a right triangle. Contrapositive: If a triangle is not a right triangle, then the square of the longest side of the triangle is not equal to the sum of the squares of the other two sides.

5. Converse: If $x \neq 0$, then $x > 2$. Inverse: If $x \not> 2$, then $x = 0$. Contrapositive: If $x = 0$, then $x \not> 2$.

6. Converse: If $x^2 \neq 9$, then $|x| \neq 3$. Inverse: If $|x| = 3$, then $x^2 = 9$. Contrapositive: If $x^2 = 9$, then $|x| = 3$.

7. Converse: If $x = 1$, then $x(x - 1) = 0$. Inverse: If $x(x - 1) \neq 0$, then $x \neq 1$. Contrapositive: If $x \neq 1$, then $x(x - 1) \neq 0$.

8. The converse is always true in Exs. 3, 4, 6 and 7.

9. The inverse is always true in Exs. 3, 4, 6 and 7. (Note that these answers are the same as those for Ex. 8.)

10. The contrapositive is true for Exs. 3 through 6.

11. For any statement $p \rightarrow q$, the contrapositive is $(\sim q) \rightarrow (\sim p)$. The contrapositive of the contrapositive is $[\sim(\sim p)] \rightarrow [\sim(\sim q)]$; that is, $p \rightarrow q$.

12. For any statement $p \rightarrow q$, the converse is $q \rightarrow p$, and the contrapositive of the converse is $(\sim p) \rightarrow (\sim q)$. This is the same as the inverse, $(\sim p) \rightarrow (\sim q)$, of the given statement.

13. Not valid. **14.** Not valid. **15.** Valid. **16.** Not valid. **17.** Not valid. **18.** Valid.

11–5 *Truth Tables*

1.

p	q	$p{\to}q$	$q{\to}p$	$\sim p$	$\sim q$	$(\sim p){\to}(\sim q)$
T	T	T	T	F	F	T
T	F	F	T	F	T	T
F	T	T	F	T	F	F
F	F	T	T	T	T	T

(Notice that the fourth and seventh columns are identical.)

2.

p	q	$p{\to}q$	$q{\to}p$	$(p{\to}q)\wedge(q{\to}p)$	$p{\leftrightarrow}q$
T	T	T	T	T	T
T	F	F	T	F	F
F	T	T	F	F	F
F	F	T	T	T	T

(Notice that the last two columns are identical.)

3.

p	$p{\wedge}p$	$(p{\wedge}p){\leftrightarrow}p$
T	T	T
F	F	T

(Notice that the given statement is a tautology.)

4.

p	$(p \lor p)$	$(p \lor p) \longleftrightarrow p$
T	T	T
F	F	T

5.

p	q	$p \rightarrow q$	$\sim p$	$(\sim p) \lor q$	$(p \rightarrow q) \longleftrightarrow [(\sim p) \lor q]$
T	T	T	F	T	T
T	F	F	F	F	T
F	T	T	T	T	T
F	F	T	T	T	T

6.

p	q	$p \rightarrow q$	$\sim q$	$p \land (\sim q)$	$\sim [p \land (\sim q)]$	$(p \rightarrow q) \longleftrightarrow \sim [p \land (\sim q)]$
T	T	T	F	F	T	T
T	F	F	T	T	F	T
F	T	T	F	F	T	T
F	F	T	T	F	T	T

7.

p	q	$p \lor q$	$\sim p$	$\sim q$	$(\sim p) \land (\sim q)$	$\sim [(\sim p) \land (\sim q)]$	$(p \lor q) \longleftrightarrow \sim [(\sim p) \land (\sim q)]$
T	T	T	F	F	F	T	T
T	F	T	F	T	F	T	T
F	T	T	T	F	F	T	T
F	F	F	T	T	T	F	T

8.

p	q	$p \vee q$	$\sim(p \vee q)$	$\sim p$	$\sim q$	$(\sim p)\wedge(\sim q)$	$\sim(p\vee q) \leftrightarrow [(\sim p)\wedge(\sim q)]$
T	T	T	F	F	F	F	T
T	F	T	F	F	T	F	T
F	T	T	F	T	F	F	T
F	F	F	T	T	T	T	T

9.

p	q	$p \wedge q$	$\sim(p \wedge q)$	$\sim p$	$\sim q$	$(\sim p)\vee(\sim q)$	$\sim(p\wedge q) \leftrightarrow [(\sim p)\vee(\sim q)]$
T	T	T	F	F	F	F	T
T	F	F	T	F	T	T	T
F	T	F	T	T	F	T	T
F	F	F	T	T	T	T	T

10.

p	q	$p \wedge q$	$\sim p$	$q \rightarrow (\sim p)$	$(p\wedge q) \rightarrow [q \rightarrow (\sim p)]$
T	T	T	F	F	F
T	F	F	F	T	T
F	T	F	T	T	T
F	F	F	T	T	T

The statement is not a tautology because it is false when p and q are both true.

11.

p	q	$p \land q$	$q \land p$	$(p \land q) \leftrightarrow (q \land p)$
T	T	T	T	T
T	F	F	F	T
F	T	F	F	T
F	F	F	F	T

The statement is a tautology.

12.

p	q	$p \land q$	$(p \land q) \rightarrow p$
T	T	T	T
T	F	F	T
F	T	F	T
F	F	F	T

The statement is a tautology.

13.

p	q	$p \land q$	$p \lor q$	$(p \land q) \rightarrow (p \lor q)$
T	T	T	T	T
T	F	F	T	T
F	T	F	T	T
F	F	F	F	T

The statement is a tautology.

14.

p	q	$\sim p$	$p \wedge (\sim p)$	$[p \wedge (\sim p)] \to q$
T	T	F	F	T
T	F	F	F	T
F	T	T	F	T
F	F	T	F	T

The statement is a tautology.

15. $\sim[p \wedge (\sim q)] \overset{\text{Ex. 9}}{\longleftrightarrow} [(\sim p) \vee q] \overset{\text{Ex. 5}}{\longleftrightarrow} (p \to q)$.

16. $\sim[(\sim p) \vee q] \overset{\text{Ex. 8}}{\longleftrightarrow} [p \wedge (\sim q)]$.

17. $\{\sim[(\sim p) \vee q] \wedge p\} \overset{\text{Ex. 8}}{\longleftrightarrow} \{[p \wedge (\sim q)] \wedge p\} \overset{\text{Ex. 3}}{\longleftrightarrow} [p \wedge (\sim q)]$.

18. $\{[p \vee (\sim q)] \wedge (p \vee q)\} \leftrightarrow \{p \wedge [q \vee (\sim q)]\} \leftrightarrow p$.

19. $\{p \to (q \to p)\} \overset{\text{Ex. 5}}{\longleftrightarrow} \{(\sim p) \vee (q \to p)\} \overset{\text{Ex. 5}}{\longleftrightarrow}$

$\{(\sim p) \vee [(\sim q) \vee p]\} \leftrightarrow [p \vee (\sim p)]$.

The given statement is a tautology.

20. $\{(p \wedge q) \wedge \sim[(\sim p) \vee (\sim q)]\} \overset{\text{Ex. 8}}{\longleftrightarrow} \{(p \wedge q) \wedge (p \wedge q)\} \overset{\text{Ex. 3}}{\longleftrightarrow}$

$(p \wedge q)$.

11–6 *Symbolic Representation of Statements*

1. (a) $(\sim p) \wedge (\sim q)$, (b) $(\sim q) \wedge p$, (c) $(\sim p) \wedge q$, (d) $(\sim p) \wedge q$, (e) $\sim[p \wedge (\sim q)]$, (f) $\sim p \vee q$, (g) $p \vee \sim q$.

2. (b) and (g).

3. (a) $p \to q$, (b) $q \to p$, (c) $\sim p \to \sim q$, (d) $q \to p$, (e) $q \leftrightarrow p$.

4. (a) I like this book and I like mathematics; (b) I do not like this book and I do not like mathematics; (c) If I like this book, then I like mathematics; (d) If I do not like mathematics, then I do not like this book; (e) I like this book if and only if I like mathematics; (f) It is not true that I like this book or I do not like mathematics; that is, I do not like this book and I do like mathematics.

5. There are many possible answers. Here is a sample for each part: (a) If $x < 2$, then $x \neq 3$. (b) If two coplanar lines are not parallel, then the lines intersect. (c) If two lines intersect, then they are not parallel. (d) If $x \geq 2$ and $x \leq 2$, then $x = 2$. (e) If $x \neq 0$, then $x < 0$ or $x > 0$. (f) If $x^2 \leq 4$ and $x^2 \geq 4$, then $x = 2$ or $x = -2$.

11-7 *Venn Diagrams*

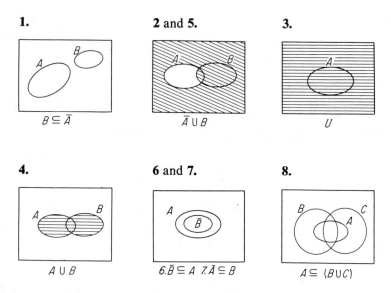

1.

$B \subseteq \bar{A}$

2 and 5.

$\bar{A} \cup B$

3.

U

4.

$A \cup B$

6 and 7.

$6. \bar{B} \subseteq A \quad 7. \bar{A} \subseteq B$

8.

$A \subseteq (B \cup C)$

In Ex. 1, note that we may have $A \cup B = C$; in Ex. 8, $A = B \cup C$.

9. The statements in Exs. 6 and 7 are equivalent; also, the statements in Exs. 2 and 5 are equivalent.

CHAPTER
TWELVE

STRUCTURE OF A FIRST
COURSE IN
GEOMETRY

The present concern over the place of geometry in our curriculum reflects several points of view on the scope of geometry. Is it simply "earth measure," as implied by the origin of the term? Is it simply a selection of some of the deductive sequences of Euclid? Is it concerned with all deductive sequences and, thus, with all of mathematics?

People who consider the subject archaic think of geometry in terms of its historical position as a selection of topics from Euclid. At the other extreme are the few people who think of geometry as including all of mathematics. The majority of people concerned with elementary mathematics view geometry as a study of proofs of relationships among figures composed of points, lines, and planes. We adopt this point of view and study figures with a recognition of their significance and application for earth measure as well as with an emphasis upon modern concepts of mathematics.

This chapter is concerned with the structure of a first course in geometry and with the development of this structure in a secondary school class.

12–1 Sequences of Topics

There are many national, state, and local groups working on mathematics curricula. Several of these groups were considered in Chapter 1.

In geometry all of these groups seem to share a concern for precise definitions. Each also emphasizes the nature of proof, including the significance of assumptions (postulates and axioms). We shall consider these concerns with reference to a particular structure of a geometry course, so that teachers may more easily apply our comments to their daily classroom teaching.

The report of the Commission on Mathematics (§1–3) includes a brief outline for a geometry program. The report is realistic in its approach, as is indicated by its decision to continue to use the ordinary postulates for geometry rather than to introduce a more elegant set of postulates.

The UICSM (§1–2) geometry program is based upon a list of topics. Such a list provides, at best, a reference for discussing the structure of a course. The treatment of each topic must depend upon the backgrounds of the students. For example, the CEEB Commission on Mathematics suggests that all of the common figures and common constructions be considered in the junior high school grades and be assumed in the first formal course in geometry. Since such an assumption is not tenable for many teachers, some provision must be made for the treatment of these topics to the extent to which they are needed by the students. This flexibility emphasizes the essential point that the study of geometry should not be considered as the sole domain of a single year's program. Rather, geometry should be present throughout the mathematics curricula. In particular, there should be many informal experiences prior to the first formal course in geometry.

Teachers have as a major concern the fact that any structure of a course can be effective only if there are textbooks available for them to use. The structure that we now propose is compatible with most textbooks, assuming that the teacher looks over sets of exercises before assigning them. This structure also is compatible with the recommendations of the Commission on Mathematics. In particular, notice the reorganization of the material to make the Pythagorean Theorem available early in the year as a basis for the distance relation on a coordinate plane. Thus, teachers should think of the items listed as units of material to be developed in order and with a thoroughness commensurate with the background of the students.

A First Course in Geometry

1. Measurements and constructions.
2. The nature of proof.
3. Triangles.

4. Parallels.
5. Coordinates and loci.
6. Similar polygons, the Pythagorean Theorem.
7. Circles.
8. Angles and arcs.
9. Areas and volumes.
10. Regular polygons.
11. Numerical trigonometry.
12. Ways of thinking.

This sequence of topics differs from that in many texts by placing the coordinates, loci, and similar polygons before the work on circles, angles, and arcs. Notice, however, that the reorganization makes it possible to reach the Pythagorean Theorem earlier than usual and so have the distance formula available for the discussion of circles. In thus rearranging any text, the teacher must look over the exercises on similar figures and not try to prove, for example, that the tangent is the mean proportional between the secant and its external segment before discussing circles.

This structure enables a teacher to place as little or as much emphasis as he likes upon the use of coordinates. Indeed, this approach may be stressed with the better students while the others continue to use primarily the traditional methods.

The remainder of our discussion of structure is concerned with the points of view recommended for the presentation of common topics of plane geometry and some related topics of solid geometry. These will be developed with reference to the suggested structural units of the course. The use of coordinates will be treated separately in Chapter 13.

12–2 Definitions

One of the major concerns of the introduction of geometric concepts is a careful attention to definitions. As in any other logical system, we recognize that it is not possible to define everything. Usually we take point and line as undefined terms. We take the property of a point being on the line or plane as an undefined relation. We speak of the line or plane as containing the point. Then we try to make careful definitions in terms of these assumed terms and relations.

Consider, for example, the definition of an angle. If you compare the definitions in recent textbooks with those in textbooks of a few decades ago, you will find considerable contrast. It was not uncommon to find

such a definition of angle as "two lines from the same point." When
considered with the postulate that a line may be extended indefinitely
in either or both directions, this definition of angle gives a pair of
intersecting lines—hardly an angle. Modern definitions are based upon
the undefined concept of line and the undefined concept of a point
separating a line into two rays of which that point is the common end
point. As in Chapter 10, *an angle is then defined as the geometric figure
formed by two rays having a common end point.* The term "geometric
figure" may be taken as undefined or may be defined on a plane as a
set of points and lines.

The concept of a point separating a line into two rays is usually
extended to that of a line separating a plane into two half-planes.
Euclid recognized, at least intuitively, this separation of a plane by a
line when he referred to the "side" of a line in the statement of his
famous fifth postulate.

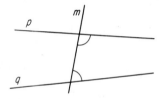

"If a line *m* intersects two lines *p, q* such that the sum of the interior angles
on the same side of *m* is less than two right angles, then the lines *p* and *q*
intersect on the side of *m* on which the sum of the interior angles is less than
two right angles."

Notice Euclid's use of "on the side of *m* on which the sum of the
interior angles is less than two right angles."

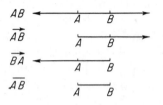

Consider a line *AB*. As in §10–1, there is a ray $\overrightarrow{AB}$ with end point

A containing B and a ray $\overrightarrow{BA}$ with end point B containing A. The line segment $\overline{AB}$ consists of the common points of the rays $\overrightarrow{AB}$ and $\overrightarrow{BA}$. Thus, we may use the concept of the intersection of two sets instead of the property of a point being between two others on a line, and may make this definition of the line segment AB:

$$\overline{AB} = \overrightarrow{AB} \cap \overrightarrow{BA}.$$

As in Chapter 10, a triangle may be defined as a union of line segments. Specifically, a triangle is a geometric figure consisting of three non-collinear points and the line segments determined by them. With suitable introduction, tenth-graders can understand this definition very well.

Triangles

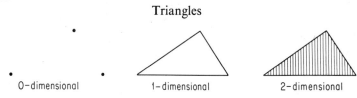

0-dimensional   1-dimensional   2-dimensional

Teachers in Russia are taught to recognize the three vertices of a triangle as a zero-dimensional triangle; the vertices and the line segments determined by them as a one-dimensional triangle; and the vertices, line segments, and all interior points as a two-dimensional triangle. The positions of the centers of gravity of these three types of triangles are then compared. This approach is also extended to tetrahedrons, with the vertices forming a zero-dimensional tetrahedron, the edges a one-dimensional tetrahedron, the surfaces of the sides a two-dimensional tetrahedron, and the sides with the interior points a three-dimensional tetrahedron. Such detailed definitions are not recommended here but rather are cited as an example of precision of terminology.

In general, each definition should have these four properties:

(i) The term to be defined should be placed in its *nearest class*.

Example: A triangle is a geometric figure.

(ii) The necessary *distinguishing properties* should be given.

Example: A triangle consists of three non-collinear points and the line segments determined by them.

(iii) The definition should be *reversible*.

Example: If a geometric figure consists of three non-collinear points and the line segment determined by them, it is a triangle.

(iv) The definition should involve *simpler terms* (that is, undefined or previously defined terms).

Careful definitions are essential for an understanding of the figures studied in geometry. To provide secondary school students with an understanding of what geometry is, one must use an intuitive approach. Euclidean geometry is sometimes described as the geometry in which figures may be moved without changing their size and shape. This intuitive idea provides the basis for superposition. However, if super-position is assumed, many of the other basic properties of figures may be proved as theorems, thus destroying the significance of many of the usual postulates. The basic role of superposition is to provide informal introductions to concepts which will be treated more formally later in the course.

Exercises

Does each definition have the desired properties? Explain.

1. A point is that which has no part.

2. A line is length without breadth.

3. A duck is a bird.

4. A circle is the locus of points at a given distance from a given point.

5. A triangle is a three-sided polygon.

6. A polygon is convex if the entire figure is on the same half-plane when each of the sides of the polygon is taken as the common edge of two half-planes.

7. A rectangle is a parallelogram with at least one right angle.

Note: In order to prove that a parallelogram is a rectangle, one must show that the definition is satisfied. Therefore, it is important to include in the definition as few properties as possible. One should not use the definition as an opportunity to list properties: four right angles, diagonals equal, opposite sides equal, diagonals bisect each other, and so forth.

.

12–3 The Nature of Proof

In both the general discussions and the treatment of geometry, postulates have additional significance when examples are given of situations in which they do not hold. For this purpose, the intuitive concepts that the students already have of the geometry of three-dimensional space and the two-dimensional geometry of points and arcs of great circles on the surface of a sphere serve very effectively.

In any geometry or other logical system, there should be an emphasis upon techniques for proving statements false as well as techniques for proving that statements are true (Chapter 11). To prove that a statement is false, one may prove that the statement can never fail to be false. In other words, an indirect method of proof may be used to show that the statement can never be true. This method of proof is suggested for the exercises at the end of this section. In many cases, an easier way to prove that a general statement is false is to give a single example or situation for which it is false. This is sufficient evidence for rejecting the premise that the statement is true, since "true" in the logical sense means "always true." Our usual postulates are significant because they involve distinguishing properties of Euclidean geometry; that is, each of these postulates is a true statement in Euclidean geometry but it may be false in a geometry based upon a different set of postulates, such as the geometry on the surface of a sphere. Here are a few examples of the use of the geometry on a sphere to show that some of our postulates are significant assumptions for Euclidean geometry, since each may be false in a geometry that is different from Euclidean geometry (that is, based upon another set of postulates).

The geometry of points and straight lines on a plane corresponds to the geometry of points and arcs of great circles on a sphere. A great circle has the center of the sphere as its center. We use the vocabulary of *meridian*, *equator*, *north* and *south poles*, and so forth, on the earth in discussing the geometry on a sphere. Thus, the equator and the meridians are great circles.

The shortest path between two points on a plane is along the line segment joining them; the shortest path between two points on a sphere is along an arc of a great circle joining them. We interpret "line" as "great circle" whenever we consider statements of plane geometry on a sphere. Under this interpretation, consider these common postulates from plane geometry:

Postulate 1. A line can be extended to any required length in either direction or both directions.

Notice that on a sphere a segment of a line (great circle) can be extended only until the circle is complete. For example, there cannot be a line 10 inches long on a sphere of radius 1 inch. Thus, in the geometry on a sphere, Postulate 1 fails.

Postulate 2. Two straight lines cannot intersect in more than one point.

Notice that Postulate 2 fails on a sphere, since any two lines intersect in two points. For example, think of two meridians having the north and south poles in common.

Postulate 3. Through two given points, one and only one line can be drawn.

On a sphere, each line (great circle) is determined as the intersection of the sphere and a plane through the center of the sphere. A plane is determined by three non-collinear points. In the case of the north and south poles, these two points and the center of the sphere lie on a single line; there are many planes through these three points; there are many lines (great circles) connecting the north and south poles. In general, there are many great circles through any two diametrically opposite points; Postulate 3 fails in the geometry on a sphere. The postulate fails because it is not always true. It applies for any two points that are not diametrically opposite, but it is not true as a general statement.

Postulate 4. The shortest distance between two points is the length of the line segment joining them.

Notice that we have interpreted lines on a sphere so that this postulate would be true. With any other interpretation, the postulate would be false.

Other examples can be found for other postulates. The geometry on a sphere also provides examples of measuring distances as well as angles in terms of degrees. There is an absolute unit of angle measure (one rotation, 360 angle degrees); there is also an absolute unit of linear measure (the circumference of a great circle, 360 arc degrees).

An intuitive recognition of the geometry of space is an essential part of any first course in geometry. With the increasing tendency to replace the traditional course in solid geometry with other studies, it becomes still more important that students learn some of the aspects of solid geometry in their earlier courses. The recognition of common figures and the use of formulas for volumes and areas are frequently considered in junior high school courses (Chapter 10). Skill in the use of formulas seems to be a reasonable part of algebra. The visualization of space figures and the recognition that we live in a three-dimensional world seem important at all levels.

In geometry there are several natural extensions of concepts of plane geometry into space which improve the student's understanding of both plane and space figures. For example, consider the definitions of plane and dihedral angles. There are also a few elementary proofs in space that can profitably be considered along with proofs on a plane. For example, when you are proving that two lines perpendicular to the same line cannot have a point in common, rephrase your proof to show that two lines perpendicular to the same plane cannot have a point in common; also that two planes perpendicular to the same line cannot have a point in common. When you discuss uniqueness of a line perpendicular to a given line and through a given point on the line, show that, like the spokes of a wheel, there are many in space.

In the discussion of postulates, the geometry of space shows the need for the condition "on a plane" in the postulate that two lines intersect or are parallel. In space, two lines may also be skew lines.

The consideration of both theorems and postulates in space often shows the need for great care in making definitions. For example, we either prove or postulate that, if two adjacent angles are supplementary, their exterior sides form a straight line. We should emphasize that this property is based upon an assumption that adjacent angles are necessarily coplanar. Think of the corner of a room. On each wall, a right angle is formed with the ceiling and the other wall. These two right angles are supplementary. Their exterior sides form a right angle rather than a straight angle on the ceiling.

Considerations of theorems and postulates on a sphere and in space provide a basis for emphasizing that theorems are true in geometries in which the definitions and postulates hold. A particular theorem may or may not be true in a geometry in which at least one of the postulates does not hold. Such dependence of the truth of statements on the given definitions and postulates illustrates an essential aspect of the nature of proof.

Exercises

1. Assume that on a plane there is at most one line perpendicular to a given line and through a given point. Then prove that on a plane two distinct lines perpendicular to a given line cannot have a point in common.

2. Assume that a line n and a plane γ are perpendicular each to each at a point P if and only if n is perpendicular to each line that is on γ and through P. Then prove that two planes α and β perpendicular to a line m at distinct points on the line cannot have a point in common.

12–4 Conjectures

Many people think of geometry in terms of proofs, without stopping to consider the source of the statements that are to be proved. Such neglect of the proper role of an intuitive approach and the extreme desirability of training students to look for relationships and to formulate their conjectures (guesses) as statements is most unfortunate. Insight can be developed most effectively by making such conjectures very freely and then testing them in reference to the postulates and previously proved statements.

Students vary as widely in their ability to make conjectures as in their ability to prove statements. Often students who do very well in one of these areas do poorly in the other. In order to challenge students of different abilities, we need exercises which are subject to different levels of interpretation. Here are two such exercises.

Triangles are often introduced as rigid figures. When this is done, ask the students how many diagonals are required to make plane polygons of 3, 4, 5, . . ., n sides rigid figures. The pattern is shown in the following array, which should be developed out of class discussion, leaving any wrong answers in the array until some student observes that the pattern is being violated:

Number of sides	3	4	5	6	7	8	9	10	12	n
Number of diagonals needed to make rigid	0	1	2	3	4	5	6	7	9	$n-3$

While you are working this out with the average students, ask the better students in how many ways the necessary diagonals can be picked for a quadrilateral and for a pentagon. In the case of the quadrilateral, one diagonal is needed and either one may be used. Thus, the diagonal may be selected in two ways. In the case of the pentagon, the two diagonals may have a common vertex (any one of the five) or they may use four of the vertices (thus avoiding any one of the five) and, hence, may be

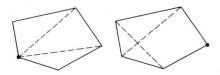

chosen in 10 ways. There are at least 40 ways for a hexagon. A complete discussion of the number of ways to make hexagon a rigid figure is not recommended for high school students nor is it worth pursuing here.

In the discussion of locus problems, there are many opportunities to challenge students of various abilities by considering both plane and space figures and by considering related exercises of different degrees of difficulty. As an example of the second approach, consider a railroad wheel with its flange. Discuss the paths of the points A, B, C, and D

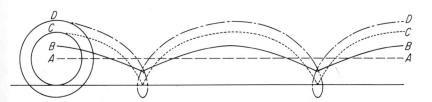

in the figure as the wheel rolls along the track. Discuss these paths in the order A, B, C, D and encourage the better students to work ahead of you so that they may be challenged to think for themselves while you are explaining the early cases.

Throughout the study of geometry, and especially after the preliminary theorems and methods of proof have been established, there should be an emphasis upon the making of conjectures and the testing of these conjectures in the postulational system under consideration. When a theorem is proved on a plane, consider it in space; consider the converse of the theorem on a plane and in space. The treatment in space can be either deductive or informal; usually the informal, or intuitive, approach is better at this level. For example, think of perpendicularity. When do you have perpendicularity on a plane? Under what conditions are perpendiculars unique? Under what circumstances are perpendiculars used in locus problems? Extend each of these considerations to space. Treat parallels in a similar way. These ideas are developed in the exercises.

Exercises

1. Describe the ways in which perpendiculars exist (a) on a plane; (b) in space.

2. Describe the situations under which perpendiculars exist and seem to be unique (a) on a plane; (b) in space.

3. Describe the use of perpendiculars in locus problems (a) on a plane; (b) in space.

4. Describe the ways in which parallelism exists (a) on a plane; (b) in space.

5. Describe the situations under which parallels exist and seem to be unique (a) on a plane; (b) in space.

6. Describe the use of parallels in locus problems (a) on a plane; (b) in space.

Note: Exercises such as these may be used effectively either as a basis for conjectures to be proved formally (especially on a plane) or as a basis for conjectures to be considered only intuitively and illustrated by figures (especially in space).

12–5 Points Deserving Emphasis

So far in this chapter we have emphasized:

(a) The need for a sequence of topics (§12–1) which will make it possible to prove the Pythagorean Theorem using similar triangles relatively early in the course, as a basis for the distance formula in coordinate geometry (Chapter 13);

(b) The importance of definitions (§12–2);

(c) The dependence of proofs upon the postulates used (§12–3); and

(d) The importance of conjectures as a basis for broadening the student's understanding and for developing his facility in geometry (§12–4).

The precise methods for using these emphases vary from topic to topic. However, the general idea of considering statements from other points of view applies throughout. For example, consider the parallel postulate in the form:

There is one and only one line through a given point and parallel to a given line.

For the better students, notice that this postulate does not hold on the surface of a sphere; consider other geometries obtained by assuming no lines or more than one line through the given point and parallel to a given line (Chapter 15). Notice the use of parallel lines in the construction of a number scale (Chapter 14).

Statements may also be extended by considering them in space as well as on a plane. The study of loci provides an excellent opportunity for doing this. Also, the study of intersections of space loci helps to develop the visualization of space figures. Furthermore, loci may be used in the development of the coordinate plane. The coordinate plane is very useful (Chapter 13); it provides a second major avenue of attack upon many problems. We may use either the postulates of geometry and an ordinary deductive proof, or we may use the postulates of algebra and the coordinate plane. The use of the coordinate plane helps the student understand the properties of real numbers and also the continuity of the number line (Chapter 16). The coordinate plane also provides the basis for the study of numerical trigonometry, where several of the formulas may be derived using the distance formula on a plane.

We conclude with a discussion of two other points deserving emphasis:

(e) A precise vocabulary and notation to avoid confusion; and

(f) A policy of "honesty" in proofs.

The latter is especially necessary when the most common postulates for plane geometry are used.

There are two proofs regarding triangles which are sometimes questioned. The proof that the base angles of an isosceles triangle are equal involves the construction of the angle bisector. However, we cannot yet prove that the construction used for this purpose produces the desired result. Accordingly, most texts simply postulate the existence of the angle bisector; a few teachers use the following proof, which emphasizes the matching of corresponding vertices in writing down the symbols for congruent triangles. They use the statement $\triangle ABC \cong \triangle RST$ to imply these six equations:

$$\angle A = \angle R, \qquad \angle B = \angle S, \qquad \angle C = \angle T,$$

$$\overline{BC} = \overline{ST}, \qquad \overline{AC} = \overline{RT}, \qquad \overline{AB} = \overline{RS}.$$

Such a matching of vertices was highly recommended by the first SMSG (§1–5) committee on geometry for both congruent and similar triangles. When this precise notation is used and $\angle A \neq \angle S$, as in the figure, it is not correct to write $\triangle ABC \cong \triangle SRT$ even though it is correct that $\triangle ABC \cong \triangle RST$.

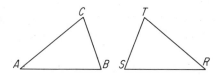

The proof that the base angles of an isosceles triangle are equal may be given using the precise notation for congruences without formally using the angle bisector. Intuitively the correspondence between congruent triangles may be visualized in terms of superposition

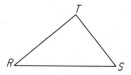

(technically, we use a mapping without moving the triangles). Under such a correspondence, a triangle may correspond to itself as well as to other triangles. Thus, for any triangle RST, we have $\triangle RST \cong \triangle RST$, since, for example, $\angle R = \angle R$, $\angle S = \angle S$, and $\overline{RS} = \overline{RS}$. In the case of an isosceles triangle ABC with $\overline{AC} = \overline{BC}$, there is another way of mapping the triangle onto itself. Intuitively we may think of the triangle as reflected in (folded over) the bisector of $\angle C$. Formally we notice that $\angle ACB = \angle BCA$, $\overline{AC} = \overline{BC}$, and $\overline{CB} = \overline{CA}$; therefore, by s.a.s. = s.a.s.,

$$\triangle ACB \cong \triangle BCA$$

and $\angle A = \angle B$, as was to be proved.

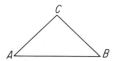

In the first SMSG geometry, there was extensive discussion of such mappings of a figure onto itself. As we have seen, any triangle is congruent to itself, $\triangle ABC \cong \triangle ABC$; also, if $\overline{AC} = \overline{BC}$, then $\triangle ACB \cong \triangle BCA$. Thus, an isosceles triangle can be mapped onto itself in two ways. In how many ways can an equilateral triangle be mapped onto itself? If $\overline{AC} = \overline{BC} = \overline{AB}$, then $\triangle ABC \cong \triangle ABC$ by identity as before; $\triangle ABC \cong \triangle BAC$, $\triangle ABC \cong \triangle ACB$, and $\triangle ABC \cong \triangle CBA$ by line reflections in the altitudes; $\triangle ABC \cong \triangle BCA$ and $\triangle ABC \cong \triangle CAB$ by rotations of 120° and 240° about the point of intersection of the altitudes. Thus, an equilateral triangle can be mapped onto itself in six ways.

The other proof that is sometimes questioned has the disadvantage of making use of the appearance of the figure. Consider the usual proof

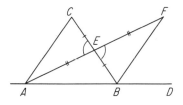

that any exterior angle of a triangle is greater than either opposite interior angle. Given a triangle ABC, you extend AB to a point D and prove that $\angle DBC$ is greater than $\angle C$. The usual method of proof involves finding the mid-point, say E, of BC; drawing AE; extending AE to a point F such that E is the mid-point of AF; drawing BF; and then comparing angles in the figure. You prove $\triangle AEC \cong \triangle FEB$ (s.a.s.), and thus know that $\angle C = \angle FBC$. Finally, you must show that $\angle FBC$ is less than $\angle DBC$, which you assert from the appearance of the figure. In particular, you assert that the whole of $\angle DBC$ is greater than one of its parts. But how do you know that $\angle FBC$ is a part of $\angle DBC$? Frankly, you don't know this as far as your stated assumptions are concerned. Rather, you think that you see it from the figure. It is true in the figure drawn, and, indeed, in any figure on a plane. However, if you are honest with your students, you must admit that you have bypassed the postulates and tried to make the reason for this step *look reasonable* rather than formally proving it. Average and better students can be trained so that they see such weaknesses in proofs.

You should be willing to admit the weaknesses in your proofs. What can you do about these weaknesses? There are postulates which cover such problems. However, most people consider such postulates ineffective in a first course. Thus, for average pupils you should accept a reason based upon the appearance of a figure when such seems necessary. For above-average pupils, you should insist that they include in their proofs an indication that they realize that they have bypassed the postulates and used the appearance of a figure. For these better pupils, you should also discuss geometries in which the figures would appear differently.

The most common geometry in which the exterior angle theorem fails is the geometry on the surface of a sphere. On a sphere, we have

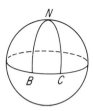

points and great circles (shortest lines or paths between two points, that is, geodesics) in place of points and lines. Thus, a triangle on a sphere is bounded by arcs of great circles. For example, any two meridians and the equator form a triangle NBC in the northern hemisphere, where

N is the north pole and B and C are on the equator. In this triangle, the angles at B and C are right angles, and thus the exterior angle at B is equal to rather than greater than $\angle C$.

Let's try the proof just developed for the exterior-angle theorem on this spherical triangle. Extend NB to a point D to form exterior $\angle DBC$; find the mid-point, say E, of BC; draw NE; extend NE to a point F such that $NE = EF$; draw BF. It remains to show that $\angle FBC$ is less than $\angle DBC$. Note that NE is a quarter of a great circle. Therefore, NF is half of a great circle and F is at the south pole, S. Each great

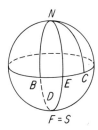

circle through N passes through S. Therefore, NB passes through S, that is, S is on the line NBD. Finally, note that a great circle through S and B must contain N. Therefore, the line FB cannot be drawn as it is dotted on the figure; rather, it must be the same line as DB. Then, $\angle FBC$ is identical with and equal to $\angle DBC$ instead of being one of its parts.

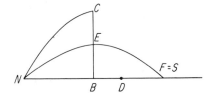

It is helpful to turn and flatten the sphere to show the figure just considered for $\triangle NBC$ as follows. The actual basis for the failure of the exterior-angle theorem on a sphere is the fact that on a sphere two lines (great circles) intersect in two points (diametrically opposite). Thus, if NE is less than one-quarter of a great circle, the exterior-angle theorem holds; if NE is equal to one-quarter of a great circle, the exterior angle is equal to the particular opposite interior angle under consideration; if *NE* is greater than one-quarter of a great circle, the exterior angle is less than the opposite interior angle under consideration. Such a case is shown here for a spherical triangle and also as it would look flattened out on a plane. In all cases, $\angle FBC$ is greater than $\angle DBC$ rather than less.

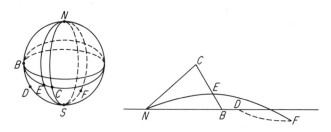

Many students can profit by a detailed development as presented here to show the significance of the assertion that the theorem holds on a plane. All students deserve an explicit recognition that this procedure of making a statement from the appearance of a figure will not be generally acceptable. In particular, they will not be allowed to call triangles right triangles or isosceles triangles just because they look that way.

Application and Additional Readings

This entire chapter has been concerned with applications to secondary school courses. For additional reading regarding experimental programs in geometry, see the publications of such groups as [42] and [48]; for an example of a regular text structured in accordance with the proposed outline, see [29].

Answers for Exercises

12–2 *Definitions*

1. No; "point" is not classified and the definition is not reversible.

2. No; "line" is not classified and the definition is not reversible.

3. No; the definition is not reversible.

4. No; the circle must, at least implicitly, be classified as a plane figure, as contrasted with a line or space figure.

5. No; for most people, a general polygon is not a simpler figure than a triangle.

6. Yes.

7. Yes.

12–3 *The Nature of Proof*

1. Given: Distinct coplanar lines m, n, and t; $n \perp t$; $m \perp t$. To prove: There does not exist a point P that is on both m and n. Proof: Suppose that the lines m and n have a point P in common. Then there would be two lines perpendicular to t and through P. By the assumption stated in the exercise, this is impossible. Therefore, by the method of indirect proof, our assumption that a point P exists on both m and n must be false. This statement is logically equivalent to the statement that was to be proved: there does not exist a point that is on both m and n.

2. Given: Distinct planes α and β and a line m; $\alpha \perp m$ at A; $\beta \perp m$ at B. To prove: There does not exist a point Q that is on both α and β. Proof: Suppose there is a point Q on α and on β. The lines QB and QA intersect and determine a plane. This plane also contains m (which is determined by B and A). Thus, $QB \perp m$ at B and $QA \perp m$ at A, which is impossible by our assumption in Ex. 1; therefore, the assumption that Q is on both α and β must be false. This statement is logically equivalent to the statement that was to be proved: there does not exist a point Q that is on both α and β.

12–4 *Conjectures*

1. (a) Line to line. (b) Line to line, line to plane, plane to line, plane to plane.

2. (a) Line to a given line through point of line,
       line to a given line through point not on line.
   (b) Line to a given line through point not on line,
       line to a given plane through point on plane,
       line to a given plane through point not on plane,

plane to a given line through point on line,
plane to a given line through point not on line,
plane to a given plane through line on plane,
plane to a given plane through line not on and not perpendicular to the plane.

3. (a) The locus of points equidistant from ends of line segment is a line perpendicular to and bisecting the segment. (b) The locus of points equidistant from ends of line segment is a plane perpendicular to and bisecting the segment; the locus of points equidistant from three noncollinear points is a line perpendicular to the plane of the three points and through the intersection of the perpendicular bisectors of the triangle having the given points as vertices; the locus of points equidistant from two parallel lines is a plane perpendicular to their plane and halfway between them.

4. (a) Line to line. (b) Line to line, line to plane, plane to line, plane to plane.

5. (a) Line to a given line through a point not on the line. (b) Line to line through a point not on the line; plane to a given plane through a point not on given plane.

6. (a) The locus of points at a given distance d from a given line m is two lines each parallel to m and at the distance d from m; the locus of points equidistant from two parallel lines is a line parallel to the given lines and halfway between them. (b) The locus of points at a given distance d from a given plane α is two planes β and γ each parallel to α and at the distance d from α; the locus of points equidistant from two parallel planes is a plane parallel to the given planes and halfway between them; the locus of points at a given distance d from a given line m is the set of lines (the lines on the surface of a cylinder) each parallel to m and at the given distance d from m.

CHAPTER

THIRTEEN

COORDINATE GEOMETRY
FOR A FIRST COURSE

One of the major recommendations of the Commission on Mathematics (§1–3) is for the systematic use of coordinates in the first formal course in geometry. The reader is probably familiar with most of the uses of coordinates. Thus the major question is: How do these uses of coordinates fit into a first course? In this chapter we shall attempt to answer this question and to review the uses of coordinates.

The goal is not the insertion of a capsule of coordinate geometry. The goal is to broaden the over-all view of geometry so that either coordinate or synthetic methods will be available for use whenever appropriate. Then the problems of geometry can be approached with a greater variety of skills and techniques.

There are some theorems that can more easily be proved using synthetic methods; there are some theorems that can more easily be proved using coordinate methods; and there are some theorems that can easily be proved either way.

13–1 The Coordinate Plane

There is a temptation to consider any classroom discussion of coordinate geometry as a self-contained unit of analytic geometry. This temptation can be minimized by considering the topics of coordinate geometry according to their applicability in the development of the major topics of a first course in geometry (§12–1).

The early units on reviewing measurements and constructions and introducing the nature of proof are not affected. The units on triangles and parallels are also not affected, since they are needed as a basis for introducing coordinates. Think of the x-axis and the y-axis as given perpendicular lines. The location on a coordinate plane of any point (x, y) may be determined after parallel lines have been introduced and a unit of measure is given. For example, the points one unit from the x-axis are on the lines $y = 1$ and $y = -1$ parallel to the x-axis. The points two units from the y-axis are on the lines $x = 2$ and $x = -2$ parallel to the y-axis. The point $(2, 1)$ is at the intersection of $x = 2$ and $y = 1$.

When the coordinate plane is introduced, each student should learn:

(a) To locate points on a coordinate plane when their coordinates are given;

(b) to sketch the graphs of simple statements;

(c) to graph simple equations and inequalities;

(d) to create statements describing simple loci;

(e) to identify points on a line having a given equation;

(f) to find the length of any line segment parallel to a coordinate axis; and

(g) to find the equation of a line through two given points when the line is parallel to a coordinate axis.

These concepts can be developed after the following statements have been accepted. Any two points with the same first coordinate are on the same line parallel to the y-axis; any two points with the same second coordinate are on the same line parallel to the x-axis. Lines parallel to the y-axis have equations of the form $x = k$; lines parallel to the x-axis have equations of the form $y = n$. Each line is a locus. We locate points (k, n) as the intersection of these loci. Some teachers prefer to call the x-coordinate the **abscissa** of the point, and the y-coordinate the **ordinate** of the point.

The distance from the origin of a point $(x, 0)$ on the x-axis may be expressed as $|x|$, or as $|x - 0|$. Also, on the x-axis the length of any line segment with end points $(x_1, 0)$ and $(x_2, 0)$ may be expressed as $|x_2 - x_1|$. On the coordinate plane, the length of any line segment with end points (x_1, y_1) and (x_2, y_1) may be expressed as $|x_2 - x_1|$;

the length of any line segment with end points (x_1, y_1) and (x_1, y_2) may be expressed as $|y_2 - y_1|$.

The exercises which follow illustrate the development of the desired concepts. Notice that this material is very susceptible to student explorations, conjectures, and discoveries; also, that additional relations among points may be developed by having students determine whether or not three points having given coordinates lie on a straight line. For example, consider three points A, B, and C on a line. The point B is said to be **between** A and C if the lengths of the line segments satisfy the equation $AB + BC = AC$.

The concept of betweenness has been essentially undefined until recent times. It may be defined for points using lengths of line segments as just noted. It may also be defined using the intersection of two rays.

As in §10–1, two points A and B determine a line $\overleftrightarrow{AB}$. They also determine a ray $\overrightarrow{AB}$ and a ray $\overrightarrow{BA}$. The intersection of these two rays is the line segment $\overline{AB}$. This line segment consists of the two end points A and B and the points *between* A and B.

Exercises

Plot on the same coordinate plane:

1. $(2, 5)$ 　　 2. $(-2, 5)$ 　　 3. $(-3, -4)$ 　　 4. $(3, -4)$

5. $(0, -2)$ 　　 6. $(-3, 0)$ 　　 7. $(5, -2)$ 　　 8. $(-2, -3)$

Draw coordinate axes, sketch each locus, and give its equation:

9. The points 2 units above the x-axis.

10. The points 3 units to the left of the y-axis.

11. The points 2 units from the origin and on the x-axis.

12. The points with coordinates which are equal.

Graph each equation or inequality on a coordinate plane and give the coordinates of any three points of the graph:

13. $y = 2$ 　　　 14. $x = -3$ 　　　 15. $x = y$

16. $x + y = 1$ 　　　 17. $y = 2x - 1$ 　　　 18. $x > 3$

19. $x > 3$ and $y < 4$ 　　 *20. $|x| + |y| = 1$ 　　 *21. $|x - y| < 1$

Find the equation of the line through and the lengths of the line segment determined by each pair of points:

22. (2, 1) and (2, 5)   **23.** (−3, 2) and (−3, 7)

24. (2, 1) and (5, 1)   **25.** (−3, 2) and (−7, 2)

26. (5, −2) and (5, 7)   **27.** (−1, −3) and (5, −3)

13–2 The Mid-point Formula

The mid-point formula for the line segment determined by any two given points (x_1, y_1) and (x_2, y_2) is derived using the fact that if three parallel lines cut off equal segments on one transversal, they cut off equal segments on every transversal. To do this, we need to be able to find the mid-point of a line segment on a coordinate axis, that is, on a number line.

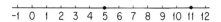

Consider the points with coordinates 5 and 11 on a number line; the length of the line segment determined by them is $11 - 5$, that is, 6. The mid-point of the line segment has coordinate $5 + \frac{1}{2}(6)$, that is, 8. Notice that $8 = \frac{1}{2}(5 + 11)$. The points with coordinates 3 and -5 on a number line determine a line segment of length $3 - (-5)$, that is, 8; the mid-point has coordinate $-5 + \frac{1}{2}(8)$, that is, -1. Notice that $-1 = \frac{1}{2}(-5 + 3)$.

Suppose that R and S are points on a number line with coordinates r and s. Then the line segment $\overline{RS}$ has length $|r - s|$. When $r < s$, as

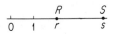

in the figure, the length is $s - r$; the mid-point has coordinate $r + \frac{1}{2}(s - r)$, that is, $\frac{1}{2}(r + s)$. This formula holds for any two points R and S on a number line.

Now consider any two points A: (x_1, y_1) and B: (x_2, y_2) on a co-ordinate plane. The line that passes through A and is parallel to the

y-axis has the equation $x = x_1$ and crosses the x-axis at $(x_1, 0)$; the line that passes through B and is parallel to the y-axis has the equation $x = x_2$ and crosses the x-axis at $(x_2, 0)$. These points with coordinates x_1 and x_2 on the x-axis determine a line segment; the mid-point D of this line segment has x-coordinate $\frac{1}{2}(x_1 + x_2)$. The line that passes

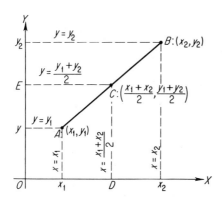

through D and is parallel to the y-axis has equation $x = \frac{1}{2}(x_1 + x_2)$. Notice that the three parallel lines

$$x = x_1, \qquad x = \tfrac{1}{2}(x_1 + x_2), \qquad \text{and} \qquad x = x_2$$

cut off equal segments on the x-axis; therefore, they cut off equal segments on the line AB. In other words, the line $x = \frac{1}{2}(x_1 + x_2)$ passes through the mid-point C of the line segment $\overline{AB}$, and C has x-coordinate $\frac{1}{2}(x_1 + x_2)$.

Similarly, the lines that pass through A and B and are parallel to the x-axis have equations $y = y_1$ and $y = y_2$. These lines intersect the y-axis in points $(0, y_1)$ and $(0, y_2)$; they determine a line segment with mid-point $\left(0, \dfrac{y_1 + y_2}{2}\right)$. The three parallel lines

$$y = y_1 \qquad y = \tfrac{1}{2}(y_1 + y_2), \qquad \text{and} \qquad y = y_2$$

cut off equal segments on the y-axis and therefore cut off equal segments on the line AB. In other words, the line $y = \frac{1}{2}(y_1 + y_2)$ passes through the mid-point C of the line segment $\overline{AB}$, and C has y-coordinate $\frac{1}{2}(y_1 + y_2)$.

We have now completed the derivation of the **mid-point formula:**
Any line segment with end points (x_1, y_1) and (x_2, y_2) has mid-point

$$\left(\frac{x_1 + x_2}{2}, \frac{y_1 + y_2}{2}\right)$$

Notice that after the coordinate plane has been introduced, the mid-point formula can be derived without any additional assumptions. This development is based upon the theorem: If three parallel lines cut off equal segments on one transversal, then they cut off equal segments on any transversal. Applications of the mid-point formula will be considered in the exercises.

Exercises

Find the mid-point of the line segment with the given end points:

1. $(1, 2)$ and $(3, 8)$ **2.** $(2, -3)$ and $(4, 7)$

3. $(-5, 4)$ and $(3, -2)$ **4.** $(-3, -7)$ and $(5, 9)$

Show that, for suitable values of the coordinates, any figure of the given type may be represented with vertices at the indicated points on a coordinate plane having mutually perpendicular axes:

5. Right triangle; $(0, 0)$, $(b, 0)$, $(0, a)$.

6. Rectangle; $(0, 0)$ $(a, 0)$, (a, b), $(0, b)$.

7. Square; $(0, 0)$, $(a, 0)$, (a, a), $(0, a)$.

8. Rhombus; $(a, 0)$, $(0, b)$, $(-a, 0)$, $(0, -b)$.

9. Parallelogram; $(0, 0)$, $(a, 0)$, $(a + b, c)$, (b, c).

10. Triangle; $(0, 0)$, $(a, 0)$, (b, c).

11. Quadrilateral; $(0, 0)$, $(a, 0)$, (b, c), (d, e).

In Exs. 12 through 15, represent the figure on a coordinate plane and prove:

12. The line segment joining the mid-points of two sides of a triangle is parallel to the third side and equal to half of it.

13. The median of a trapezoid is parallel to the bases and equal to one-half their sum.

14. The diagonals of a parallelogram bisect each other.

15. The lines joining the mid-points of the opposite sides of a quadrilateral bisect each other.

16. A line segment $\overline{RS}$ has end point R: $(1, 3)$ and mid-point M: $(2, 7)$. Find the coordinates of S.

17. Repeat Ex. 16 for R: $(2, -5)$ and M: $(5, -8)$.

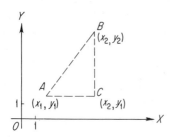

13–3 The Slope of a Line

Given any two points A: (x_1, y_1) and B: (x_2, y_2), either the line AB is parallel to a coordinate axis or a right triangle ACB with legs parallel to the coordinate axes may be formed by using C: (x_2, y_1) as the third vertex. Then the sides $\overline{AC}$ and $\overline{BC}$ have lengths $|x_2 - x_1|$ and $|y_2 - y_1|$. The ratio $\dfrac{y_2 - y_1}{x_2 - x_1}$ of the directed segments $\overline{CB}$ and $\overline{AC}$ is defined to be the slope of the line segment $\overline{AB}$.

Slope is important primarily as a property of lines rather than of line segments. Any two points A: (x_1, y_1) and B: (x_2, y_2) determine a line AB. This line is parallel to the y-axis if and only if $x_2 = x_1$. If $x_2 = x_1$, the ratio $\dfrac{y_2 - y_1}{x_2 - x_1}$ is undefined, since we cannot divide by zero. If $x_2 \neq x_1$, the ratio $\dfrac{y_2 - y_1}{x_2 - x_1}$ is defined for any points A and B on the line.

Properties of similar figures are needed to prove that the ratio $\dfrac{y_2 - y_1}{x_2 - x_1}$ has the same value whatever points A and B are selected on the line. This value is called the **slope** m of the line; we write

$$m = \frac{y_2 - y_1}{x_2 - x_1}.$$

A proof that the slope m of a line does not depend upon the selection of the points A and B may be found in [29; p. 285]. Notice that the slope is defined for any line that is not parallel to the y-axis; the slope of any line parallel to the x-axis is zero.

Slope is often an optional topic in a first course in geometry. It is usually introduced for lines through the origin; then defined in general, as we have done; then it is proved that, for lines that are not parallel to the y-axis, two lines are parallel if and only if they have the same slope.

The equation of any line that is "determined" may now be found. We shall consider these cases:

(a) a line through two arbitrary points,
(b) a line through two points on the coordinate axes,
(c) a line through any given point and parallel to a given line, and
(d) a line through a point on the y-axis and parallel to a given line.

Let A: (x_1, y_1) and B: (x_2, y_2) be any two given points. If $x_1 = x_2$, the line AB has equation $x = x_1$. If $x_1 \neq x_2$, a point P: (x, y) is on

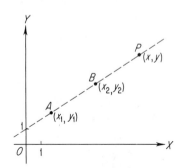

the line AB if and only if the slope $\dfrac{y - y_1}{x - x_1}$ of the line segment $\overline{AP}$ is equal to the slope $\dfrac{y_2 - y_1}{x_2 - x_1}$ of the line segment $\overline{AB}$. This assertion is equivalent to the statement that through a given point A there is one and only one line parallel to the given line AB; that is, with a given slope. We use the expressions for the slopes and write

$$\frac{y - y_1}{x - x_1} = \frac{y_2 - y_1}{x_2 - x_1}$$

as the equation of a line through any two points A: (x_1, y_1) and B: (x_2, y_2), where $x_1 \neq x_2$. This equation is called the **two-point form** of the equation of the line.

Let A: $(a, 0)$ and B: $(0, b)$ be two given points on the coordinate axes. If $a = 0$, both A and B are on the y-axis and the line AB has equation $x = 0$. If $a \neq 0$, the line AB consists of points (x, y) such that

$$\frac{y - 0}{x - a} = \frac{b - 0}{0 - a},$$

that is, the points with coordinates satisfying the two-point form of the equation of the line. We may rewrite this equation in the forms

$$(-a)y = b(x) + (-a)b,$$

$$\frac{y}{b} = -\frac{x}{a} + 1,$$

$$\frac{x}{a} + \frac{y}{b} = 1.$$

The last equation is called the **intercept form** of the equation of the line. The number a is the x-coordinate of the point at which the line cuts the x-axis and is called the **x-intercept** of the line. The number b is the y-coordinate of the point at which the line cuts the y-axis and is called the **y-intercept** of the line. Notice that a line parallel to a coordinate axis fails to have two intercepts and cannot be written in intercept form.

Let A: (x_1, y_1) be any given point, and let m be the slope of a given line. The coordinates of each point P: (x, y) on the line through A with slope m satisfy the equation

$$\frac{y - y_1}{x - x_1} = m.$$

When written in the form

$$y - y_1 = m(x - x_1),$$

this equation is called the **point-slope form** of the equation of the line.

Let A: $(0, b)$ be any point on the y-axis, and let m be the slope of any given line. Then the point-slope form of the equation is

$$y - b = m(x - 0)$$

and may be written in the form

$$y = mx + b.$$

This equation is called the **slope-intercept form** of the equation of the line. Notice that it is the y-intercept, that is, the y-coordinate of the point at which the line cuts the y-axis, that is used.

Practice in using these four forms of the equations of a line is provided in the exercises. Notice that, if an equation of a line is given in one form, it may be rewritten in each of the other forms. For example, this equation in two-point form,

$$\frac{y-1}{x-1} = \frac{3-1}{2-1},$$

may be written in point-slope form as

$$y - 1 = 2(x - 1),$$

may be written in slope-intercept form as

$$y = 2x - 1,$$

and may be written in intercept form as

$$\frac{x}{\frac{1}{2}} + \frac{y}{-1} = 1.$$

Notice also that, for any given equation, it is possible to find as many points as desired on the line. For example, if the equation is $y = 2x + 3$, then each point has coordinates of the form $(x, 2x + 3)$. If $x = 1$, $y = 5$; if $x = -1$, $y = 1$; if $x = 5$, $y = 13$, and so forth. Each of the points $(1, 5)$, $(-1, 1)$, and $(5, 13)$ is on the line whose equation is $y = 2x + 3$. Any two of these points may be used to write an equation for the line in two-point form. For example,

$$\frac{y-5}{x-1} = \frac{13-5}{5-1}.$$

Exercises

Consider lines with the given equations. In Exs. 1 through 4, find two points on each line and write an equation for each line in two-point form.

1. $y = 3x - 5$ 2. $2x + 3y = 6$

3. $x = 5 - y$ 4. $y = -2$

5. Write an equation for each line in Exs. 1 through 4 in point-slope form.

6. Write an equation for each line in Exs. 1 through 4 in slope-intercept form.

7. Write an equation for each line in Exs. 1, 2, and 3 in intercept form.

8. Draw the graph of each line in Exs. 1 through 4 on a coordinate plane.

Find an equation for a line:

9. Through (2, 3) and (4, 5).

10. Through (0, 3) and (5, 0).

11. Through $(0, -2)$ with slope $\frac{3}{2}$.

12. With x-intercept 5 and y-intercept 4.

Assume (a) that the coordinate axes have been selected so that none of the lines under discussion is parallel to the y-axis, and (b) that two lines on a coordinate plane are parallel if and only if they have the same slope. Then prove each of these statements for lines on a coordinate plane:

13. If two lines are parallel to the same line, they are parallel to each other.

14. If a line intersects one of two parallel lines, then it intersects the other also.

15. If a line is parallel to one of two intersecting lines, then it intersects the other.

16. Lines parallel to intersecting lines intersect.

17. Quadrilateral $ABCD$ is a parallelogram when its vertices are A: (0, 0), B: (5, 7), C: (7, 13), and D: (2, 6),

13–4 The Distance Formula

After the Pythagorean Theorem has been proved, it may be used to obtain a general formula for the length of any line segment on a coordinate plane. Let the end points of the line segment have coordinates (x_1, y_1) and (x_2, y_2). As in §13–3, either the line segment is parallel to a coordinate axis, or a right triangle may be formed with the vertex of the right angle at (x_2, y_1). The lengths of the legs of the right triangle are $|x_2 - x_1|$ and $|y_2 - y_1|$; by the Pythagorean Theorem, the length of the hypotenuse is

$$d = \sqrt{(x_2 - x_1)^2 + (y_2 - y_1)^2}.$$

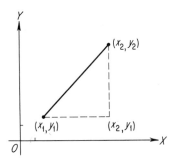

This is the **distance formula** on a plane. It holds also when the line segment is parallel to a coordinate axis, since $|x_2 - x_1| = \sqrt{(x_2 - x_1)^2}$ and $|y_2 - y_1| = \sqrt{(y_2 - y_1)^2}$.

The treatment of circles can now be considered from both a synthetic and a coordinate point of view.

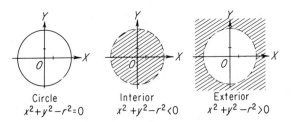

Circle
$x^2 + y^2 - r^2 = 0$

Interior
$x^2 + y^2 - r^2 < 0$

Exterior
$x^2 + y^2 - r^2 > 0$

The distance formula can be used to obtain proofs of many common theorems in coordinate geometry. Several of these are considered in exercises. The proof of the following theorem provides an opportunity to use inequalities as well as equations.

If two chords of a circle are unequal, the longer chord is nearer the center.

Consider the lengths of the chords as $2q$ and $2t$, where $2q > 2t$. Call their distances from the center of the circle p and s, respectively. The radius of the circle with equation $x^2 + y^2 = r^2$ is r. Consider the chord with end points (p, q) and $(p, -q)$ and the chord with end points (s, t) and $(s, -t)$. These chords are equal to the given chords, since in the same circle or equal circles chords equally distant from the center

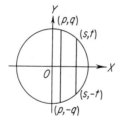

are equal. The statement that the end points of the chords are on the circle is $p^2 + q^2 = r^2$ and $s^2 + t^2 = r^2$. Thus, $p^2 + q^2 = s^2 + t^2$. Given that $2q > 2t$, and that p, q, s, and t are distances (that is, non-negative), then $q > t$, $q^2 > t^2$, and, subtracting the inequality from the equality, we have

$$\begin{array}{ll} p^2 + q^2 = s^2 + t^2 \\ \quad\ \ q^2 > \qquad\ t^2 \\ \hline p^2 \qquad < s^2 \end{array}$$

whence $p < s$ as was to be proved. Obviously, the statements require previous consideration of inequalities (§8–1).

The converse of this theorem may be proved in a similar manner (Ex. 7). Other applications are also considered in the exercises.

The distance formula enables us to classify triangles when the co-ordinates of their vertices are given. A triangle is isosceles if at least two of its sides are equal, equilateral if all three sides are equal, and right if the sum of the squares of two sides is equal to the square of the third side.

Exercises

Find the length of the line segment with end points:

1. (1, 3) and (4, 7)   **2.** (2, −3) and (7, 9)

3. (−1, 5) and (2, −3)   **4.** (−3, −4) and (−7, −15)

Find the lengths of the sides and tell whether the triangle with the given vertices is (a) *an isosceles triangle,* (b) *an equilateral triangle,* (c) *a right triangle.*

5. (4, 5), (3, 7), and (6, 6)

6. (−1, 15), (7, −12), and (−3, −5)

Prove on a coordinate plane:

7. A line $x = p$ is tangent to the circle with equation $x^2 + y^2 = r^2$ if $p^2 = r^2$; is a secant if $p^2 < r^2$; does not intersect the circle if $p^2 > r^2$.

8. The diagonals of a rectangle are equal.

9. An isosceles triangle has two equal medians.

10. The sum of the squares of the distances from any point P on the plane of a rectangle to the end points of one diagonal of the rectangle is equal to the sum of the squares of the distances from P to the end points of the other diagonal.

13–5 Perpendicular Lines

Two lines on a coordinate plane are parallel if and only if they are both parallel to the y-axis or if they have the same slope (§13–3). We now use the Pythagorean Theorem and prove that if neither of two lines is parallel to the x-axis and if the lines are perpendicular, then the product of their slopes is −1.

Consider two lines p and q on a coordinate plane. If at least one of the lines is parallel to the x-axis, then the lines are perpendicular if and only if the other line is parallel to the y-axis. If neither line is parallel to the x-axis, then each line intersects the x-axis. Suppose that one line intersects the x-axis at $A: (a, 0)$ and that the other line intersects the x-axis at a point $B: (b, 0)$, where $b > a$. This assumption implies that the lines do not intersect on the x-axis. When the lines intersect on the x-axis, either a new coordinate system may be used with a different choice of the x-axis or a new proof may be given with A and B selected on a line $y = k$, $k \neq 0$.

If $p \perp q$, call their point of intersection C and draw the altitude $\overline{CD}$ of $\triangle ABC$. Since $b > a$, we may choose $r > 0$ such that $\overline{AD} = r^2$, and thus D has coordinates $(a + r^2, 0)$. In any right triangle ABC with right angle at C and altitude $\overline{CD}$, we know that $\overline{CD}^2 = (\overline{AD})(\overline{DB})$, since the altitude to the hypotenuse is the mean proportional between the segments of the hypotenuse. Therefore, we may choose s such that

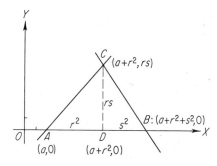

$\overline{CD} = rs$ and $\overline{DB} = s^2$. Then we have $C: (a + r^2, rs)$ and $B:$ $(a + r^2 + s^2, 0)$, as in the figure. The slope of AC is $\dfrac{rs - 0}{(a + r^2) - a}$, that is, $\dfrac{s}{r}$. The slope of BC is $\dfrac{rs - 0}{(a + r^2) - (a + r^2 + s^2)}$, that is, $-\dfrac{r}{s}$. The product of the slopes of the two lines is $\dfrac{s}{r}\left(-\dfrac{r}{s}\right)$, that is, -1. We have proved that the product of the slopes of the perpendicular lines p and q is -1. As a matter of convenience, in this text we shall assume the converse statement without proof: If the product of the slopes of two lines is -1, then the lines are perpendicular.

Exercises

Assume that the lines are not parallel to coordinate axes and prove:

1. A line perpendicular to one of two parallel lines is perpendicular to the other.

2. Two lines perpendicular to the same line are parallel.

3. Two lines perpendicular, respectively, to two intersecting lines intersect.

Prove:

4. The diagonals of a square are mutually perpendicular.

5. The altitudes of a triangle are concurrent.

13–6 The Conic Sections

In §13–4 the distance formula was used to classify triangles with given vertices on a coordinate plane as isosceles, equilateral, or right. We now use the distance formula to derive the equations of figures which are defined in terms of distances.

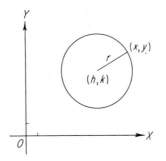

A **circle** may be defined as the set of points P: (x, y) at a distance r from a given point (h, k); these points satisfy the equation

$$(x - h)^2 + (y - k)^2 = r^2.$$

An **ellipse** with center at the origin and major axis along the x-axis may be defined as the set of points P: (x, y) such that the sum of the distances of each point P from the points F_1: $(-\sqrt{a^2 - b^2}, 0)$ and F_2: $(+\sqrt{a^2 - b^2}, 0)$ is $2a$. By the distance formula,

$$\overline{PF_1}^2 = (x + \sqrt{a^2 - b^2})^2 + y^2 \quad \text{and} \quad \overline{PF_2}^2 = (x - \sqrt{a^2 - b^2})^2 + y^2.$$

Then, since $\overline{PF_1} + \overline{PF_2} = 2a$, we have

$$\sqrt{(x + \sqrt{a^2 - b^2})^2 + y^2} + \sqrt{(x - \sqrt{a^2 - b^2})^2 + y^2} = 2a,$$

which can be written in the form

$$\frac{x^2}{a^2} + \frac{y^2}{b^2} = 1. \tag{1}$$

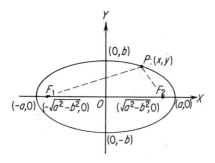

In general, an ellipse with center (h, k) has an equation of the form

$$\frac{(x - h)^2}{a^2} + \frac{(y - k)^2}{b^2} = 1. \tag{2}$$

A **hyperbola** with center at the origin and major axis along the x-axis may be defined as the set of points $P: (x, y)$ such that a difference

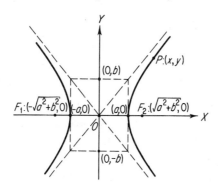

of the distances of each point P from F_1: $(-\sqrt{a^2 + b^2}, 0)$ and F_2: $(+\sqrt{a^2 + b^2}, 0)$ is $2a$.

By the distance formula,

$$\overline{PF_1^2} = (x + \sqrt{a^2 + b^2})^2 + y^2$$

and

$$\overline{PF_2^2} = (x - \sqrt{a^2 + b^2})^2 + y^2.$$

Then, since $\overline{PF_1} - \overline{PF_2} = \pm 2a$, we have

$$\sqrt{(x + \sqrt{a^2 + b^2})^2 + y^2} - \sqrt{(x - \sqrt{a^2 + b^2})^2 + y^2} = \pm 2a,$$

which can be written in the form

$$\frac{x^2}{a^2} - \frac{y^2}{b^2} = 1. \tag{3}$$

In general, a hyperbola with center (h, k) and major axis parallel to the x-axis has an equation of the form

$$\frac{(x - h)^2}{a^2} - \frac{(y - k)^2}{b^2} = 1; \tag{4}$$

a hyperbola with center (h, k) and major axis parallel to the y-axis has an equation of the form

$$\frac{(y - k)^2}{a^2} - \frac{(x - h)^2}{b^2} = 1. \tag{5}$$

A **parabola** with focus at F: $(0, a)$ and the line $y = -a$ as directrix may be defined as the set of points P: (x, y) such that $\overline{PF}$ is equal to

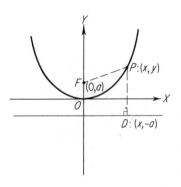

the distance of P from the directrix. As in the figure, draw PD with $D: (x, -a)$. Then the lines PD and $y = -a$ are perpendicular, $\overline{PD}$ is the distance of P from the directrix, and we have

$$\overline{PD} = y + a,$$
$$\overline{PF} = \sqrt{x^2 + (y - a)^2}.$$

Since $\overline{PD} = \overline{PF}$, we have

$$y + a = \sqrt{x^2 + (y - a)^2},$$
$$y^2 + 2ay + a^2 = x^2 + y^2 - 2ay + a^2,$$

which can be expressed as

$$x^2 = 4ay. \tag{6}$$

In general, a parabola with vertex (h, k) and directrix parallel to the x-axis has an equation of the form

$$(x - h)^2 = 4a(y - k); \tag{7}$$

a parabola with vertex (h, k) and directrix parallel to the y-axis has an equation of the form

$$(y - k)^2 = 4a(x - h). \tag{8}$$

These curves (circle, ellipse, hyperbola, and parabola) are called conic sections because they may be obtained as plane sections of a cone, as in the figure. Think of a cone as generated by revolving a line m through

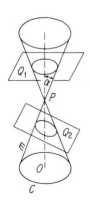
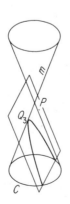
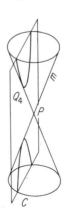

a fixed point P so that the line traverses a circle C which has center $O \neq P$ and is on a plane perpendicular to the line PO. The line m will then make a constant angle α with the line OP. Let Q be any point different from P on the cone. The cone has two nappes; the positions of m are called the elements of the cone. A plane through Q_1 and perpendicular to OP intersects the cone in a circle. A plane through Q_2 and intersecting all of the elements of the cone on one of the nappes (the lower one in the figure) but not perpendicular to OP intersects the cone in an ellipse. A plane through Q_3 and parallel to an element of the cone intersects the cone in a parabola. Any other plane through a point Q_4 and which does not contain an element of the cone intersects the cone in a hyperbola. In other words, a plane through Q intersects the cone in a circle if the plane is perpendicular to OP; intersects the cone in an ellipse if the angle θ between the plane and OP is greater than α, intersects in a hyperbola if $\theta < \alpha$, and intersects in a parabola if $\theta = \alpha$.

It is usually desirable to base any geometric proof on the most general possible case of the statement to be proved. For this reason, some people might object to the arbitrary selection of the origin as the center of the ellipse, the center of the hyperbola, and the vertex of the parabola in the development of their equations. Such an objection is not a significant one, since the center or vertex may be considered in any other position after a translation of the axes

$$x' = x + h, \qquad y' = y + k.$$

Notice that the form of the equations for each conic section in terms of (h, k) may be obtained by the substitution

$$x = x' - h, \qquad y = y' - k.$$

Any objection to the selection of an axis or directrix of a conic section parallel to a coordinate axis may be similarly resolved by rotating the axes through some angle θ:

$$x = x' \cos \theta - y' \sin \theta$$
$$y = x' \sin \theta + y' \cos \theta.$$

Exercises

Prove:

1. Any parabola with vertex (h, k) and directrix parallel to the x-axis has an equation of the form (7).

2. Any parabola with vertex (h, k) and directrix parallel to the y-axis has an equation of the form (8).

3. Any ellipse with center at (h, k) has an equation of the form (2).

4. Any hyperbola with center (h, k) and major axis parallel to the x-axis has an equation of the form (4).

5. Any hyperbola with center (h, k) and major axis parallel to the y-axis has an equation of the form (5).

Exercises on Paper Folding

Draw a circle 6 inches in diameter on wax paper. Think of the circle as having equation $x^2 + y^2 = 9$ on a coordinate plane. Each point of the plane is a point of the circle, an interior point of the circle, or an exterior point of the circle. Select 20 points S_n of the circle spaced as evenly as possible.

1. Pick a point P on the given circle and fold each of the points S_n onto P. Describe the pattern formed by the folds.

2. Pick a point P at the center of the circle and fold each of the points S_n onto P. (a) Describe the pattern formed by the folds. (b) Find the equation of the curve to which the lines of the folds are tangent.

3. Pick a point P inside the circle but not at its center O and fold each point S_n onto P. (a) Describe the pattern formed by the folds. (b) For each S_n, let B_n be the intersection of OS_n and the line along the fold obtained when S_n is folded onto P. Prove that for each B_n we have $\overline{OB_n} + \overline{PB_n} = 3$ inches and, thus, that the points B_n are points of an ellipse. (In more advanced courses, it can be shown that the lines along the folds are tangent to the ellipse at the points B_n.)

4. Pick a point P outside the circle and fold each point S_n onto P. (a) Describe the pattern formed by the folds. (b) For each S_n let B_n be the intersection of OS_n and the line along the fold obtained when S_n is folded onto P. Prove that, for each B_n, we have $\overline{PB_n} - \overline{OB_n} = 3$ inches and, thus, that the points B_n are points of a hyperbola. (In more advanced courses, it can be shown that the lines along the folds are tangent to the hyperbola at the points B_n.)

Draw a line m and select 20 points S_n spaced as evenly as possible on m.

5. Pick a point P that is not on m and fold each point S_n onto P. (a) Describe the pattern formed by the folds. (b) For each S_n let B_n be the intersection of the line perpendicular to m at S_n and the line along the fold obtained when S_n is folded onto P. Prove that the points B_n are on a parabola with directrix m and focus P. (c) Prove that the lines along the folds are tangents to this parabola.

13–7 Other Uses of Coordinates

Projections, circular (that is, trigonometric) functions, and areas may be considered on a coordinate plane. Measures of most angles cannot be easily represented except in terms of circular functions.

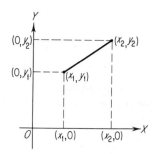

The **projection** of any line segment with end points (x_1, y_1) and (x_2, y_2) onto the x-axis is $|x_2 - x_1|$; the projection onto the y-axis is $|y_2 - y_1|$.

Any angle θ may be placed in **standard position** on a coordinate plane with its vertex at the origin, its initial side along the positive x-axis, and the angle measured in a counterclockwise sense. Each of the **circular functions** may then be defined in terms of the coordinates of any point P different from the vertex on the terminal side of the angle. We take $\overline{OP} = \sqrt{x^2 + y^2} = r$.

$$\sin \theta = \frac{y}{r}, \qquad \cos \theta = \frac{x}{r}, \qquad \tan \theta = \frac{y}{x},$$

$$\csc \theta = \frac{r}{y}, \qquad \sec \theta = \frac{r}{x}, \qquad \cot \theta = \frac{x}{y}.$$

These ratios are called **trigonometric ratios** when $0 < \theta < 180°$. Notice that the position of P on the coordinate plane determines the signs of x and y and, thus, the sign of each circular function.

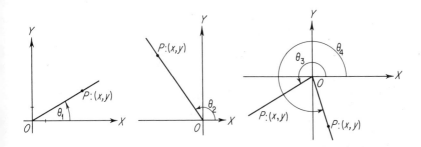

Each point P: (x, y) on the coordinate plane but not at the origin O may now be identified in terms of the distance $\overline{OP}$ and an angle θ in standard position. Notice that $x = r \cos \theta$ and $y = r \sin \theta$; thus, P has coordinates $(r \cos \theta, r \sin \theta)$. The numbers r and θ are called the **polar coordinates** of P. If P is on the unit circle with center at the origin, then $r = 1$ and P has coordinates $(\cos \theta, \sin \theta)$, and $\sin^2 \theta + \cos^2 \theta = 1$.

The distance formula (§13–4) and the polar coordinates of a point may be used to derive the **law of cosines**. Consider any $\triangle ABC$ with $\angle A$ in standard position. Then we have,

A: $(0, 0)$,
B: $(c, 0)$, and
C: $(b \cos A, b \sin A)$.

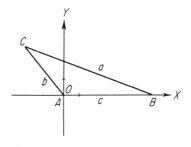

By the distance formula,

$$\overline{BC}^2 = (b \cos A - c)^2 + (b \sin A - 0)^2$$
$$a^2 = b^2 \cos^2 A - 2bc \cos A + c^2 + b^2 \sin^2 A$$
$$a^2 = b^2 (\sin^2 A + \cos^2 A) - 2bc \cos A + c^2$$
$$a^2 = b^2 + c^2 - 2bc \cos A$$

The area S of any $\triangle ABC$ with vertices A: (x_1, y_1), B: (x_2, y_2), and C: (x_3, y_3) may be expressed as a determinant:

$$S = \pm\tfrac{1}{2} \begin{vmatrix} x_1 & y_1 & 1 \\ x_2 & y_2 & 1 \\ x_3 & y_3 & 1 \end{vmatrix} = \tfrac{1}{2}[x_1(y_2 - y_3) - y_1(x_2 - x_3) + x_2 y_3 - x_3 y_2].$$

The proof is left as an exercise (Ex. 6); the sign is to be selected so that the area is non-negative. The positive sign will be used when a figure is traversed in a counterclockwise sense ABC; the negative sign, when a figure is traversed in a clockwise sense $A'B'C'$.

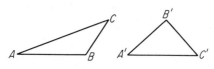

Figure 1

The area of any quadrilateral $ABCD$ on a coordinate plane may also be expressed in terms of the coordinates. Intuitively, one considers the largest and smallest rectangles with sides parallel to the coordinate axes and on lines passing through the vertices of the given quadrilateral. The area of $ABCD$ is half the sum of the areas of the rectangles $RSTU$

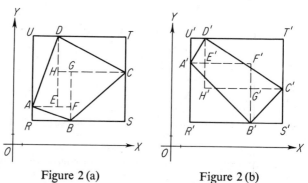

Figure 2 (a)   Figure 2 (b)

and *EFGH*. The area of *A'B'C'D'* is half the difference of the areas of the rectangles *R'S'T'U'* and *E'F'G'H'*.

Finally, we should not overlook a use of coordinates on a number line to assure ourselves that all possible values of a variable have been considered. For example, think of two circles with radii *r* and *r'* and centers *O* and *O'*. The problem is to describe the possible intersections

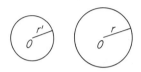

of the circles in terms of the relative values of *r*, *r'*, and $\overline{OO'}$. Assume that $r \geq r'$. The circles do not intersect if $\overline{OO'} < r - r'$ or $\overline{OO'} > r + r'$; they are tangent if $\overline{OO'} = r + r'$ or if $\overline{OO'} = r - r'$; they intersect in two points if $r - r' < \overline{OO'} < r + r'$. We know that all possible cases have been considered because all segments on the number line have been considered.

Exercises

In Exs. 1 *through* 4, *find the projection of the line segments with the given end points:* (a) *onto the x-axis;* (b) *onto the y-axis.*

1. (2, 3) and (5, 9)   2. (0, 1) and (3, −2)

3. (2, −5) and (−3, 2)   4. (3, 1) and (3, 4)

5. Derive the law of cosines in the form

$$b^2 = a^2 + c^2 - 2ac \cos B.$$

6. Derive a formula for the area of a triangle in terms of the coordinates of its vertices.

7. Derive a formula for the area of any quadrilateral in terms of the coordinates of its vertices.

Application and Additional Readings

This chapter has been concerned with the use of coordinates. Most topics are recommended for all geometry students. All topics are recommended for the better students. Much of the classroom application of coordinate geometry in plane geometry courses must be left to the ingenuity of the individual teacher, who is expected to base the level and intensity of the treatment upon the caliber of the students.

Additional readings may be found in traditional college texts in analytic geometry and [14].

Answers for Exercises

13–1 *The Coordinate Plane*

1 through 8.   **9.**

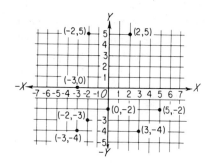   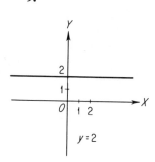

10.   **11.**

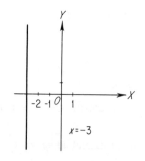   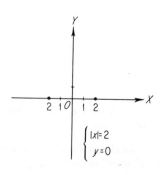

12.

13.

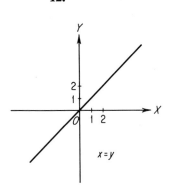

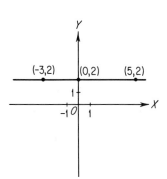

14.

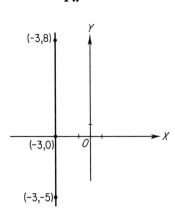

In Exs. 13 through 21, there are many possible correct selections of points satisfying the conditions.

15.

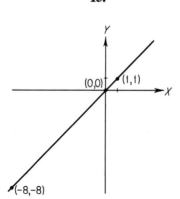

16.

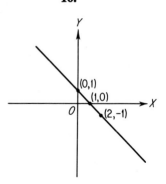

17.

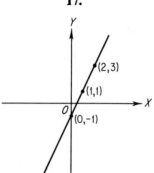

18.

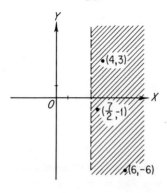

19.

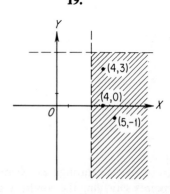

20. **21.**

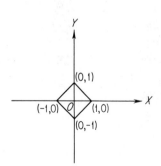 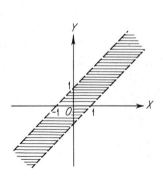

22. $x = 2$; 4. **23.** $y = -3$; 5. **24.** $y = 1$; 3.

25. $y = 2$; 4. **26.** $x = 5$; 9. **27.** $y = -3$; 6.

13–2 *The Mid-point Formula*

1. (2, 5). **2.** (3, 2). **3.** (−1, 1). **4.** (1, 1).

5. Let ABC be any right triangle, $\angle C = 90°$, $\overline{BC} = a$, and $\overline{CA} = b$. The triangle on a coordinate plane with vertices C': (0, 0), A': $(b, 0)$,

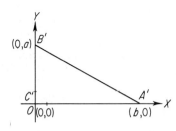

and B': $(0, a)$ has $\angle C' = 90°$, and thus, by *s.a.s.* = *s.a.s.*, is congruent to the given triangle. In other words, we may use such a triangle $A'B'C'$ to represent any given right triangle ABC on a coordinate plane.

6. Consider any rectangle $ABCD$ with sides a and b; suppose $\overline{AB} = a$ and $\overline{AD} = b$. Then take A': $(0, 0)$, B': $(a, 0)$, C': (a, b), and D': $(0, b)$ on a coordinate plane. Notice that $A'B' \parallel C'D'$, $A'D' \parallel B'C'$, and $\angle A' = 90°$, whence $A'B'C'D'$ is a rectangle with the same dimensions as the given rectangle $ABCD$. Thus, $A'B'C'D'$ may be used to represent $ABCD$.

7. Label the points A': $(0, 0)$, B': $(a, 0)$, C': (a, a), and D': $(0, a)$. Then $A'B'C'D'$ is a rectangle (Ex. 6) with a pair of adjacent sides equal $(\overline{A'B'} = \overline{A'D'})$ and thus is a square. Any square may be represented in this way by taking a as the length of a side of the square.

8. We use the fact that a quadrilateral is a rhombus if the diagonals bisect each other and are perpendicular to each other. Label the

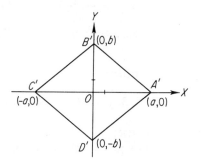

points A': $(a, 0)$, B': $(0, b)$, C': $(-a, 0)$, and D': $(0, -b)$. Then $A'B'C'D'$ is a rhombus, since the diagonals $\overline{A'C'}$ and $\overline{B'D'}$ are perpendicular and bisect each other. The lengths a and b may be chosen so that any rhombus may be so represented.

9. Label the points A': $(0, 0)$, B': $(a, 0)$, C': $(a + b, c)$, and D': (b, c). Notice that $\overline{A'B'} = \overline{D'C'} = a$, $\overline{A'D'} = \overline{B'C'} = b$, $A'B' \parallel D'C'$ and $A'D' \parallel B'C'$, and c may be selected to make angle A' equal to any angle A of a given parallelogram. Since the two sides $\overline{AB}$ and $\overline{AD}$ and $\angle A$ suffice to determine any parallelogram, any parallelogram $ABCD$ may be represented by a parallelogram $A'B'C'D'$ with vertices of the given form.

10. Any right triangle MNP with $\angle N = 90°$ is determined by $\angle N$ and sides $\overline{MN}$ and $\overline{NP}$. Any triangle RST, whether it is a right triangle or not, has at least one acute angle R and an associated right triangle

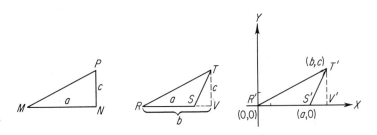

RVT where $\overline{TV}$ is the altitude from T to the line RS. When R' is taken at $(0, 0)$, the vertex T is determined by its coordinates b and c; that is, by the lengths of $\overline{R'V'}$ and $\overline{V'T'}$; also the vertex S' is determined by the length a of $\overline{RS}$. Thus, for any given triangle RST, the vertices R': $(0, 0)$, S': $(a, 0)$, and T': (b, c) may be determined to obtain triangle $R'S'T'$, which may be used to represent triangle RST.

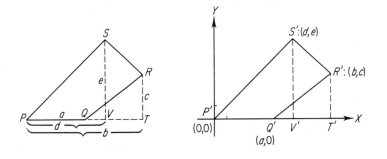

11. Any quadrilateral has at least one acute angle, P. Given any quadrilateral $PQRS$ with $\overline{PQ} = a$, we may take P': $(0, 0)$ and Q': $(a, 0)$. Draw altitudes $\overline{RT}$ and $\overline{SV}$ to the line PQ. For $\overline{PT} = b$ and $\overline{RT} = c$, we take R': (b, c); for $\overline{PV} = d$ and $\overline{VS} = e$, we take S': (d, e). For P' at $(0, 0)$, PQ along the positive x-axis, and R in the first quadrant (that is, with both coordinates positive), the points Q', R', and S' are uniquely determined by the given figure and themselves determine with P' a quadrilateral which may be used to represent the given quadrilateral $PQRS$ on a coordinate plane.

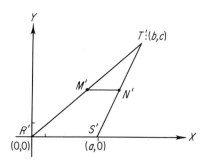

12. Represent the triangle by R': $(0, 0)$, S': $(a, 0)$, and T': (b, c), as in Ex. 10. Let M' be the mid-point of $\overline{R'T'}$ and N' the mid-point of $\overline{S'T'}$. Then, by the mid-point formula, we have

$$M': \left(\frac{b}{2}, \frac{c}{2}\right) \quad \text{and} \quad N': \left(\frac{a+b}{2}, \frac{c}{2}\right).$$

The line $M'N'$ is parallel to the x-axis and, thus, to $R'S'$, since the y-coordinates of M' and N' are equal. The length of $\overline{R'S'}$ is a; the length of $\overline{M'N'}$ is $\left|\dfrac{a+b}{2} - \dfrac{b}{2}\right|$, that is, $\dfrac{a}{2}$. Thus, $\overline{M'N'} = \tfrac{1}{2}\overline{R'S'}$.

13. A quadrilateral $PQRS$ is a trapezoid if $PQ \parallel RS$. We may represent the trapezoid on a coordinate plane with $P'Q'$ on the x-axis, P' at $(0, 0)$, Q' at $(a, 0)$ where $\overline{PQ} = a$, and R' with a positive y-coordinate. Since $SR \parallel PQ$, the altitudes $\overline{SA}$ and $\overline{RB}$ onto PQ are equal; suppose $\overline{SA} = h$. Then S' and R' have y-coordinate h; they may have any distinct numbers b and d, respectively, as x-coordinate, where $b < d$ for a convex figure. We take S' at (b, h) and R' at (d, h). Any trapezoid $PQRS$ may be represented on a coordinate plane in this manner with vertices at $(0, 0)$, $(a, 0)$, (d, h), and (b, h) for suitable choices of values for a, b, d, and h. Let M' be the mid-point of $\overline{P'S'}$ and N' be the mid-point of $\overline{R'Q'}$. Then we have

$$M': \left(\frac{b}{2}, \frac{h}{2}\right) \quad \text{and} \quad N': \left(\frac{a+d}{2}, \frac{h}{2}\right).$$

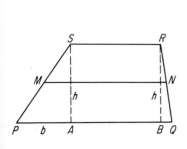 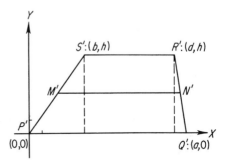

The line $M'N'$ is parallel to the x-axis and, thus, to $P'Q'$, since the y-coordinates of M' and N' are equal. The length of $\overline{M'N'}$ is $\left|\dfrac{a+d}{2} - \dfrac{b}{2}\right|$, that is, $\frac{1}{2}[a + (d - b)]$. The length of $\overline{P'Q'}$ is a, the length of $\overline{S'R'}$ is $(d - b)$. Thus, the length of $\overline{M'N'}$ is one-half the sum of the bases of the trapezoid.

14. Any given parallelogram $ABCD$ may be represented on a coordinate plane by $A'B'C'D'$, as in Ex. 9, with A': $(0,0)$, B': $(a, 0)$, C': $(a + b, c)$, and D': (b, c). The mid-point of the diagonal $\overline{A'C'}$ is $\left(\dfrac{a+b}{2}, \dfrac{c}{2}\right)$; the mid-point of the diagonal $\overline{B'D'}$ is $\left(\dfrac{a+b}{2}, \dfrac{c}{2}\right)$. Since the two diagonals have the same point as their mid-point, each passes through the mid-point of the other; that is, the diagonals bisect each other.

15. Any given quadrilateral $PQRS$ may be represented on a co-ordinate plane by $P'Q'R'S'$, as in Ex. 11, with P': $(0, 0)$, Q': $(a, 0)$, R': (b, c), and S': (d, e). The sides $\overline{P'Q'}$ and $\overline{R'S'}$ are opposite sides and have mid-points $\left(\dfrac{a}{2}, 0\right)$ and $\left(\dfrac{b+d}{2}, \dfrac{c+e}{2}\right)$, respectively. The line segment joining these mid-points itself has mid-point $\left(\dfrac{a+b+d}{4}, \dfrac{c+e}{4}\right)$.

Similarly, the sides $\overline{P'S'}$ and $\overline{Q'R'}$ are opposite sides and have mid-points $\left(\dfrac{d}{2}, \dfrac{e}{2}\right)$ and $\left(\dfrac{a+b}{2}, \dfrac{c}{2}\right)$, respectively. The line segment joining these mid-points itself has mid-point $\left(\dfrac{a+b+d}{4}, \dfrac{c+e}{4}\right)$. Since the line segments joining the mid-points of the opposite sides of the quadrilateral have the same mid-point, they bisect each other.

16. (3, 11).   **17.** (8, −11).

13–3 *The Slope of a Line*

There are many possible correct answers in Exs. 1 through 4.

1. $(0, -5), (1, -2), \dfrac{y-(-5)}{x-0} = \dfrac{-2-(-5)}{1-0}$.

2. $(0, 2), (3, 0), \dfrac{y-2}{x-0} = \dfrac{0-2}{3-0}$.

3. $(1, 4), (2, 3), \dfrac{y-4}{x-1} = \dfrac{3-4}{2-1}$.

4. $(0, -2), (3, -2), \dfrac{y-(-2)}{x-0} = \dfrac{(-2)-(-2)}{3-0}$.

5. (1) $y - (-5) = 3(x - 0)$;   (2) $y - 2 = -\frac{2}{3}(x - 0)$;
(3) $y - 4 = (-1)(x - 1)$;   (4) $y - (-2) = 0(x - 0)$.

6. (1) $y = 3x + (-5)$;   (2) $y = -\frac{2}{3}x + 2$;   (3) $y = (-1)x + 5$;
(4) $y = 0(x) + (-2)$.

7. (1) $\dfrac{x}{\frac{5}{3}} + \dfrac{y}{-5} = 1$;   (2) $\dfrac{x}{3} + \dfrac{y}{2} = 1$;   (3) $\dfrac{x}{5} + \dfrac{y}{5} = 1$.

8. Note that any one of the forms of the equation of a line may be used to graph the line. However, unless the line passes through $(0, 0)$, the intercept form is the easiest to graph. When the two-point form is used, first graph the two points; when the point-slope form is used, first graph the point (x_1, y_1) and the point $(x_1 + k, y_1 + km)$, where m is the slope and k is a convenient number of units; when the slope-intercept form is used, first graph the points $(0, b)$ and $(k, b + km)$;

when the intercept form is used, first graph the points $(a, 0)$ and $(0, b)$. In each case, draw the line through the two points and check to see that a third point whose coordinates satisfy the given equation is on the line that was drawn.

(1)   (2)   (3)   (4)

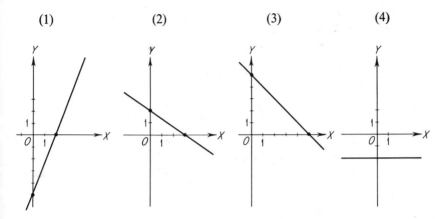

Note: In Exs. 9 through 12, other equivalent forms of the equations are also acceptable.

9. $\dfrac{y-3}{x-2} = \dfrac{5-3}{4-2}$; that is, $y = x + 1$.

10. $\dfrac{x}{5} + \dfrac{y}{3} = 1$.

11. $y + 2 = \dfrac{3}{2}x$.

12. $\dfrac{x}{5} + \dfrac{y}{4} = 1$.

13. Given: Lines a, b, c, such that $a \parallel b$ and $c \parallel b$. To prove: $a \parallel c$. *Proof:* The line b is taken not parallel to the y-axis, so that it has a slope m. Then the line a has slope m, since $a \parallel b$; also, the line c has slope m, since $c \parallel b$. Finally, $a \parallel c$, since each has slope m.

14. Given: Lines a, b, and c such that a intersects b and $b \parallel c$. To prove: a intersects c. *Proof:* Let m be the slope of the line b. Then since $b \parallel c$, the slope of c is also m. Since the line a intersects the line b, the slope of a is not m. Finally, since a and c have different slopes, a intersects c.

15. Given: Lines a, b, and c such that $a \parallel b$ and b intersects c. To prove: a intersects c. *Proof:* As in Ex. 14, let m be the slope of the line b; the slope of a is also m; the slope of c is not equal to m; a and c have different slopes and thus intersect.

16. Given: Lines a, b, c, and d such that $a \parallel c$, $b \parallel d$, and c intersects d. To prove: a intersects b. *Proof:* Let m be the slope of c. Then m is the slope of the line a, since $a \parallel c$; the slope of d is not m, since c intersects d; the slope of b is not m, since $b \parallel d$; and a intersects b, since a and b have different slopes.

17. AB and CD each have slope $\frac{7}{8}$; AD and BC each have slope 3; $AB \parallel CD$ and $AD \parallel BC$; thus, by definition, $ABCD$ is a parallelogram.

13–4 *The Distance Formula*

1. 5. **2.** 13. **3.** $\sqrt{73}$. **4.** $\sqrt{137}$. **5.** $\sqrt{5}$, $\sqrt{5}$, $\sqrt{10}$; (a) yes, (b) no, (c) yes. **6.** $\sqrt{793}$, $\sqrt{149}$, $2\sqrt{101}$; (a) no, (b) no, (c) no.

7. Given: Circle $x^2 + y^2 = r^2$, $x = p_1$ where $p_1 > r$, $x = p_2$ where $p_2 = r$, $x = p_3$ where $p_3 < r$. To prove: The line $x = p_1$ does not intersect the circle; $x = p_2$ is tangent to the circle; $x = p_3$ is a secant of the circle. *Proof:* Solving the equation $x^2 + y^2 = r^2$ of the circle simultaneously with the equation $x = p_1$ of the line, $p_1{}^2 + y^2 = r^2$,

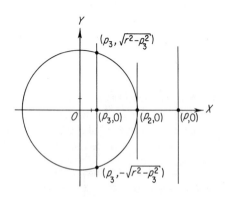

that is, $y^2 = r^2 - p^2$. But $p_1{}^2 > r^2$; therefore, $(r^2 - p_1{}^2)$ is negative and y is imaginary; in other words, this line does not intersect the circle. Using the line $x = p_2$, $y^2 = r^2 - p_2{}^2$. But $r^2 = p_2{}^2$ because $r = p_2$; therefore, $y = 0$ and the only point common to $x^2 + y^2 = r^2$ and $x = p_2$ is the point $(p_2, 0)$; hence, $x = p_2$ is tangent to the circle. Using the line $x = p_3$, $y^2 = r^2 - p_3{}^2$. But $r^2 > p_3{}^2$ because $r > p_3$; therefore, $(r^2 - p_3{}^2)$ is positive and y has two distinct real roots. Hence, $x = p_3$ cuts $x^2 + y^2 = r^2$ at $(p_3, \sqrt{r^2 - p_3{}^2})$ and $(p_3, -\sqrt{r^2 - p_3{}^2})$, and $x = p_3$ is a secant of the circle.

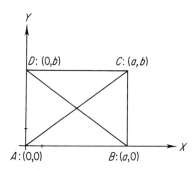

8. Given: Rectangle $ABCD$ with A: $(0, 0)$, B: $(a, 0)$, C: (a, b), D: $(0, b)$. To prove: $\overline{AC} = \overline{DB}$. *Proof:* By the distance formula: $\overline{AC} = \sqrt{(a - 0)^2 + (b - 0)^2} = \sqrt{a^2 + b^2}$; $\overline{BD} = \sqrt{(a - 0)^2 + (0 - b)^2} = \sqrt{a^2 + b^2}$; hence, $\overline{AC} = \overline{BD}$, since each equals $\sqrt{a^2 + b^2}$.

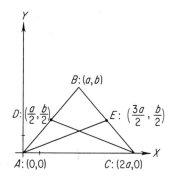

9. Given: Isosceles triangle ABC, $\overline{AB} = \overline{BC}$ with $\overline{AE}$ and $\overline{CD}$ as medians, A: $(0,0)$, B: (a,b), C: $(2a,0)$. To prove: $\overline{AE} = \overline{CD}$. *Proof:* By the mid-point formula, we have E: $\left(\dfrac{3a}{2}, \dfrac{b}{2}\right)$ and D: $\left(\dfrac{a}{2}, \dfrac{b}{2}\right)$.

By the distance formula, $\overline{AE} = \sqrt{\left(\dfrac{3a}{2}\right)^2 + \dfrac{b^2}{4}} = \dfrac{\sqrt{9a^2 + b^2}}{2}$ and $\overline{CD}$

$= \sqrt{\left(2a - \dfrac{a}{2}\right)^2 + \left(-\dfrac{b}{2}\right)^2} = \sqrt{\left(\dfrac{3a}{2}\right)^2 + \left(\dfrac{b}{2}\right)^2} = \dfrac{\sqrt{9a^2 + b^2}}{2}$; hence,

$\overline{AE} = \overline{CD}$, since each equals $\dfrac{\sqrt{9a^2 + b^2}}{2}$.

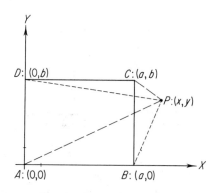

10. Given: Rectangle $ABCD$ with A: $(0,0)$, B: $(a,0)$, C: (a,b), D: $(0,b)$, and P: (x,y) any point on the plane of the rectangle. To prove: $\overline{PC}^2 + \overline{PA}^2 = \overline{PB}^2 + \overline{PD}^2$. *Proof:* By the distance formula, $\overline{PC} = \sqrt{(x-a)^2 + (y-b)^2}$; $\overline{PA} = \sqrt{x^2 + y^2}$; $\overline{PB} = \sqrt{(x-a)^2 + y^2}$; $\overline{PD} = \sqrt{x^2 + (y-b)^2}$. Thus, $\overline{PC}^2 + \overline{PA}^2 = (x-a)^2 + (y-b)^2 + x^2 + y^2$; $\overline{PB}^2 + \overline{PD}^2 = (x-a)^2 + y^2 + x^2 + (y-b)^2$; hence, $\overline{PC}^2 + \overline{PA}^2 = \overline{PB}^2 + \overline{PD}^2$.

13–5 Perpendicular Lines

1. Given: $a \parallel b$, $r \perp a$, slope of a is m. To prove: $r \perp b$. *Proof:* Slope of b is m, since $a \parallel b$ and parallel lines have the same slope.

Slope of r is $-\dfrac{1}{m}$, because $r \perp a$; hence, their slopes must be negative reciprocals. The slope of b and the slope of r are negative reciprocals;

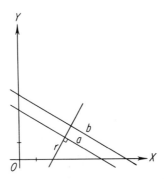

hence, $r \perp b$, because two lines whose slopes are negative reciprocals are perpendicular.

2. Use the figure for Ex. 1. Given: $a \perp r$ and $b \perp r$, a and b are distinct lines, and the slope of r is m. To prove: $a \parallel b$. *Proof:* The slope of a is $-\dfrac{1}{m}$ and the slope of b is $-\dfrac{1}{m}$, because the slopes of perpendicular lines are negative reciprocals; then $a \parallel b$, because two distinct lines having the same slope are parallel.

3. Given: Intersecting lines a with slope m and b with slope n, lines $r \perp a$ and $s \perp b$. To prove: r intersects s. *Proof:* The slopes m and n are not equal, since the lines a and b intersect. Thus, $\dfrac{1}{m} \neq \dfrac{1}{n}$ and $-\dfrac{1}{m} \neq -\dfrac{1}{n}$. The slope of r is $-\dfrac{1}{m}$; the slope of s is $-\dfrac{1}{n}$; r and s intersect.

4. Given: Square $ABCD$ with A: $(0, 0)$, B: $(a, 0)$, C: (a, a), D: $(0, a)$. To prove: $\overline{AC} \perp \overline{BD}$. *Proof:* The slope of $\overline{AC}$ is $\dfrac{a}{a} = 1$. The slope of $\overline{BD} = \dfrac{a}{-a} = -1$. Since 1 and -1 are negative reciprocals, $\overline{AC} \perp \overline{BD}$.

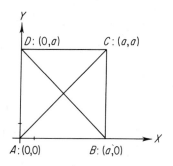

5. Given: $\triangle ABC$ with altitudes CD, AE, and BF, A: $(0, 0)$, B: $(b, 0)$, C: (a, c). To prove: AE, BF, and DC are concurrent. *Proof:* Since $CD \perp AB$, $CD \parallel y$-axis and the equation of CD is $x = a$. The slope of AC is $\dfrac{c}{a}$ and the slope of BF, the altitude to AC, is $-\dfrac{a}{c}$; in the same manner, the slope of BC is $\dfrac{c}{a - b}$ and the slope of AE, the altitude

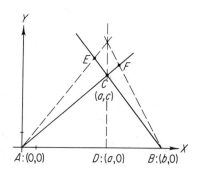

to BC, is $-\dfrac{a - b}{c}$ or $\dfrac{b - a}{c}$, because an altitude is perpendicular to the side to which it is drawn, and the slopes of perpendicular lines are negative reciprocals. By the point-slope formula, the equation of AE is $y = \dfrac{b - a}{c} x$ and the equation of BF is $y = -\dfrac{a}{c}(x - b)$. Solving these two equations simultaneously, $\dfrac{b - a}{c} x = -\dfrac{a}{c}(x - b)$, that is,

$x = a$ and $y = \dfrac{ab - a^2}{c}$. Thus, the coordinates of the point of inter-

section of AE and BF are $\left(a, \dfrac{ab - a^2}{c}\right)$, which is also a point on $x = a$;

therefore, AE, BF, and DC are concurrent.

13–6 *Conic Sections*

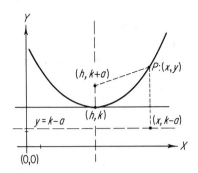

1. A parabola is defined as the locus of P such that the distance from P to the focal point is equal to the distance from P to the directrix. Using this definition and the distance formula,

$$\sqrt{(x - h)^2 + (y - k - a)^2} = y - k + a.$$

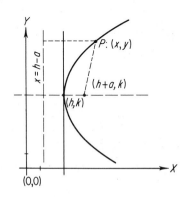

Squaring both sides of this equation, $(x - h)^2 + y^2 + k^2 + a^2 - 2ky - 2ay + 2ak = y^2 + k^2 + a^2 - 2ky + 2ay - 2ak$. Collecting terms, $(x - h)^2 = 4ay - 4ak$, or $(x - h)^2 = 4a(y - k)$, as in (7).

2. The exercise is set up in the same manner as Ex. 1. The initial equation is: $\sqrt{(x - h - a)^2 + (y - k)^2} = x - h + a$. Following the same processes as in Ex. 1, $x^2 + h^2 + a^2 - 2hx - 2ax + 2ah + (y - k)^2 = x^2 + h^2 + a^2 - 2hx + 2ax - 2ah; (y - k)^2 = 4ax - 4ah$, or $(y - k)^2 = 4a(x - h)$, as in (8). See Figure at bottom of page 281.

3. If the center of the ellipse is at (h, k), then the foci will be at $(-\sqrt{a^2 - b^2} + h, k)$ and $(\sqrt{a^2 - b^2} + h, k)$. Use the definition of an ellipse which states that an ellipse is the locus of a point $P: (x, y)$

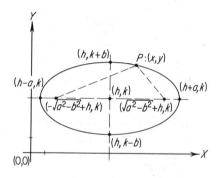

the sum of whose distances from the two foci is constant. Then substituting in the distance formula gives:

$$2a = \sqrt{(x + \sqrt{a^2 - b^2} - h)^2 + (y - k)^2}$$
$$+ \sqrt{(x - \sqrt{a^2 - b^2} - h)^2 + (y - k)^2}.$$

Then

$$4a^2 + (x + \sqrt{a^2 - b^2} - h)^2 + (y - k)^2$$
$$- 4a\sqrt{(x + \sqrt{a^2 - b^2} - h)^2 + (y - k)^2}$$
$$= (x - \sqrt{a^2 - b^2} - h)^2 + (y - k)^2,$$

which simplifies to

$$a^2 + x\sqrt{a^2 - b^2} - h\sqrt{a^2 - b^2}$$
$$= a\sqrt{(x + \sqrt{a^2 - b^2} - h)^2 + (y - k)^2}.$$

Squaring both sides of this equation and simplifying, we have

$$-b^2x^2 - b^2h^2 + 2b^2hx = -a^2b^2 + a^2(y - k)^2;$$

dividing through by $(-b^2)$,

$$x^2 - 2hx + h^2 = a^2 - \frac{a^2}{b^2}(y - k)^2;$$

and dividing through by a^2 and simplifying,

$$\frac{(x - h)^2}{a^2} + \frac{(y - k)^2}{b^2} = 1, \text{ as in (2)}.$$

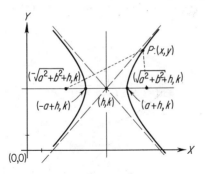

4. By definition, a hyperbola is the locus of points P the difference of whose distances from the foci is $\pm 2a$; thus, use of the distance formula gives the following equation:

$$\pm 2a = \sqrt{(x + \sqrt{a^2 + b^2} - h)^2 + (y - k)^2}$$
$$- \sqrt{(x - \sqrt{a^2 + b^2} - h)^2 + (y - k)^2},$$

or

$$\sqrt{(x - \sqrt{a^2 + b^2} - h)^2 + (y - k)^2} \pm 2a$$
$$= \sqrt{(x + \sqrt{a^2 + b^2} - h)^2 + (y - k)^2}.$$

Squaring both sides of the equation and simplifying:

$$x\sqrt{a^2 + b^2} - h\sqrt{a^2 + b^2} - a^2$$
$$= \pm a\sqrt{(x - \sqrt{a^2 + b^2} - h)^2 + (y - k)^2}.$$

Squaring and collecting terms again:

$$b^2x^2 - 2b^2hx + b^2h^2 = a^2b^2 + a^2(y - k)^2.$$

Dividing through by b^2 and factoring the left member:

$$(x - h)^2 = a^2 + \frac{a^2}{b^2}(y - k)^2.$$

Subtracting $\dfrac{a^2}{b^2}(y - k)^2$ from both sides and dividing through by a^2:

$$\frac{(x - h)^2}{a^2} - \frac{(y - k)^2}{b^2} = 1, \text{ as in (4).}$$

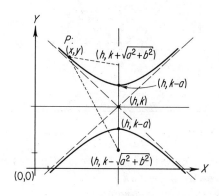

5. This exercise is set up in the same manner as Ex. 4. The initial equation is:

$$\pm 2a = \sqrt{(x - h)^2 + (y - k + \sqrt{a^2 + b^2})^2}$$
$$- \sqrt{(x - h)^2 + (y - k - \sqrt{a^2 + b^2})^2}.$$

Following the same algebraic processes as in Ex. 4,

$$k\sqrt{a^2+b^2} - y\sqrt{a^2+b^2} + a^2$$
$$= \pm a\sqrt{(x-h)^2 + (y-k-\sqrt{a^2+b^2})^2};$$
$$b^2y^2 - 2b^2ky + b^2k^2 = a^2(x-h)^2 + a^2b^2;$$
$$(y-k)^2 = \frac{a^2}{b^2}(x-h)^2 + a^2; \quad \frac{(y-k)^2}{a^2} - \frac{(x-h)^2}{b^2} = 1,$$

as in (5).

Exercises on Paper Folding

1. Each fold is along the perpendicular bisector of a chord $\overline{PS_n}$. Thus, each fold is along a line through the center of the circle. The pattern of the folds is a set of lines through the center of the circle.

2. (a) Each fold is along a line $1\frac{1}{2}''$ from the center of the circle, since each fold is along the perpendicular bisector of a radius $\overline{PS_n}$. The pattern of the folds is a set of lines tangent to a circle having the same center as the given circle and having radius $1\frac{1}{2}''$. (b) $x^2 + y^2 = \frac{9}{4}$.

3. (a) The folds seem to be along lines bounding an ellipse. (b) Each fold will be along the perpendicular bisector of a line segment PS_n.

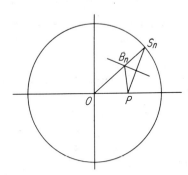

Each point of the fold, and in particular B_n, will be equidistant from P and S_n. Thus, $\overline{PB_n} = \overline{B_nS_n}$. Notice that $\overline{OB_n} + \overline{B_nS_n} = 3''$, since $\overline{OS_n}$ is a radius of the given circle. Thus, $\overline{OB_n} + \overline{PB_n} = 3''$, and B_n is on an ellipse with foci at O and P, as was to be proved.

Note: There is a "brute force" method for proving that the lines are tangent to the ellipse at the points B_n. The significant property of the point P is its distance from the center O of the given circle. Thus, we may take P at $(2h, 0)$, where $0 < h$, since P is not at the center and $h < \frac{3}{2}$, since P is an interior point of the circle. Then the center of the ellipse is at $(h, 0)$, the center of $\overline{OP}$. Let each point S_n have coordinates (x_n, y_n). The line OS_n has equation

$$y = \frac{y_n}{x_n} x;$$

the mid-point of $\overline{PS_n}$ has coordinates $\left(\dfrac{x_n + 2h}{2}, \dfrac{y_n}{2}\right)$; the line PS_n has

slope $\dfrac{y_n}{x_n - 2h}$; the line along the fold has slope $\dfrac{x_n - 2h}{-y_n}$ and equation

$$y - \frac{y_n}{2} = \frac{2h - x_n}{y_n}\left(x - \frac{x_n + 2h}{2}\right).$$

The ellipse with center at $(h, 0)$ and focus at $(0, 0)$ with the constant sum of the distances of its points from the foci $3''$ has equation

$$\frac{4(x - h)^2}{9} + \frac{4y^2}{9 - 4h^2} = 1.$$

The proof consists of showing that the line intersects the ellipse in two coincident points. We shall demonstrate the method in Ex. 5.

4. (a) The folds seem to be along lines bounding a hyperbola. (b) Each fold will be along the perpendicular bisector of a line segment

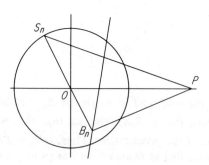

$\overline{PS}_n$. Each point of the fold, and in particular B_n, will be equidistant from P and S_n. Thus, $\overline{PB}_n = \overline{B_nS}_n$. Notice that $\overline{B_nS}_n = \overline{B_nO} + \overline{OS}_n = \overline{B_nO} + 3''$, since $\overline{OS}_n$ is a radius of the given circle. Thus, $\overline{PB}_n - \overline{OB}_n = 3''$ and the points B_n are on a hyperbola, as was to be proved.

The method for proving that the lines are tangent to the hyperbola at the points B_n is similar to that for Ex. 3.

5. (a) The folds seem to be along lines that are tangent to a parabola. (b) Each fold will be along the perpendicular bisector of a line segment $\overline{PS}_n$. Each point on the fold, and in particular B_n, will be equidistant

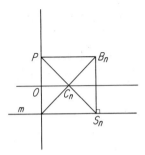

from P and S_n. Since $\overline{B_nS}_n$ is perpendicular to m, the point B_n is also equidistant from P and m. In other words, each point B_n is on a parabola with directrix m and focus P. (c) Select the coordinate axes such that the line m has equation $y = -a$ and that P has coordinates $(0, a)$. Select the points S_n to have coordinates $(n, -a)$. Then the mid-point C_n of each $\overline{PS}_n$ has coordinates $\left(\dfrac{n}{2}, 0\right)$; the line $\overline{PS}_n$ has slope $\dfrac{2a}{-n}$; the line along the fold through C_n has slope $\dfrac{n}{2a}$ and equation

$$y = \frac{n}{2a}\left(x - \frac{n}{2}\right).$$

The parabola with directrix m and focus P has equation $x^2 = 4ay$, as derived in the text material. The x-coordinates of the points of intersection of the line $y = \dfrac{nx}{2a} - \dfrac{n^2}{4a}$ and the parabola $x^2 = 4ay$ satisfy the equations $x^2 = 4a\left(\dfrac{nx}{2a} - \dfrac{n^2}{4a}\right)$, $x^2 = 2nx - n^2$, $x^2 - 2nx + n^2 = 0$, and $(x - n)^2 = 0$. Thus, the line intersects the parabola at one and only one point $\left(n, \dfrac{n^2}{4a}\right)$; in other words, the line is tangent to the parabola at this point B_n. We have proved that the lines along the folds are tangent to the parabola having the given line as directrix and the given point as focus.

13-7 *Other Uses of Coordinates*

1. (a) 3; (b) 6. **2.** (a) 3; (b) 3. **3.** (a) 5; (b) 7. **4.** (a) 0 (a point at $(3, 0)$); (b) 3.

5. Use the figure shown for the derivation of the law of cosines in the text, but interchange A and B, also a and b, to form the figure needed

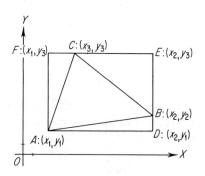

for this proof with A: $(c, 0)$, B: $(0, 0)$, and C: $(a \cos B, a \sin B)$. By the distance formula:

$$\overline{AC}^2 = (a \cos B - c)^2 + (a \sin B - 0)^2$$
$$b^2 = a^2 \cos^2 B - 2ac \cos B + c^2 + a^2 \sin^2 B$$
$$b^2 = a^2(\sin^2 B + \cos^2 B) - 2ac \cos B + c^2$$
$$b^2 = a^2 + c^2 - 2ac \cos B.$$

6. Given triangle $A'BC$, A: (x_1, y_1), B: (x_2, y_2), C: (x_3, y_3); draw lines through A, B, and C parallel to the coordinate axes. This forms rectangle $ADEF$ with D: (x_2, y_1), E: (x_2, y_3), and F: (x_1, y_3). The area of $\triangle ABC$ = area of rectangle $ADEF$ − area of $\triangle ADB$ − area $\triangle BEC$ − area $\triangle CFA$. $\square ADEF = (x_2 - x_1)(y_3 - y_1)$; $\triangle ADB = \frac{1}{2}(x_2 - x_1)(y_2 - y_1)$; $\triangle BEC = \frac{1}{2}(y_3 - y_2)(x_2 - x_3)$; $\triangle CFA = \frac{1}{2}(x_3 - x_1)(y_3 - y_1)$. $\triangle ABC = (x_2 - x_1)(y_3 - y_1) - \frac{1}{2}[(x_2 - x_1)(y_2 - y_1) + (x_2 - x_3)(y_3 - y_2) + (x_3 - x_1)(y_3 - y_1)]$. To obtain the form shown in the text, multiply to remove all parentheses, and collect like terms: $\triangle ABC = \frac{1}{2}x_2y_3 - \frac{1}{2}x_2y_1 - \frac{1}{2}x_1y_3 + \frac{1}{2}x_1y_2 - \frac{1}{2}x_3y_2 + \frac{1}{2}x_3y_1$; regroup and factor to obtain: $\triangle ABC = \frac{1}{2}[x_1(y_2 - y_3) - y_1(x_2 - x_3) + x_2y_3 - x_3y_2]$, as in the text.

7. Consider Figure 2 (a) on page 264 with A: (x_1, y_1); B: (x_2, y_2); C: (x_3, y_3); D: (x_4, y_4), and, therefore, E: (x_4, y_1); F: (x_2, y_1); G: (x_2, y_3); H: (x_4, y_3); R: (x_1, y_2); S: (x_3, y_2); T: (x_3, y_4); and U: (x_1, y_4). Since $ABCD$ is made up of $\frac{1}{2}(BSCG) + \frac{1}{2}(CTDH) + \frac{1}{2}(DUAE) + \frac{1}{2}(ARBF) + EFGH$, we may write $ABCD$ as $\frac{1}{2}(RSTU + EFGH)$. Thus, the area in terms of the vertices is $\frac{1}{2}[(x_3 - x_1)(y_4 - y_2) + (x_2 - x_4)(y_3 - y_1)]$.

Consider Figure 2 (b) on page 264 with A': (x_1, y_1); B': (x_2, y_2); C': (x_3, y_3); D': (x_4, y_4); and, therefore, E': (x_4, y_1); F': (x_2, y_1); G': (x_2, y_3); H': (x_4, y_3); R': (x_1, y_2); S': (x_3, y_2); T': (x_3, y_4); and U': (x_1, y_4). Since $A'B'C'D'$ is made up of $\frac{1}{2}(B'S'C'G') + \frac{1}{2}(C'T'D'H') + \frac{1}{2}(D'U'A'E') + \frac{1}{2}(A'R'B'F') - E'H'G'F'$, we may write $A'B'C'D'$ as $\frac{1}{2}(R'S'T'U' - E'H'G'F')$. Thus, the area in terms of the vertices is $\frac{1}{2}[(x_3 - x_1)(y_4 - y_2) - (x_4 - x_2)(y_3 - y_1)]$. Notice that, in terms of the coordinates of the vertices, this formula is equivalent to the formula for Fig. 1.

CHAPTER FOURTEEN

NUMBER SCALES AND PERSPECTIVE

The use of the real number line as a basis for a coordinate plane in Euclidean geometry was considered in Chapter 13. We now consider the use of parallel lines in constructing a number scale on a line in Euclidean geometry. A similar technique may be used to obtain a number scale on a line in affine geometry, a plane geometry that is not Euclidean. In this geometry, parallel lines are assumed to intersect at a point on the horizon line (often called the **ideal line** or the **line at infinity**) of the plane. This approach provides a basis for discussing perspective figures and for developing new insight into the classification of conics.

Student discussion may be motivated by the consideration of the following problem in perspective. An artist has drawn a railroad track with the rails appearing to converge on the horizon in his picture. How should he space telephone poles down the side of the track so that they will appear to be equally spaced?

14–1 Constructing Integral Points on a Euclidean Line

We need two points, an origin P_0 and a unit point P_1, to determine a number scale on a line. Given points P_0 and P_1 on a line m, we shall consider the construction of integral points P_n on m. Draw a line s

parallel to m. Then draw parallel lines through P_0 and P_1 intersecting s in S_0 and S_1.

To find P_2, draw $S_0 P_1$ and a line through S_1 parallel to $S_0 P_1$ cutting m in a point P_2. Notice that two parallelograms, $P_0 P_1 S_1 S_0$ and $P_1 P_2 S_1 S_0$, have been formed; thus, $\overline{P_0 P_1} = \overline{S_0 S_1}$, and $\overline{S_0 S_1} = \overline{P_1 P_2}$, as opposite sides of parallelograms. To find P_3, draw a line through P_2 parallel to $P_1 S_1$ to find S_2 on s; draw a line through S_2 parallel to $S_1 P_2$ to find P_3 on m. Continue in this manner to find $P_4, P_5, \ldots$ on m. To find P_{-1}, draw a line through P_0 parallel to $P_1 S_0$ to find S_{-1} on s; draw a line

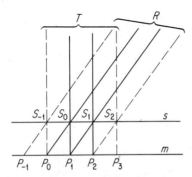

through S_{-1} parallel to $P_0 S_0$ to find P_{-1} on m. Continue this process to find $P_{-2}, P_{-3}, P_{-4}, \ldots$ on m.

Relative to our future work, it will be helpful if you think of lines parallel to $P_0 S_0$ as in a direction R; also, if you think of lines parallel to $P_1 S_0$ as in a direction T. However, your interpretation of "direction" must allow you to travel either way along the lines. Then, to find P_4, you could draw a line through P_3 in the direction R to find S_3 on s, and draw a line through S_3 in the direction T to find P_4 on m. We use the symbol

$$P_0 P_1 P_2 \ldots \overset{R}{\underset{\wedge}{=}} S_0 S_1 S_2 \ldots$$

to show the correspondence of points (P_0 with S_0, P_1 with S_1, P_2 with $S_2, \ldots$) on lines in the direction R. In more advanced discussions, we say that the points $P_0, P_1, P_2, \ldots$ are **perspective** with the points S_0, $S_1, S_2, \ldots$ with respect to R. We use the symbol

$$S_0 S_1 S_2 \ldots \overset{T}{\underset{\wedge}{=}} P_1 P_2 P_3 \ldots$$

to show the correspondence of points on lines in the direction T. The complete pattern used in the construction of integral points P_{n+1} from points P_n is given for integral values of n by the statement

$$P_n \overset{R}{=\!=} S_n \overset{T}{=\!=} P_{n+1}.$$

You may read this as, "Each P_n is collinear in the direction R with S_n; each S_n is collinear in the direction T with P_{n+1}." The pattern for the construction of points P_{n-1} from points P_n, as used for negative numbers, is given by

$$P_n \overset{T}{=\!=} S_{n-1} \overset{R}{=\!=} P_{n-1}.$$

Exercises

1. Use the method demonstrated in this section and construct points $P_{-3}, P_{-2}, \ldots, P_5, P_6$.

2. Given P_0 and P_1, construct $P_4, P_6, P_8, P_{-2},$ and P_{-4}.

3. Given $P_0, P_1,$ and P_x with $x > 1$, construct $P_{x+1}, P_{x+2},$ and P_{x-1}.

Hint: Use $P_0 P_1 \overset{R}{=\!=} S_0 S_1 \overset{T}{=\!=} P_x P_{x+1}$ to construct P_{x+1}.

4. Repeat Ex. 3 with $0 < x < 1$.

5. Given $P_0, P_x,$ and P_y, where $0 < x < y$, construct $P_{x+y}, P_{y+x},$ and P_{y-x}.

Hint: Use $P_0 P_y \overset{R}{=\!=} S_0 S_y \overset{T}{=\!=} P_x P_{x+y}$ to construct P_{x+y}.

6. Given $P_0, P_{-1},$ and P_x, where $0 < x$; construct P_{x+1} and P_{x-1}.

7. Describe the method that you use for deciding whether a point $P_x (x \neq 0)$ on a number scale is a positive point or a negative point, that is, a point with a positive coordinate or a point with a negative coordinate.

Draw figures illustrating each statement:

8. The sum of two positive points is positive.

9. The difference of two positive points may be either positive or negative.

10. For any point P_x, there is an integer n such that $n(P_1) = P_n$ is "greater than" P_x.

14–2 Lines in Other Geometries

We now use the appearance of railroad tracks to introduce lines in two other geometries: affine and hyperbolic. Affine lines are used in this section in the development of number scales; hyperbolic lines are considered in Chapter 15. Considered as a set of points, an **affine line** consists of an ordinary Euclidean line with its **ideal point**, that is, its point "at the horizon," added. The lines used in the discussion of perspective are affine lines.

Think of a straight railroad track on a level plane. The rails seem to have a point in common at the horizon. Sometimes we speak of this ideal point as the **point at infinity**, P_∞, on the line. As in the case of railroad tracks, any two parallel lines in our geometry have the same point at infinity. For example, all the lines in the direction R in §14–1 have the same point at infinity, R_∞; all the lines in the direction T have the same point at infinity, T_∞.

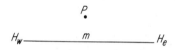

We shall assume for the present that there is only one point at infinity on each line. This means that, if you look down the railroad track in each direction, say east and west, the two horizons are at the same point. If you find that hard to believe, consider the consequences of having two horizon points, H_e and H_w, on a line m, as in the figure. Now consider a point P that is not on the line. Would you like to have one line through P parallel to m, or two? If you would like one, should it be PH_e or PH_w? Perhaps you would like H_wPH_e all on one line. Then this line would intersect m in two points H_w and H_e. But we usually postulate that on a plane two points determine exactly one line. Thus, either we have a two-dimensional geometry, as on the surface of a sphere, in which "lines" (great circles) may intersect in two points, or we must assume that the horizon points H_e and H_w are the same point. We could also get a good recognizable geometry called hyperbolic geometry, also called Lobatchevskian geometry, by taking H_e and H_w as distinct points and taking PH_e and PH_w as distinct lines in hyperbolic geometry. But we would have two lines through the given point P, with each line parallel to m (one to the east and one to the west). You may study this geometry in the future. For our purposes, you should think of reaching the *same* point on the horizon whether you travel east or west. This may seem to indicate to you that you must travel halfway around the world in each case, and thus should think of an east-west line as "tied together" into a circle by its point on the horizon, that is, its ideal point. This notion has several merits, as we shall see.

Think of H_e and H_w as the same point, H. Then H is the ideal point of the line m. This point does not exist in Euclidean geometry; it is a point of the line in affine geometry. How can we draw an affine line? We must make our drawing in Euclidean geometry. If, as in the previous figure, we draw a line with H at H_e (or H_w), then it does not appear to be accessible from the side H_w (or H_e). The ideal point H must be accessible from both sides. In order to show this, we picture the affine line as a circle with the special point H identified; similarly, we may picture a Euclidean line as a circle with the point H missing. In each geometry, the circle should be thought of as having a radius that is unboundedly large, even though each circle that we draw has a finite radius. Briefly, any straight line (we simply say "line") in our ordinary Euclidean geometry is like a circle with one point missing and a radius that is unboundedly large. A straight line in affine geometry is like a circle with one point selected as the point at infinity and with a radius that is unboundedly large.

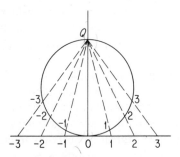

Here is another way to compare a Euclidean and an affine line. Draw a circle (to represent an affine line) tangent to a number line (Euclidean line with a scale) at the origin. Let Q be the point on the circle diametrically opposite the point of tangency. You can make a scale on the circle by joining Q to each point with coordinate n on the number line and labeling the other point at which the secant cuts the circle with the coordinate n, as in the figure.

Notice that the diameter $\overline{QO}$ divides the circle into two semicircles. Except for its end points, one semicircle has points with positive numbers as its coordinates; the other semicircle has points with negative numbers as its coordinates. The point O has coordinate O; the point Q has coordinate ∞, where P_∞ is the point on the horizon on the given line. Thus, the circle represents an affine line with the ideal point Q; if the point Q is removed, the rest of the circle may be "stretched out" to obtain a Euclidean line.

Exercises

1. Use a circle tangent to a number line to construct a scale from -8 to $+8$ on the circle.

2. Repeat Ex. 1 using the x-axis as the number line, a unit circle with center at the origin of the coordinate plane, and P_∞ at $(0, 1)$.

3. Use an extension of the method of Ex. 1 for a coordinate plane and a sphere to give a method for assigning coordinates to points on a sphere. What will the points on the horizon on the plane correspond to on the sphere?

4. Repeat Ex. 3, using the extension of the method of Ex. 2.

5. Use the figure for Ex. 1 and explain: A Euclidean line is divided into two half-lines by any point on it; two points are required to divide an affine line into two half-lines.

14–3 Constructing Integral Points on an Affine Line

Let us return to the visual image of the railroad track with its associated point at the horizon. The problem of constructing integral

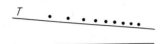

points is precisely the problem that an artist has in spacing telephone poles down the track so that the poles appear to be equidistant. This problem is the same whether the point at the horizon is on the plane

(in the picture) or not. It is easier to solve the problem when the point
at the horizon is assumed to be on the plane. That is why we are
considering the affine line.

In the problem, two telephone poles are needed to determine how
far apart they are to be placed. On the number scale, two points,
P_0 and P_1, are needed to determine the scale.

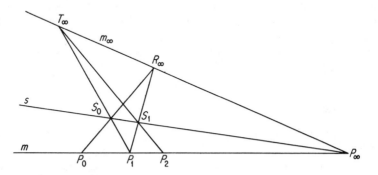

Consider a line m with points P_0 and P_1 given. Call the point at the
horizon on the line P_∞. Then draw a line m_∞ to represent the horizon
line. Note that in Euclidean geometry our assumption in §14–2 of a
single horizon point meant that the horizon could be represented by
a line. Our construction will be essentially the same as in §14–1.

Draw a line s through P_∞, that is, parallel to m. Pick a point R_∞
on m_∞. Draw

$$P_0 R_\infty \text{ to find } S_0 \text{ on } s;$$

$$P_1 R_\infty \text{ to find } S_1 \text{ on } s;$$

$$P_1 S_0 \text{ to find } T_\infty \text{ on } m_\infty;$$

$$T_\infty S_1 \text{ to find } P_2 \text{ on } m.$$

Then to find P_3, use $P_2 R_\infty$ to find S_2 and $T_\infty S_2$ to find P_3. To find P_{-1},
use $P_0 T_\infty$ to find S_{-1} and $R_\infty S_{-1}$ to find P_{-1}.

As in §14–1, the construction is completely described by the symbolic
statements:

$$P_n \stackrel{R_\infty}{\underset{\wedge}{=\!=}} S_n, \quad S_n \stackrel{T_\infty}{\underset{\wedge}{=\!=}} P_{n+1}, \quad P_n \stackrel{T_\infty}{\underset{\wedge}{=\!=}} S_{n-1}, \quad S_{n-1} \stackrel{R_\infty}{\underset{\wedge}{=\!=}} P_{n-1}.$$

Exercises

1. Use the method shown in this section and construct points P_{-3}, P_{-2}, . . ., P_5, P_6 on an affine line.

2. Copy P_0, P_1, and P_∞, spaced as in Ex. 1, onto another line. Use a different-appearing choice of the lines s and m_∞, and repeat Ex. 1. Compare your results with those obtained in Ex. 1. They should match exactly.

3. Take P_1 on the left of P_0, take P_∞ on the right of P_0, and construct P_2, P_3, P_4, . . . until one of these is on the right of P_∞.

4. Explain what has happened in Ex. 3 using Ex. 5 of §14–2.

5. Identify the locus of positive points on the scales in Exs. 1 and 3.

6. Repeat Ex. 5 for the locus of negative points.

7. Given P_0, P_1, P_x, P_∞ in that order on an affine line, construct P_{x+1}, P_{x+2}, and P_{x+3}.

8. Given P_0, P_x, P_1, and P_∞ in that order, repeat Ex. 7.

9. Given P_0, P_x, P_y, and P_∞ in that order, construct P_{x+y}, P_{y+x}, and P_{y-x}.

10. Given P_x, P_0, P_y, and P_∞ in that order, construct P_{y+x}, P_{x+y}, P_{y-x}, and P_{x-y}.

11. Sketch a long, straight street or railroad track in perspective with telephone poles appearing to be equally spaced and of equal heights.

12. Four coplanar points, 0, X_∞, Y_∞, and U, are given with no three collinear. As in the figure, take OX_∞ as the x-axis, OY_∞ as the y-axis, and

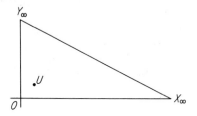

U as $(1, 1)$. Draw $X_\infty U$ to find $(0, 1)$; $Y_\infty U$, to find $(1, 0)$. Construct points with these coordinates:

  (a) $(2, 1)$;   (b) $(2, 0)$;   (c) $(3, 0)$;
  (d) $(0, 2)$;   (e) $(3, 2)$;   (f) $(-1, 0)$.

13. Use the points $(0, 0, 0)$, $(1, 1, 1)$, X_∞, Y_∞, and Z_∞ to develop a co-ordinate system for affine three-dimensional space. Construct points with each of these coordinates:

(a) (1, 1, 0);   (b) (1, 0, 0);   (c) (0, 1, 0);
(d) (0, 1, 1);   (e) (0, 0, 1);   (f) (1, 0, 1);
(g) (2, 1, 0);   (h) (2, 0, 0);   (i) (2, 1, 1).

14–4 Multiplication and Division in Euclidean Geometry

Given any two line segments of lengths a and b, we can find segments of lengths $a + b$ and $a - b$, as in §14–1. To find segments of length ab and $a \div b$, we need also a segment of length 1. We then use the fact

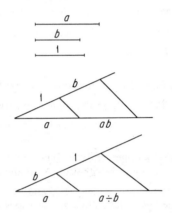

that a line parallel to one side of a triangle divides the other two sides proportionally. The proportions

$$\frac{1}{a} = \frac{b}{ab} \quad \text{and} \quad \frac{b}{a} = \frac{1}{a \div b}$$

provide the basis for the constructions, as in the figures.

Exercises

1. Select line segments a, b, and 1, where $a \approx 1\frac{1}{2}$ and $b \approx \frac{2}{3}$. Construct segments of lengths ab, $a \div b$, and $b \div a$.

2. Repeat Ex. 1 for $a \approx 3$ and $b \approx 2$.

*3. Explain why an additional assumption is needed before the method of this section can be used with the methods of §§14–1 and 14–3.

14-5 Constructing Rational Points

In affine geometry, rational points are constructed after defining harmonic sets of points. We shall instead introduce an assumption that will enable us to extend the method of §14-4 to construct any point with a rational number as its coordinate on the given scale.

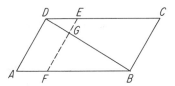

We assume that in any parallelogram $ABCD$ the diagonal DB divides any line EF which is parallel to AD so that $\overline{EG}:\overline{GF} = \overline{AF}:\overline{FB}$. The proof in Euclidean geometry is left as Exercise 1.

Example. Construct two intersecting number scales in ordinary Euclidean geometry (§14-1). Note that the scales do not need to be

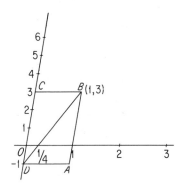

perpendicular and that they may have different units. To construct the point with coordinate $\frac{1}{4}$, construct a parallelogram $ABCD$ with A: $(1, -1)$, B: $(1, 3)$, C: $(0, 3)$, and D: $(0, -1)$; draw DB; use E: $(0, 0)$ and F: $(1, 0)$ to obtain G: $(\frac{1}{4}, 0)$.

Exercises

A

1. Prove that the assumption $\dfrac{\overline{EG}}{\overline{GF}} = \dfrac{\overline{AF}}{\overline{FB}}$ is a correct assumption in Euclidean geometry.

2. As in the illustrative example, construct points with coordinates $\frac{2}{3}$, $\frac{3}{2}$, and $\frac{2}{5}$.

3. Give a construction for any point with a rational coordinate $\dfrac{p}{q}$.

4 through 6. Construct $\frac{1}{4}$ and repeat Exs. 2 and 3 for points on an affine line.

Hint: See Ex. 12 of §14–3.

B

The constructions on a Euclidean line considered up to this time have been based upon P_0 and P_1 as given points. Actually you can start with any two points with known rational coordinates on the line. Use the methods that we have considered and give constructions for P_0 and P_1 when the listed points are given.

1. P_2 and P_3 **2.** P_{-2} and P_{-1}

3. P_2 and P_4 **4.** P_{-1} and P_3

5. $P_{1/2}$ and $P_{3/2}$ **6.** $P_{1/4}$ and $P_{3/4}$

7. $P_{1/2}$ and $P_{2/3}$ **8.** $P_{-1/2}$ and $P_{3/2}$

14–6 Perspective Figures

The study of perspective figures was started by artists. As in the case of the problem of locating telephone poles beside a railroad track, perspective is primarily concerned with lines and points. The poles will appear to be the same distance from the track if and only if the bases of the poles are all on a line through the point P_∞ on the horizon

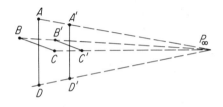

and the tracks. The poles will appear to be of the same height if and
only if their tops are all on a line through P_∞. Any two poles will
appear to be of the same shape if and only if the line joining
corresponding points passes through P_∞. Consider the poles $ABCD$ and
$A'B'C'D'$ in the figure. The lines joining corresponding points are all
distinct and all pass through P_∞. We describe this situation by saying
that the poles are perspective with respect to P_∞; we write

$$ABCD \stackrel{P_\infty}{\underset{\wedge}{=\!=}} A'B'C'D'.$$

This is the same notation that we used in §§14–1 and 14–3. In each
of those cases, the figures were perspective with respect to the specified
points.

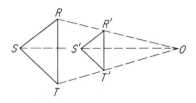

Two triangles RST and $R'S'T'$ are **perspective with respect to a point**
O if the lines joining corresponding vertices are distinct and all pass

through O. We write $RST \stackrel{O}{\underset{\wedge}{=\!=}} R'S'T'$.

Two triangles ABC and $A'B'C'$ are **perspective with respect to a line**
m if the points of intersection of corresponding sides are distinct and

all lie on m. We write $ABC \stackrel{m}{\underset{\wedge}{=\!=}} A'B'C'$. The definitions of triangles

perspective with respect to a point and of triangles perspective with

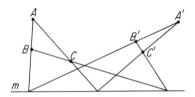

respect to a line may be rephrased for other polygons. They apply whether the points and lines are ordinary or at the horizon.

Exercises

1. Define and sketch two quadrilaterals (a) that are perspective from a point O; (b) that are perspective from a line m.

2. Draw a figure showing a square perspective with respect to a point with (a) a square; (b) a rectangle.

3. The figure shows a tetrahedron $ABCD$ cut by a plane in triangle $B'C'D'$. Note that $BCD \overset{A}{\underset{\wedge}{=}} B'C'D'$. The lines BC and $B'C'$ intersect at

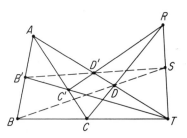

T; CD and $C'D'$, at R; BD and $B'D'$, at S. Prove that the points R, S, and T are on a line.

4. The statement proved in Ex. 3 may be stated for triangles on different planes as: If two triangles are perspective from a point, they are perspective from a line. The statement and its converse are true whether the triangles are on the same or different planes. It is known as the Theorem of Desargues. Assume this theorem and give a construction laying out a pattern of 10 trees such that there are ten rows with three trees on each row.

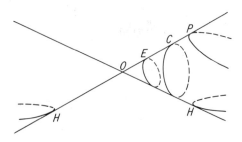

5. The figure at the bottom of page 302 shows a circle C perspective with respect to the point O with the ellipse E, the hyperbola H, and the parabola P. Use the figure to explain why each of these plane figures is often called a conic. Each of these conic sections is non-degenerate, since it does not consist of one or more straight lines or of a single point.

14-7 Classifications of Conics

We now consider the non-degenerate conics: ellipses, parabolas, and hyperbolas. We consider a circle as a special case of an ellipse. Our purpose is to compare the classification of conics with the classification of roots of quadratic equations.

The general quadratic equation in one variable

$$ax^2 + bx + c = 0 \tag{1}$$

with real coefficients has roots

$$\frac{-b + \sqrt{b^2 - 4ac}}{2a} \quad \text{and} \quad \frac{-b - \sqrt{b^2 - 4ac}}{2a},$$

which are classified, as in the array, according to the value of the discriminant $b^2 - 4ac$.

$b^2 - 4ac$	Roots
Positive	Real and unequal
Zero	Real and equal
Negative	Conjugate imaginary (unequal)

A general quadratic equation in two variables,

$$Ax^2 + Bxy + Cy^2 + Dx + Ey + F = 0, \tag{2}$$

with real coefficients has a non-degenerate conic as its graph if the following condition (which we assume here without proof) is satisfied:

$$\begin{vmatrix} 2A & B & D \\ B & 2C & E \\ D & E & 2F \end{vmatrix} \neq 0$$

that is, if $8ACF + 2BDE - 2CD^2 - 2AE^2 - 2B^2F \neq 0$.

These graphs are usually classified in the second course in algebra according to the value of $B^2 - 4AC$:

B^2-4AC	Conic
Positive	Hyperbola
Zero	Parabola
Negative	Ellipse

The similarity between the arrays for $b^2 - 4ac$ and $B^2 - 4AC$ should be clear. We shall seek the geometric basis for associating a hyperbola with distinct real roots, associating a parabola with real and equal roots, and associating an ellipse with imaginary roots. In order to do this, we recognize that, for large numerical values of x and/or y (that is, for points near the horizon line), only the second-degree terms of the equation (2) need to be considered. Thus, we have

$$Ax^2 + Bxy + Cy^2 = 0. \tag{3}$$

The equation (3) may be considered as a quadratic equation in the ratio $\dfrac{x}{y}$:

$$A\left(\frac{x}{y}\right)^2 + B\left(\frac{x}{y}\right) + C = 0$$

and is then easily compared with the equation (1). Under this comparison, a hyperbola corresponds to two real, distinct values of this ratio; a parabola corresponds to real and equal values of this ratio; an ellipse corresponds to imaginary values of this ratio. These values of the ratio $\dfrac{x}{y}$ correspond to the reciprocals of slopes of lines through the origin and, in that sense, to directions. Thus, we have an association of

a hyperbola with two distinct directions,
a parabola with a single direction,
an ellipse with imaginary directions.

These are the ways in which each curve becomes unbounded: a hyperbola in two senses along each of its asymptotes, a parabola in one sense along its axis, and an ellipse in no directions on the real plane.

This interpretation of the classification of conics may be visualized by associating an ideal line with a Euclidean plane. This line is analogous to the ideal point considered in §14–2. In §14–2 we associated an affine line with a circle on which one point was designated as the ideal point; the circle without the ideal point corresponds to a Euclidean line. We now associate an affine plane with a cylinder on which one line is

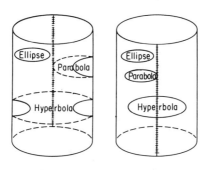

Figure 1   Figure 2

designated as the ideal or horizon line. The cylinder without this ideal line corresponds to a Euclidean plane. In talking with students, it is convenient to refer to this ideal line as a "zipper" of the plane. In a sense, we roll up the line and "button it" with its ideal point; we roll

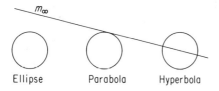

Ellipse   Parabola   Hyperbola

up the plane and "zip" it with its ideal line. When the plane is turned so that the zipper is not in view, we see the graphs of equations of the form (2), as in Euclidean geometry (Fig. 1). When the plane is turned so that the zipper is in view (Fig. 2), we see that the ellipse does not intersect the ideal line (imaginary roots for the directions in which the ellipse becomes unbounded). The parabola is tangent to the ideal line (real and equal roots for the directions in which the parabola becomes unbounded). The hyperbola crosses the special line in two distinct points (real and unequal roots for the directions in which the hyperbola becomes unbounded).

We may also visualize the intersections of the conics with the ideal line simply by designating one line on the plane as this line. The drawing of each conic as a circle is based upon the results discussed in Ex. 5 of §14–6. The visualization of the figures is often helped by thinking of the ideal line as sliding across the plane of the circle.

Application and Additional Readings

The construction of number scales on a Euclidean line is recommended for all students studying geometry. The construction of number scales on an affine line provides an interesting supplementary topic for the better students. At some stage every student of Euclidean geometry should be led to recognize the existence of other geometries. The number scales considered in this chapter provide one basis for doing this at a necessarily intuitive level. The classification of conics is intended primarily to provide background for teachers. Additional reading may be found in Chapter 15 and the references for that chapter.

Answers for Exercises

14–1 *Constructing Integral Points on a Euclidean Line*

1.

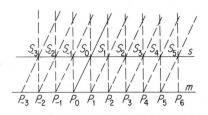

2.

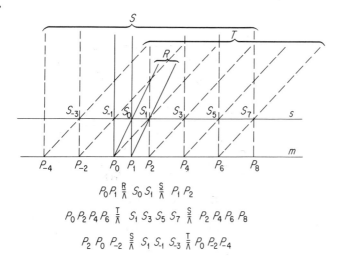

$$P_0 P_1 \overset{R}{\underset{\wedge}{=}} S_0 S_1 \overset{S}{\underset{\wedge}{=}} P_1 P_2$$

$$P_0 P_2 P_4 P_6 \overset{T}{\underset{\wedge}{=}} S_1 S_3 S_5 S_7 \overset{S}{\underset{\wedge}{=}} P_2 P_4 P_6 P_8$$

$$P_2 P_0 P_{-2} \overset{S}{\underset{\wedge}{=}} S_1 S_{-1} S_{-3} \overset{T}{\underset{\wedge}{=}} P_0 P_{-2} P_{-4}$$

3.

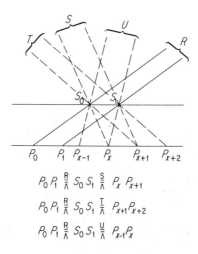

$$P_0 P_1 \overset{R}{\underset{\wedge}{=}} S_0 S_1 \overset{S}{\underset{\wedge}{=}} P_x P_{x+1}$$

$$P_0 P_1 \overset{R}{\underset{\wedge}{=}} S_0 S_1 \overset{T}{\underset{\wedge}{=}} P_{x+1} P_{x+2}$$

$$P_0 P_1 \overset{R}{\underset{\wedge}{=}} S_0 S_1 \overset{U}{\underset{\wedge}{=}} P_{x-1} P_x$$

Notice that, since $P_{x+1} \equiv P_{1+x}$, the construction might as readily have been performed using the sequence of perspectivities $P_0 P_x \overset{R}{\underset{\wedge}{=}} S_0 S_x$ $\overset{V}{\underset{\wedge}{=}} P_1 P_{1+x}$. (The direction, V, is not shown in this figure.)

4.

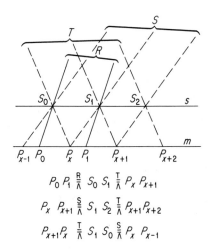

$$P_0\, P_1\, \overset{R}{\overline{\underline{\wedge}}}\, S_0\, S_1\, \overset{T}{\overline{\underline{\wedge}}}\, P_x\, P_{x+1}$$

$$P_x\, P_{x+1}\, \overset{S}{\overline{\underline{\wedge}}}\, S_1\, S_2\, \overset{T}{\overline{\underline{\wedge}}}\, P_{x+1}\, P_{x+2}$$

$$P_{x+1}\, P_x\, \overset{T}{\overline{\underline{\wedge}}}\, S_1\, S_0\, \overset{S}{\overline{\underline{\wedge}}}\, P_x\, P_{x-1}$$

5.

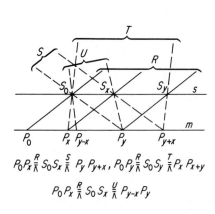

$$P_0\, P_x\, \overset{R}{\overline{\underline{\wedge}}}\, S_0\, S_x\, \overset{S}{\overline{\underline{\wedge}}}\, P_y\, P_{y+x}\,,\; P_0\, P_y\, \overset{R}{\overline{\underline{\wedge}}}\, S_0\, S_y\, \overset{T}{\overline{\underline{\wedge}}}\, P_x\, P_{x+y}$$

$$P_0\, P_x\, \overset{R}{\overline{\underline{\wedge}}}\, S_0\, S_x\, \overset{U}{\overline{\underline{\wedge}}}\, P_{y-x}\, P_y$$

6.

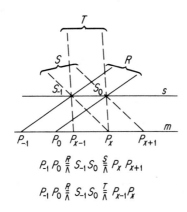

$$P_{-1}\,P_0 \overset{R}{\underset{\wedge}{=}} S_{-1}\,S_0 \overset{S}{\underset{\wedge}{=}} P_x\,P_{x+1}$$

$$P_{-1}\,P_0 \overset{R}{\underset{\wedge}{=}} S_{-1}\,S_0 \overset{T}{\underset{\wedge}{=}} P_{x-1}\,P_x$$

7. A point P_x is a positive point if it is on the same side of P_0 as P_1; a negative point, if it is on the opposite side of P_0 from P_1.

8.

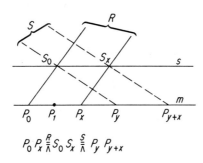

$$P_0\,P_x \overset{R}{\underset{\wedge}{=}} S_0\,S_x \overset{S}{\underset{\wedge}{=}} P_y\,P_{y+x}$$

9.

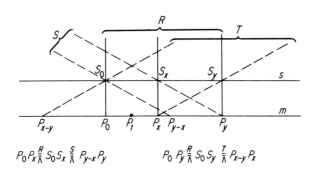

$$P_0\,P_x \overset{R}{\underset{\wedge}{=}} S_0\,S_x \overset{S}{\underset{\wedge}{=}} P_{y-x}\,P_y \qquad P_0\,P_y \overset{R}{\underset{\wedge}{=}} S_0\,S_y \overset{T}{\underset{\wedge}{=}} P_{x-y}\,P_x$$

10.

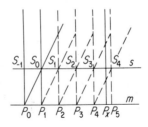

Notice that in this case our arbitrary selection of P_0, P_1, and P_x required $n \geq 5$.

14–2 *Lines in Other Geometries*

1.

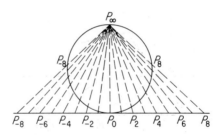

2.

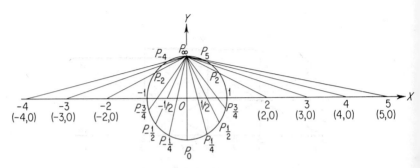

Notice that this construction may be extended for -8 to $+8$ as needed for the exercise or any other given interval.

3. If sphere S is tangent to a coordinate plane at the point O: $(0,0)$ on the plane, and $\overline{OP}$ is a diameter of the sphere, let point P on the sphere represent the ideal point, P_∞. Lines passing through P_∞ and any point (x, y) on the coordinate plane will puncture the sphere at one and only one point. Using O and P as poles, and lines of latitude and longitude (like those used in mapping the earth's surface) as the basis for identifying coordinates on the sphere, each puncture point now has a unique set of spherical coordinates which relate that point to the point (x, y) with which it is associated on the plane. The point P_∞ is the exception to the statement that each point on the sphere is uniquely related to a point on the plane, since P_∞ is related to all of the horizon points of the plane.

4. If the coordinate plane has its point $(0, 0)$ as the center of sphere S having radius 1, the plane cuts the sphere into two hemispheres. The sphere's diameter $\overline{QP}$, which is perpendicular to the coordinate plane, passes through $(0, 0)$. As in Ex. 3, let P represent P_∞, and use Q and P as poles for a spherical coordinate system. Thus, the lines joining P_∞ and the points (x, y) on the plane will relate the points on the "equator" of the sphere with the coincident points (x, y) of the circle $x^2 + y^2 = 1$. The points on the hemisphere which has Q as its pole will be uniquely related to the points of the plane which are inside the circle $x^2 + y^2 = 1$ (notice that Q represents $(0, 0)$). Except for P, the points on the other hemisphere will be uniquely related to the points (x, y) outside the circle $x^2 + y^2 = 1$. As in Ex. 3, P_∞ is related to all the horizon points of the plane.

5. The Euclidean line is divided into two half-lines by P_0 and, indeed, by any other point P_k. For the affine line, two points, such as P_0 and P_∞, are needed; any P_k and P_∞ may be used.

14–3 *Constructing Integral Points on an Affine Line*

1.

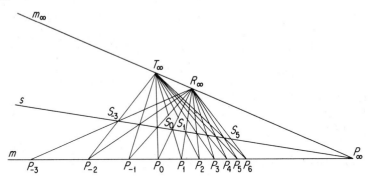

2.

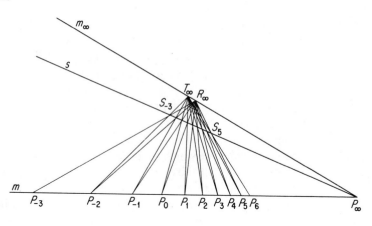

3.

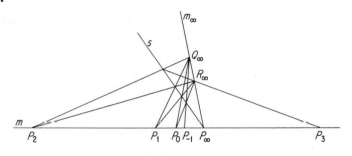

4. In Ex. 3, the affine line m including the point P_∞ is comparable to a Euclidean circle with an unbounded radius. The points P_∞ and P_0 divide this Euclidean representation of the affine line into two "arcs," that is, into two segments of the affine line. One of these "arcs," $P_0P_{-1}P_\infty$, is in full view in the drawing. This "arc" contains all the negative points of the affine line. The positive points arise on the other "arc," portions of which are visible in the drawing to the left of P_0 and to the right of P_∞. The explanation may be stated briefly, as in the answers for Ex. 5 and Ex. 6.

5. In each case, the positive points on the line are the interior points of the line segment $\overline{P_0P_1P_\infty}$.

6. In each case, the negative points on the line are the exterior points of the line segment $\overline{P_0P_1P_\infty}$.

7.

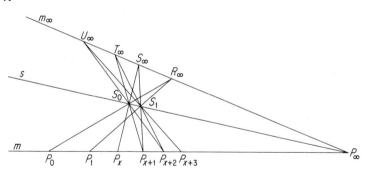

8.

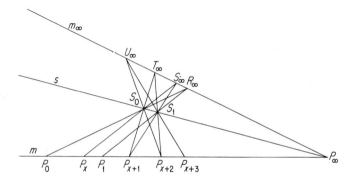

9.

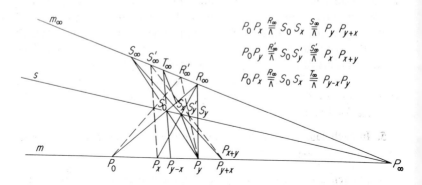

$$P_0\, P_x \stackrel{R_\infty}{\overline{\overline{\wedge}}} S_0\, S_x \stackrel{S_\infty}{\overline{\wedge}} P_y\, P_{y+x}$$

$$P_0 P_y \stackrel{R'_\infty}{\overline{\wedge}} S_0 S'_y \stackrel{S'_\infty}{\overline{\overline{\wedge}}} P_x\, P_{x+y}$$

$$P_0 P_x \stackrel{R_\infty}{\overline{\wedge}} S_0\, S_x \stackrel{T_\infty}{\overline{\overline{\wedge}}} P_{y-x} P_y$$

10.

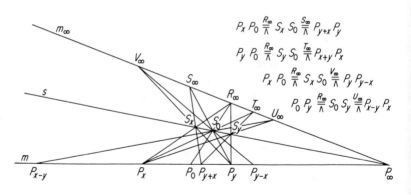

$$P_x\, P_0 \stackrel{R_\infty}{\overline{\overline{\wedge}}} S_x\, S_0 \stackrel{S_\infty}{\overline{\wedge}} P_{y+x}\, P_y$$

$$P_y\, P_0 \stackrel{R_\infty}{\overline{\wedge}} S_y\, S_0 \stackrel{T_\infty}{\overline{\wedge}} P_{x+y}\, P_x$$

$$P_x\, P_0 \stackrel{R_\infty}{\overline{\wedge}} S_x\, S_0 \stackrel{V_\infty}{\overline{\wedge}} P_y\, P_{y-x}$$

$$P_0\, P_y \stackrel{R_\infty}{\overline{\wedge}} S_0\, S_y \stackrel{U_\infty}{\overline{\wedge}} P_{x-y}\, P_x$$

Note that P_{x-y} and P_{y-x} are of opposite signs.

11.

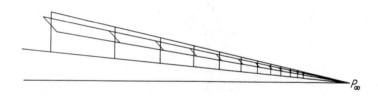

12.

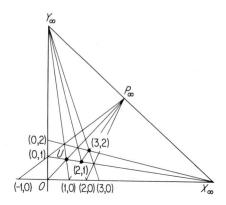

13.

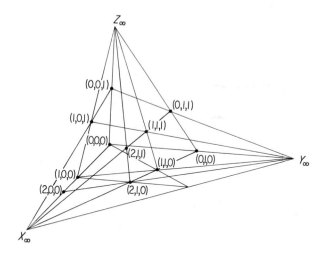

Note that, in practice, $(1, 1, 0)$ is chosen in accordance with the appearance of the figure, even though it is determined as the intersection of the XY-plane and the line through Z_∞ and $(1, 1, 1)$.

14–4 *Multiplication and Division in Euclidean Geometry*

1.

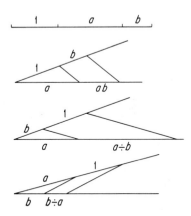

2.

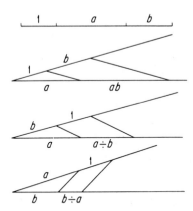

3. We have previously used only the assumption that the opposite sides of a parallelogram are equal. This enabled us to compare distances on a line or on parallel lines. In order to compare distances on intersecting lines, we need similar figures or an equivalent assumption. See §14–5.

14-5 *Constructing Rational Points*

A

1. Given: Parallelogram $ABCD$ with diagonal DB; line segment $EGF \parallel AD$ with E on DC, G on DB, and F on AB. To prove: $\dfrac{\overline{EG}}{\overline{GF}} = \dfrac{\overline{AF}}{\overline{FB}}$. *Proof:* $\triangle DEG \sim \triangle DCB$, and $\triangle BFG \sim \triangle BAD$, since a line parallel to a side of a triangle determines a triangle similar to the original triangle. Then, since corresponding sides of similar triangles are in proportion:

$$\frac{\overline{EG}}{\overline{CB}} = \frac{\overline{DG}}{\overline{DB}} \quad \text{and} \quad \frac{\overline{GF}}{\overline{DA}} = \frac{\overline{BG}}{\overline{BD}}.$$

Since opposite sides of a parallelogram are equal, $\overline{CB} = \overline{DA}$, and by substitution,

$$\frac{\overline{EG}}{\overline{DA}} = \frac{\overline{DG}}{\overline{DB}}. \quad \text{Then, as in algebra,}$$

$$\frac{\overline{EG}}{\overline{DG}} = \frac{\overline{DA}}{\overline{DB}}, \quad \text{and} \quad \frac{\overline{GF}}{\overline{BG}} = \frac{\overline{DA}}{\overline{DB}}, \text{ whence}$$

$$\frac{\overline{EG}}{\overline{DG}} = \frac{\overline{GF}}{\overline{BG}}, \quad \text{and} \quad \frac{\overline{EG}}{\overline{GF}} = \frac{\overline{DG}}{\overline{BG}}.$$

Since a line parallel to one side of a triangle and cutting the other two sides divides the two sides proportionately:

$$\frac{\overline{DG}}{\overline{BG}} = \frac{\overline{AF}}{\overline{BF}}.$$

Then, by substitution,

$$\frac{\overline{EG}}{\overline{GF}} = \frac{\overline{AF}}{\overline{BF}}, \text{ as was to be proved.}$$

2.

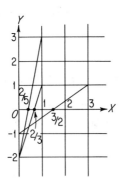

3.

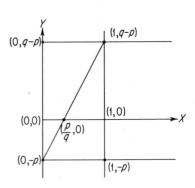

4.

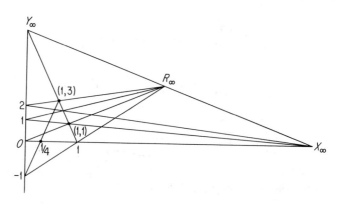

The explanation is the same as that for the illustrative example of this section, with lines which meet at an ideal point (such as Y_∞, R_∞, or X_∞) playing the role of the parallel lines of the example.

5.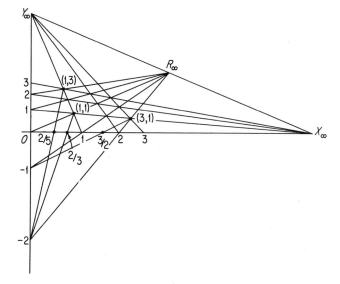

6.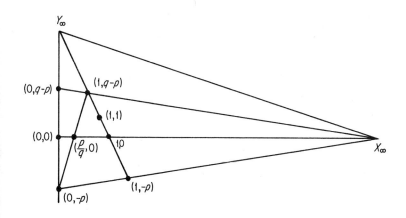

Notice that, in this affine figure, our "parallelogram" is the figure whose vertices are $(0, -p)$, $(1, -p)$, $(1, q - p)$, and $(0, q - p)$. In this respect, it is the same as the figure for Ex. 4.

B

1.

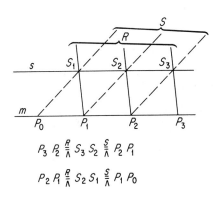

$$P_3\, P_2 \;\overset{R}{\overline{\wedge}}\; S_3\, S_2 \;\overset{S}{\overline{\wedge}}\; P_2\, P_1$$

$$P_2\, P_1 \;\overset{R}{\overline{\wedge}}\; S_2\, S_1 \;\overset{S}{\overline{\wedge}}\; P_1\, P_0$$

2.

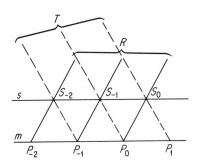

3.

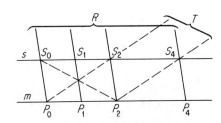

4.

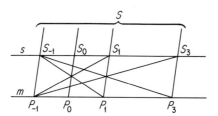

Notice that in Ex. 4 the intersection of the diagonals of a parallelogram is used to determine the midpoint of a side.

5.

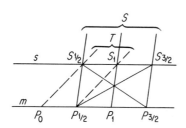

6.

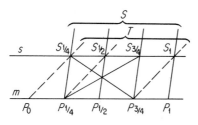

7.

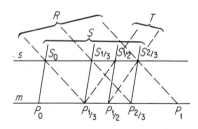

8.

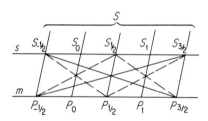

14–6 *Perspective Figures*

1a. Two quadrilaterals *RSTU* and *R'S'T'U'* are perspective with respect to a point *O* if the lines joining corresponding vertices are distinct and all pass through *O*.

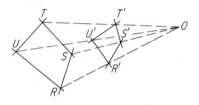

1b. Two quadrilaterals $ABCD$ and $A'B'C'D'$ are perspective with respect to a line m if the points of intersection of corresponding sides are distinct and all lie on m.

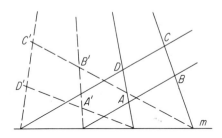

2.

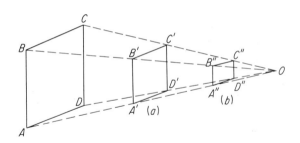

3. Note that BC, CD, and BD are on the plane BCD, whence T, R, and S are on the plane BCD; similarly, $B'C'$, $C'D'$, and $B'D'$ are on the plane $B'C'D'$, and thus T, R, and S are on the plane $B'C'D'$ Therefore, the points R, S, and T are on the line of intersection of the planes BCD and $B'C'D'$.

4. Think of the trees as at A, B, C, D, B', C', D', R, S, and T in Ex. 3. See figure in text.

5. Each plane figure is obtained as the intersection of a plane and a cone and thus is called a conic.

CHAPTER

FIFTEEN

░▒

THE PLACE OF SOLID AND OTHER GEOMETRIES IN THE SECONDARY SCHOOLS

Contemporary efforts to revise·the first course in geometry are confusing to teachers, since each·revision is based upon one or more of three distinct goals:

(a) The development of a single year's course including both plane and solid geometry,

(b) The inclusion of coordinate geometry as an integral part of the course, and

(c) The inclusion of intuitive discussions of a few geometries other than Euclidean.

The most common result of such efforts is a book which is far too long for a single year's course. In such a case, the individual teacher must assume the responsibility for selecting the topics that are to be covered. Textbooks which are comprehensive in scope will be necessary until there has been general agreement among teachers as to the topics to be covered.

The opinions expressed in the present chapter are based upon the philosophy that some geometry should be included in each secondary school course and should be developed according to the maturity and ability of the pupils in the class. It is the authors' firm conviction that there exist learning experiences in geometry which challenge and inspire students in ways that cannot be matched in any other area.

Nowhere else can be found such a wealth of non-trivial exercises for students at each level of maturity. Geometry offers all students opportunities for the development of reasoning, creative imagination, insight, and the ability to analyze problems.

15–1 Solid Geometry

The precise extent of the solid geometry which should be included in a first formal course in geometry depends to a considerable degree upon the amount of work done in the junior high school years. Many of the space figures and related formulas are developed on an intuitive basis by junior high school teachers. The figures and formulas certainly should be reviewed or introduced (as the situation requires) in a first course in geometry.

The following goals are suggested for the teaching of solid geometry in a secondary school mathematics program:

(a) At least by the end of the first course in geometry, each student should recognize such common space figures as the cube, rectangular box, parallelepiped, prism, cylinder, pyramid, cone, sphere, and a few of the special types of prisms and pyramids. He should know, and be able to use, a formula for the volume of each of these solids. He should know, and be able to use, a formula for the surface of a cube, a rectangular box, a cylinder, and a sphere. Capable students would profit by knowing other formulas as well.

(b) Skill in the use of formulas for volumes and surfaces should be developed in the second course in algebra.

(c) The proofs of a few theorems from solid geometry should be included in their natural places in the first course; a few proofs should remain for the senior year; many of the traditional proofs may be omitted entirely.

(d) The visualization of figures in space should be stressed in all secondary school mathematics courses.

In a first course in geometry, several aspects of solid geometry should be considered. As discussed in Chapters 10 and 12, points and lines should be left undefined. A geometric figure on a plane is a set of points and lines. Planes may be defined, but a description in terms of the properties of a plane should suffice. For example, a plane may be determined by three points that are not on the same line, by two intersecting lines, by a line and a point not on the line, or by two parallel lines.

A **plane** is a set of points such that:

(a) The set contains three non-collinear points;
(b) If two points of a line are in the set, then all points of the line are in the set; and
(c) Any two lines of points in the set either intersect or are parallel.

This definition is reversible. Note that part (a) of the definition stipulates that the set contains at least a plane; part (c) stipulates that the set does not include all points of three-dimensional space, since skew lines are excluded. The drawing of lines and planes in space should be stressed; models can be helpful. Symmetry with respect to a plane and perpendicularity of planes and lines should be considered, as well as parallelisms (§12–4).

The discussion of loci in space provides one of the most fruitful opportunities for developing space concepts. There are three-dimensional problems related to nearly all locus problems on a plane. Intersections of loci in space are particularly interesting and useful.

Another opportunity for developing space concepts may be found in the discussion of projections. Extend the projection of line segments onto the coordinate axes to the projection of line segments, surfaces, and volumes onto planes. For example, consider the possible projections of a circle (or a rectangle) onto a plane. Think also of the possible projections of a rectangular box or of a sphere onto a plane.

Still another opportunity may be found in three-dimensional tick-tack-toe. Any adult who doubts the ability of this game to develop the space perception of young children should try playing the game with some second- or third-grade children.

The introduction of perspective drawing provides an opportunity for discussing Greek architecture, Italian art, and other cultural topics. Space concepts are strengthened when one considers the apparent convergence in the distance of a straight railroad track and extends this concept to the drawing of telephone poles equally spaced along the track (Chapter 14).

There are many theorems involving lines and planes in space which can be proved using only techniques from plane geometry. For example, consider this extension of a theorem from plane geometry:

If three or more parallel planes intercept equal segments on one transversal, they intercept equal segments on every transversal.

Think of the planes α, β, and γ as cutting off equal segments on a line m, and take n as another transversal. If m and n intersect, they are coplanar; their plane intersects the parallel planes in parallel lines; these parallel lines cut off equal segments on n, as in plane geometry. If m and n do not intersect, let M be a point of m and N be a point of n.

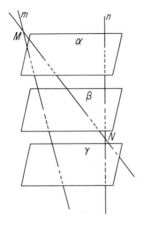

Then m and the line MN are coplanar; hence, the parallel planes cut off equal segments on MN. Also, MN and n are coplanar; hence, the parallel planes cut off equal segments on n.

Consider the mensuration formulas of solid geometry. These are usually introduced in the junior high school, reviewed in the first formal course in geometry, applied in the second course in algebra, and unified by means of the prismoidal formula near the end of the high school program. The development of mensuration formulas for solid figures throughout the courses of secondary school mathematics should be typical of the development of all geometric concepts. In particular, the unification of concepts near the end of the high school program should be sought for all areas of mathematics, whether the student

plans to continue his work in mathematics or to conclude it at the high
school level.

The **prismoidal formula**, $V = \dfrac{H}{6}(B_1 + 4M + B_2)$, for the volume V
of a solid with height H, area of first base B_1, area of mid-section M,
and area of second base B_2, can be interpreted for practically all of the
solids considered in secondary schools. For example, it can be used
for all rectangular parallelepipeds, cylinders, prisms, pyramids, cones,
prismatoids, prismoids, spheres, spherical segments, spheroids, conoids,

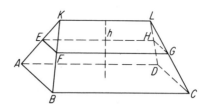

wedges, and ellipsoids. For example, in the given figure, think of the
wedge $ABCDLK$ as having a rectangular base, $ABCD$, and edge
$\overline{KL} \parallel \overline{BC}$. The plane of the mid-section, $EFGH$, is parallel to the base.
In $\triangle ABK$, $\overline{EF} \parallel \overline{AB}$ and $\overline{EF} = \tfrac{1}{2}\overline{AB}$; similarly, $\overline{HG} \parallel \overline{DC}$ and $\overline{HG} =$
$\tfrac{1}{2}\overline{DC}$. In trapezoid $BCLK$, median $\overline{FG} \parallel \overline{BC}$ and $\overline{FG} = \tfrac{1}{2}(\overline{BC} + \overline{KL})$;
similarly, $\overline{EH} \parallel \overline{AD}$ and $\overline{EH} = \tfrac{1}{2}(\overline{AD} + \overline{KL})$. Let $\overline{AB} = w$, $\overline{BC} = b$,
$\overline{KL} = c$, and the height be h. Then

$$\overline{AB} = \overline{CD} = w, \qquad \overline{EF} = \overline{GH} = \tfrac{1}{2}w;$$

$$\overline{BC} = \overline{AD} = b, \qquad \overline{FG} = \overline{EH} = \tfrac{1}{2}(b + c).$$

The expression used in the prismoidal formula may now be evaluated:

the lower base $B_1 \quad = bw$;

the mid-section $M \quad = (\tfrac{1}{2}w)(\tfrac{1}{2})(b + c) = \dfrac{w}{4}(b + c)$;

the upper base $B_2 \quad = c(0) = 0$; and

the volume is $V \quad = \dfrac{h}{6}[bw + w(b + c) + 0] = \dfrac{wh}{6}(2b + c)$.

A summary of the uses of the prismoidal formula may be found in [34]. Teachers who wish to introduce calculus will find that the proof of the prismoidal formula and its restriction to a certain class of figures can be given, using the techniques of elementary calculus. The proof is given in [34].

The pupil's power to visualize space figures also can be developed by using problems of the surveying type, in which edges of a tetrahedron or other polyhedron are to be determined. Still another approach is through the intersections of lines, planes, and solid figures. At the high school level, much of the emphasis on these intersections should be

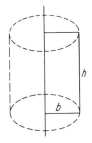

on visualizing the intersection and on drawing the figure rather than on the computation of volume or area.

Rotations of solid as well as plane figures may be considered. The solid figures generated by rotating plane figures are particularly important. For example, a cylinder with radius b and height h may be generated by rotating a rectangle with sides b and h about one of its sides of length h. Finally, when geometry is considered in terms of patterns in shapes, or properties, the use of figures on a line, on a plane, and in space provides a broad comprehension of geometry and of the universe in which we live that can be developed in no other way.

Exercises

Show that the formula for the volume of each figure can be considered as a special case of the prismoidal formula:

1. Cube
2. Pyramid
3. Sphere
4. Prism
5. Cylinder
6. Cone

15–2 Spherical Geometry

Solid geometry and the geometry on a sphere are the most common and accessible other geometries for consideration along with plane geometry. Mensuration formulas for spheres are considered in junior high school. The measures of dihedral angles should be used in the first formal course in geometry to increase the pupil's understanding of latitude and longitude.

The geometry of points and arcs of great circles on a sphere is a two-dimensional geometry comparable to that of points and line segments on a plane. The geometry on the surface of a sphere can be used very effectively to show that several of the postulates of Euclidean plane geometry serve to distinguish Euclidean from other geometries (§12–3).

When the figures are restricted to a small region on a sphere, most of the theorems of plane geometry may still be used. When the figures are not so restricted, some theorems and assumptions fail. For example, consider these corresponding statements where on a sphere "line" is interpreted as "arc of a great circle."

Any two lines:
> (*on a plane*) intersect in one and only one point or are parallel.
> (*on a sphere*) intersect at a pair of diametrically opposite points.

Given any line *m* and a point *P* that is not on *m*, there exist:
> (*on a plane*) exactly one line through *P* and parallel to *m*.
> (*on a sphere*) no lines through *P* and parallel to *m*.

The sum of the interior angles of a triangle:
> (*on a plane*) is 180°.
> (*on a sphere*) is greater than 180° and less than 540°.

Similar triangles:
> (*on a plane*) may be of different sizes.
> (*on a sphere*) are of the same size (area).

Lines perpendicular to the same line:
> (*on a plane*) are parallel.
> (*on a sphere*) all pass through two points (called the poles of the given line).

On an ordinary plane, we have a standard unit for the measure of angles, that is, one revolution. On a sphere, we also have a standard unit for the measure of distances, that is, the circumference of a great circle, the common length of all lines. Near the end of the student's high school program, it is appropriate to include a unit on spherical triangles culminating in the proof that the area of a spherical triangle may be expressed in terms of the angle sum of the triangle.

15–3 Elliptic and Hyperbolic Geometries

On a plane, two lines intersect in at most one point; on a sphere, in two diametrically opposite points. A model for elliptic geometry may be obtained by thinking of diametrically opposite points on a sphere as a single point. Then, in this geometry, points correspond to diameters of the sphere; and lines correspond to planes through the center of the sphere. Thus, the points and lines of elliptic geometry may also be visualized as diameters and planes through the center of a sphere.

Elliptic (or Riemannian) geometry is important as a consistent geometry in which most of the postulates of Euclidean geometry hold but in which the parallel postulate does not, since any two lines on a plane intersect. Elliptic plane geometry is also important because the geometry of ideal points and ideal lines (see §14–2) associated with Euclidean space is an elliptic geometry.

Hyperbolic (or Lobatchevskian) geometry may be distinguished from Euclidean geometry by this property:

Given any line m and a point P that is not a point of m, there are at least two lines through P which do not intercept m. As illustrated by the figure, there are then infinitely many lines t through P which do not

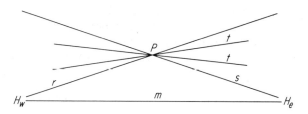

intersect m. This property is based upon the existence of two ideal points H_e and H_w, as mentioned in §14–2. The lines PH_e and PH_w are each *parallel* to m in hyperbolic geometry.

A model for hyperbolic plane geometry may be obtained by using the circles which intersect a fixed circle at right angles. Then the points on the fixed circle are the "ideal" points; the points inside the fixed circle are ordinary points. In this model (see the figure), two lines (*r* and *s*) intersect if they have an interior point (*P*) in common; two lines (*r* and *m*, also *s* and *m*) are parallel if they have a point (*Q*, or *T*)

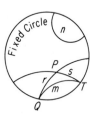

of the fixed circle in common; two lines (*m* and *n*) are non-intersecting but not parallel in all other cases [32; pp. 256–257 and 276–278].

The comparison of properties of spherical and Euclidean plane geometry may now be extended to include elliptic and hyperbolic geometries. The following abbreviations are used:

(P): in Euclidean plane geometry.
(S): in spherical geometry.
(E): in elliptic geometry.
(H): in hyperbolic geometry.

Any two lines:
(P): intersect in one and only one point or are parallel.
(S): intersect at a pair of diametrically opposite points.
(E): intersect in one and only one point.
(H): intersect in one and only one point, are parallel, or are non-intersecting.

Given any line *m* and a point *P* that is not on *m*, there exist through *P* and parallel to *m*:
(P): exactly one line.
(S): no lines.
(E): no lines.
(H): two lines.

The sum of the interior angles of any triangle is:
(P): 180°.
(S): greater than 180° but less than 540°.
(E): greater than 180°.
(H): less than 180°.

Similar triangles have the same shape and:
(P): may be of different sizes.
(S): have the same size.
(E): have the same size.
(H): have the same size.

Lines perpendicular to the same line:
(P): are parallel.
(S): all pass through two points (poles of the given line).
(E): all pass through a single point (pole of the given line).
(H): are non-intersecting (also not parallel) lines.

The elliptic and hyperbolic geometries are often called the **non-Euclidean geometries**. Note that there are other geometries, such as spherical geometry, which are *not Euclidean*; in other words, note that "non-Euclidean" and "not Euclidean" have different meanings.

The four plane geometries—Euclidean, spherical, elliptic, and hyperbolic—are significant as the *only* plane geometries in which lines are continuous (§16–1) and in which two types of transformations such as translations and rotations (§16–2) are possible.

15–4 Finite Geometries

There is much talk about "non-Euclidean" geometries by people who fail to recognize that "non-Euclidean" and "not Euclidean" have different meanings. There are many geometries that are not Euclidean; only two of these, see §15–3, are non-Euclidean. For high school students, the emphasis should be on the existence of geometries other than Euclidean. Finite geometries and spherical geometries, as well as the two non-Euclidean geometries, serve this purpose very well.

In a finite geometry there are only a finite number of points on a line. We shall consider an example in which there are three points on each line and three lines through each point. To emphasize that "point" and "line" are undefined and subject to various interpretations, we interpret

"point"   as   "student in a class,"
"line"   as   "committee."

We interpret the property of a point being on a line or of the line being through a point as a student being a member of a committee. Then, for a given class of students, we make these seven assumptions [32; p. 15]:

1. There exists at least one committee.

2. Every committee has at least three members.

3. Any two committees have at least one member in common.

4. If *A* and *B* are students, there exists a committee of which both are members.

5. If *A* and *B* are students, there exists at most one committee of which both are members.

6. Not all students are members of the same committee.

7. No committee has more than three members.

Notice that the students are identified by letters, and that each assumption must be true of all students of the class whatever letters may be used to identify them. For example, the fourth assumption must be true of students *C* and *D* as well as *A* and *B*.

The theorems in a finite geometry may be proved as in any other geometry. Several examples are given in the exercises.

Exercises

Each exercise should be considered relative to the seven assumptions given in this section.

1. Restate the assumptions in terms of points and lines.

2. State the sixth assumption in *if-then* form.

Prove:

3. There are at least four students.

4. Any two students are both members of exactly one committee.

5. Any two committees have exactly one member in common.

6. Each committee has exactly three members.

Note: It can also be proved [32; pp. 16–17] that there are exactly seven students in the class and exactly seven committees.

15–5 A Hierarchy of Geometries

High school teachers may feel that there will be an endless stream of new geometries. There could be, if abstract geometries are included. However, many of the most important geometries fit into a hierarchy that is somewhat like a family tree.

Briefly, we have

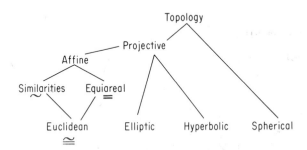

This structure of the hierarchy of geometries can be used to show the significance of the various postulates of Euclidean geometry and to show the relation of Euclidean geometry to the other geometries. Notice that spherical geometry is not a special case of projective geometry, since on a sphere two lines intersect in two points.

Topology is considered in Chapter 16 as a very general geometry. Each of the other geometries can be obtained by placing additional restrictions upon the transformations and figures considered in topology. For example, in projective geometry, lines are considered; in affine geometry, parallel lines. Euclidean geometry may be considered as a special case of affine geometry in which corresponding figures must be of the same shape ($\sim$) and size ($=$); this same restriction on affine geometry may be obtained by assuming the Pythagorean distance formula.

Application and Additional Readings

Three new but not yet generally accepted goals for a first course in geometry have been recognized. Solid geometry has been discussed in §15–1, coordinate geometry in Chapter 13, and other geometries in the remaining sections of this chapter. The primary purpose of this chapter has been to help teachers understand that students can and should recognize the existence of geometries other than Euclidean. Such geometries should be mentioned to all students and studied in modest detail by the better students.

Additional reading on solid and spherical geometry may be found in many places; additional readings on the other geometries may be found in [28], [40], and [32].

Answers for Exercises

15-1 *Solid Geometry*

In Exercises 1 through 6, use the ordinary letters and take:

1. $H = s$, $B_1 = s^2$, $M = s^2$, $B_2 = s_2$.

2. $H = h$, $B_1 = 0$, $M = \dfrac{B}{4}$, $B_2 = B$.

3. $H = 2r$, $B_1 = 0$, $M = \pi r^2$, $B_2 = 0$.

4. $H = h$, $B_1 = B$, $M = B$, $B_2 = B$.

5. $H = h$, $B_1 = \pi r^2$, $M = \pi r^2$, $B_2 = \pi r^2$.

6. $H = h$, $B_1 = 0$, $M = \dfrac{\pi r^2}{4}$, $B_2 = \pi r^2$.

15-4 *Finite Geometries*

1. (1) There exists at least one line.
    (2) Every line has at least three points.
    (3) Any two lines have at least one point in common.
    (4) If A and B are points, there is at least one line AB.
    (5) If A and B are points, there is at most one line AB.
    (6) Not all points are on the same line.
    (7) No line has more than three points.

2. Each of these statements is satisfactory:

If m is a committee, then not all students are members of m.

If m is a committee, then there is at least one student who is not a member of m.

In Exercises 3 through 6, the parenthetical references are to the given assumptions.

3. There exists a committee m (1) with at least three students as members (2). There is at least one student who is not on the committee m (6), thus implying the existence of at least four students.

4. Any two students are members of one (4) and only one (5) committee.

5. Any two committees have one (3) and only one (5) member in common.

6. Each committee has at least three (2) and no more than three (7) members.

◼▦▦▦▦▦▦▦▦▦▦▦▦▦▦▦▦▦▦▦▦▦▦▦▦▦▦▦▦▦▦▦▦▦◼

TOPOLOGY

Topology is often considered to be a very general geometry having many of the other geometries as special cases (§15–5). The discussion of topology in this chapter is based upon an article, "Topology for Secondary Schools" [33], written several years ago by one of the authors of this book.

When a topologist is asked a mathematical question, he will frequently demonstrate his use of visual images. For example, a few years ago, a topologist was asked a question regarding properties of surfaces. He suggested that the questioner visualize the Hawaiian Islands as mountains on dry land and consider the effect of the sea level gradually rising until the islands were completely submerged. Many topologists use such visual images, but they seldom interpret their subject to us in this way. We shall use a visual-image approach in presenting a few very elementary but fundamental topological concepts.

16–1 Topology

The word "topology" undoubtedly has very vague connotations for most teachers of mathematics. We shall endeavor to bring the word to life for you with an intuitive understanding of topology as a geometry with some of the properties of ordinary geometry—Euclidean geometry.

We shall endeavor to convince you that topology has significance and meaning for mathematics teachers and for pupils in secondary schools.

There is a trend toward the teaching of the underlying principles of any subject. Sometimes these principles are considered in the sense of the basic postulates or assumptions. They form the core of the subject, the underlying reasons for all its properties and theorems.

As teachers of mathematics, we must all strive to recognize and emphasize the fundamental principles of mathematics. Only in this way can we impart the power and effectiveness of mathematics to our students.

Continuity is another fundamental concept of mathematics. It is *the* basic property of topology. It is also a basic property of high school algebra and geometry. In algebra, continuity underlies the extension of the set of rational numbers to the set of real numbers. It enables us to say that any polynomial $p(x)$ that is negative when $x = a$ and positive when $x = b$ must have at least one zero on the interval (a, b) (Fig. 1).

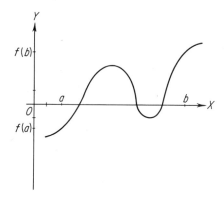

Figure 1

Accordingly, continuity is the principle underlying our intuitive idea that there are no holes in the line, that one cannot cross a line without passing through a point of the line. Euclid tacitly assumed continuity in the sense that there are no holes in a circle. He assumed that any line segment joining the center O of a circle to a point P outside the circle must contain a point of the circle (Fig. 2). Thus, continuity is one of the fundamental concepts of Euclidean geometry.

Topology includes the study of the properties of Euclidean geometry that depend upon continuity. Formally, topology is the study of properties left invariant under continuous transformations. Before discussing topology, let us consider a few transformations and clarify

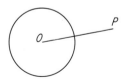

Figure 2

what is meant by saying that a property is invariant under a transformation or under a set of transformations.

16–2 Transformations

Ordinary geometry—Euclidean geometry—is the geometry of rigid motions, that is, Euclidean geometry is the study of properties that are invariant under rigid motions. Any rigid motion on a Euclidean plane may be expressed as a transformation of points (x, y) to points (x', y'), where

$$x' = x \cos \theta - y \sin \theta + a,$$

$$y' = x \sin \theta + y \cos \theta + b.$$

In other words, any rigid motion on a plane may be expressed in terms of a rotation

$$x' = x \cos \theta - y \sin \theta,$$

$$y' = x \sin \theta + y \cos \theta$$

about the origin and a translation (that is, a specified amount of sliding in a specified direction):

$$x' = x + a, \qquad y' = y + b.$$

For example, in Fig. 3 we may think of triangle $A'B'C'$ as obtained by a translation of triangle ABC. In Fig. 4 we may think of triangle

$A'B'C'$ as obtained by a rotation of triangle ABC about the point O. Under each of these transformations (that is, under translations and rotations), we find that size, shape, area, and magnitudes of angles are unchanged, or invariant. Then, since any rigid motion on the plane may be expressed in terms of translations and rotations, the above

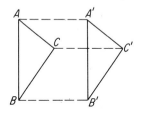

Figure 3

properties are invariant under all rigid motions, that is, under all Euclidean transformations.

Let us now consider a transformation that is not a rigid motion. For example, let us consider a uniform stretching or, as it is technically called, a dilation, such as that given by the equations:

$$x' = 2x, \qquad y' = 2y.$$

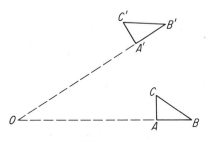

Figure 4

Under this transformation, every point on the plane is moved twice as far from the origin as it was originally. As in Fig. 5, we find that under any dilation continuity, the shape of figures and the magnitudes of angles are unchanged (invariant), but size, lengths of segments, and areas are changed (are not invariant).

In topology continuity is the only underlying invariant. The assumption of continuity may be formally stated in several ways. With a few unnecessary limitations due to the nature of the space in which we live, we may visualize the assumption of continuity as implying simply that there can be no cutting, no tearing apart, and no folding together. If two points are joined by a curve, that curve cannot be cut. If a point is

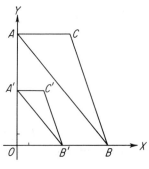

Figure 5

on a curve, it must remain on that curve even though the curve may be twisted, stretched, and distorted in many ways.

Exercises

1. Draw a triangle with vertices at A: $(0, 0)$, B: $(2, 0)$, and C: $(3, 1)$. Then find the vertices and draw the triangle $A'B'C'$ if $x' = x + 3$ and $y' = y - 2$.

2. Repeat Ex. 1 if $x' = -x$ and $y' = -y$.

3. Repeat Ex. 1 if $x' = 3x$ and $y' = 3y$.

4. Repeat Ex. 1 if $x' = y$ and $y' = -x$.

5. Repeat Ex. 1 if $x' = -x$ and $y' = y$.

6. Repeat Ex. 1 if $x' = y$ and $y' = x$.

7. Describe each of the transformations in Exercises 1 through 4.

16–3 Topologically Equivalent Curves

Try to imagine a geometry in which size and shape are unimportant. For example, consider a curve as represented by a very elastic string.

If, as in Fig. 6, the ends of the string are not joined and the string does not cross itself, we call the curve a simple open curve. The string may be continuously transformed, that is without any cutting or folding together, into each of the curves represented in Fig. 6. In topology these curves are equivalent, since any one may be made into any other by a topological, that is, a continuous, transformation. They are

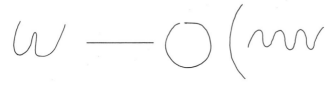

Figure 6

equivalent in topology in the same sense that two congruent triangles are equivalent in Euclidean geometry. Size and shape have no meaning in topology, but there are still some underlying common properties—those that depend only upon continuity.

The central figure in Fig. 6 may be considered as a circle with a segment missing. It is not equivalent to a circle, since one is not allowed

Figure 7

to cut the circle or remove a segment. A circle is a simple closed curve, that is, a curve such that one can start at any point, traverse the complete curve, and return to the starting point without passing through any point twice and without jumping from one arc of the curve to another. In general, any simple closed curve may be visualized as a very elastic string with its ends joined and which does not cross itself (§10–3). Such a string or curve may be continuously transformed into a circle, a square, a trapezoid, or any convex polygon. It may be transformed into any of the shapes in Fig. 7.

Some children may do better art work than that in Fig. 7. However, we hope that you are sufficiently impressed by the variety of shapes of simple closed curves. In topology all of these curves are equivalent. All simple open curves (Fig. 6) are topologically equivalent in that any one can be continuously transformed into any other one. Similarly, all simple closed curves (Fig. 7) are topologically equivalent. We may also consider curves (Fig. 8) that are equivalent to a figure eight or curves

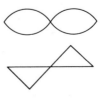

Figure 8

equivalent to more complicated curves. Indeed, the study of knots forms a part of topology.

Exercises

Draw at least three very different-appearing curves that are topologically equivalent to each given curve:

1.   **2.**   **3.**   **4.**

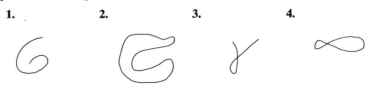

16–4 The Jordan Curve Theorem

In Euclidean geometry, any two equivalent curves have the same shape, size, and area. What do the curves in Fig. 7 have in common? Shape, size, angles, and straight lines are certainly not common properties here. What is left to be considered? Let us remind ourselves that we are probing at the foundations of mathematics. The common property that we seek must be a fundamental property. Some of you may consider it a trivial property because of its simplicity. We prefer to believe that the really basic properties of mathematics are inherently simple.

Probably many of you have now found a common property of the simple closed curves in Fig. 7. The property that we have in mind may be stated very simply: Any simple closed curve has an inside and an outside. The circle, the gingerbread boy, and the other curves in Fig. 7 have an inside and an outside. This property may be emphasized by coloring or shading the inside or bounded region of the curves. In the case of the right-hand figure in Fig. 7, the inside may be found by starting at an exterior point and crossing the curve just once. The designation of the bounded region as the inside is conventional but not strictly necessary. Indeed, we have probably all heard the story of the drunk going around and around a large tree crying, "Let me out," "Let me out."

In advanced mathematics we say that *any simple closed curve in a plane divides the plane into two regions.* This is the **Jordan Curve Theorem.** The curve is the common boundary of the two regions, and one cannot cross from one region to another without crossing the curve. The Jordan Curve Theorem is a very powerful theorem and yet a very simple theorem. It is independent of the size and shape of the curve. It is a topological theorem.

How can such a simple theorem have any significance? It provides a basis for Euclid's assumption that any line segment joining the center of a circle to a point outside the circle must contain a point of the circle. It provides a basis for the existence of a zero of a polynomial on any interval on which the polynomial changes sign. It provides a basis for Venn diagrams in any two-valued logic. For example, true statements may correspond to points inside the curve, false statements to points outside the curve. This simple theorem regarding the existence of an inside and an outside of any simple closed curve may also be used to answer questions raised by a problem on which most of you have probably spent many hours.

Consider three houses in a row and three other objects in a second row on a plane surface. The problem is to join each house to each of three objects by an arc on the plane in such a way that no two arcs cross. This problem often arises with three houses and three utilities. Tucker and Bailey [46] consider three houses, a haystack, a well, and a dovecote. Whatever the objects are called, the problem is equivalent to joining each x to each o in Fig. 9. It is easy to designate paths from one house, say the x on the left, to each of the three objects. One can also designate the three paths from the second house, as in Fig. 10.

Figure 9

Then one can designate two of the paths from the third house, as in Fig. 10, but it is not possible on a Euclidean plane to draw the path from the third house to the remaining object below. This assertion is

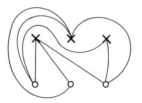

Figure 10

based upon the fact that the simple closed curve indicated in Fig. 11 divides the plane into two regions; the third house is inside the curve (shaded area), the remaining object is outside, and the two cannot be joined without crossing the curve.

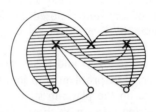

Figure 11

Another problem that is based upon the properties of a simple closed curve may be found in *Mathematics and the Imagination*, by Kasner and Newman [25]. A Persian Caliph reportedly endeavored to select the best suitor for his daughter by posing two problems. The problems appear very similar at first sight. The suitors were asked to

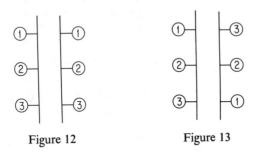

Figure 12   Figure 13

draw arcs joining the corresponding numbers in each of two figures (Fig. 12 and Fig. 13) in such a way that the arcs do not intersect with each other or the given figures. In the case of Fig. 12 the problem is trivial (Fig. 14). However, we can be confident that the Caliph's daughter died an old maid if her father insisted upon a solution of the

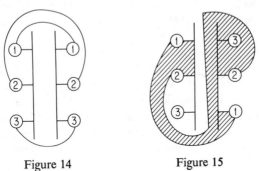

Figure 14   Figure 15

second problem. The first and second pairs of numbers may be joined, but the third pair cannot be joined. This assertion is also based upon the properties of a simple closed curve, as indicated in Fig. 15. One element of the third pair is inside the curve (shaded area) and the other is outside. By the Jordan Curve Theorem, the two points cannot be joined in the plane without crossing the curve.

16–5 Topologically Equivalent Surfaces

There also exist topologically equivalent surfaces corresponding to the sets of equivalent curves that we have considered. For example, many surfaces are topologically equivalent to a sphere. In particular, all convex polyhedrons, all surfaces of solids bounded by planes and such that any line segment joining points of the surface contains only points of the solid, are topologically equivalent to a sphere. We also consider spheres with handles. A sphere with one handle (Fig. 16) may take on many forms. If we shrink the sphere into the handle, we obtain a doughnut, as indicated in the sequence of figures in Fig. 17. If the sphere is visualized as a tennis ball without enough air in it, so that the top may be pushed in, the sphere with one handle may be

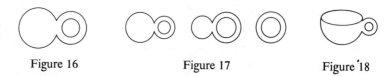

Figure 16   Figure 17   Figure 18

continuously transformed into a teacup (Fig. 18). We may also make the sphere with one handle into a builder's block with one hole in it or a single tile. A student once stated that a doughnut was topologically equivalent to a flower pot. For a moment the instructor was worried. Then he remembered the drain hole in the bottom of the pot. The drain hole is necessary. Flower pots, single tiles, doughnuts, and tea-cups are all topologically equivalent. We may spend many pleasant hours considering topological invariances, but let us now turn to consequences of topological invariances, problems and properties based upon these invariances. There are many elementary and many advanced topological problems. For example, spheres with handles may be associated with the integrability of algebraic functions. Such problems seem far removed from the topic of topology for secondary schools. However, coloring maps should appeal to everyone.

16–6 The Four-Color Problem

A preschool child will frequently color a whole sheet of paper a single color. It is possible to color a map of a single country with one

color. In general, two countries are colored different colors if they
have a common arc on their boundary. If they have only single points
on their common boundary, they do not need to be colored different
colors. We may color a green island in a blue ocean with two colors.
Similarly, we may construct a map that may be colored with three
colors. For example, we may consider an island divided into two
countries, as in Fig. 19. We have now seen that maps may be colored
using one, two, or three colors. Furthermore, if a country with more
than one neighbor has an odd number of neighbors, as in Fig. 20,

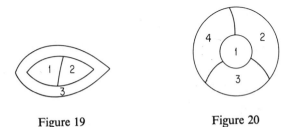

Figure 19   Figure 20

four colors are needed. In the map of the United States, the state of
Kentucky has an odd number of neighbors. One color, two colors,
three colors, four—do we ever need more? This is an open question.
No one knows the answer. However, before you start assigning this
problem to pupils in elementary school, we should mention that four
colors are sufficient for maps containing up to 38 countries. Thus, any
maps requiring more than four colors, if such exist, must have more
than 38 countries. This problem is independent of the size and shape
of the countries. It is a topological problem.

16–7 Traversable Networks

One of the famous topological problems is concerned with the bridges
in the city of Koenigsberg. There was a river flowing through the city,
two islands in the river, and seven bridges, as in Fig. 21. The people of
Koenigsberg loved a Sunday stroll and thought it would be nice to take
a walk and cross each bridge exactly once. But no matter where they

started or what route they tried, they could not cross each bridge exactly once. This caused considerable discussion. Gradually it was observed that the basic problem was concerned with paths between the two sides of the river A, B, and the two islands C, D, as in Fig. 22. With this geometric representation of the problem, it was no longer necessary to discuss the problem in terms of walking across the bridges. Instead, one could discuss whether or not the curve (Fig. 22) associated with the problem is traversable, that is, whether or not one could start at some point of the curve and traverse each arc exactly once. The curve is often called the graph of the problem. In this form, the problem could be considered by people who had never even been to

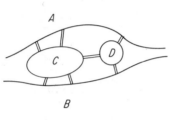

Figure 21

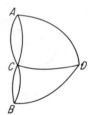

Figure 22

Koenigsberg. The problem was solvable if and only if its graph was traversable.

When is a graph traversable in a single trip? One can walk around any city block, and it is not necessary to start at any particular point. In general, one may traverse any simple closed curve in a single trip. This may surprise some children in the case of figures like the one at the right in Fig. 7, but it is a basic property of all simple closed curves. We next consider walking around two blocks and down the street separating them (Fig. 23). This problem is a bit more interesting in that it is necessary to start at B or E. Furthermore, if one starts at B, one ends at E, and conversely. Note that it is permissible to pass through a vertex several times, but one can traverse an arc only once. The peculiar property of the vertices B and E is based upon the fact that there are three arcs terminating at each of these vertices, whereas the other vertices are each on two arcs. A similar observation led a famous mathematician by the name of Euler to devise a complete theory for traversable graphs.

Euler classified the vertices of a graph as odd or even. A vertex that is on an odd number of arcs is called an odd vertex; a vertex that is on an even number of arcs is called an even vertex. Since every arc has two ends, there must be an even number of odd vertices in any graph. Any graph or network that has only even vertices is traversable and the trip may be started at any vertex. Furthermore, the trip will terminate at its starting point. If a graph contains two odd vertices, it is traversable, but the trip must start at one of the odd vertices. It will then terminate at the second odd vertex. If a graph has more than two odd

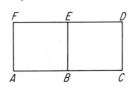

Figure 23

vertices, it is not traversable in a single trip. In general, a graph with $2k$ odd vertices may be traversed in k distinct trips. The graph in Fig. 22 has four odd vertices. It cannot be traversed in a single trip, and the famous problem of the seven Koenigsberg bridges does not have a solution in our geometry. The discussion of this problem in the article by Tucker and Bailey [46] is concluded with the statement that Tucker had actually walked across each of the bridges exactly once in 1935. There were eight bridges at that time.

Frequently we see in advanced mathematical theories only complicated manipulations and intricate statements involving precisely worded definitions and theorems. It is refreshing as well as enlightening to look back occasionally at the roots of the theory and see the problems that started great minds working for generalizations that have led to present theories. The Koenigsberg bridge problem is independent of the size and shape of the objects under consideration. It is a topological problem. It has, in fact, been considered by some writers to be the starting point of the theory of topology.

Exercises

Tell whether or not each network is traversable. If it is necessary to start at a particular vertex to traverse the network, identify the possible starting points.

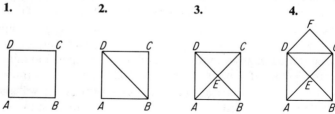

16–8 The Moebius Strip

Let us conclude our consideration of topology with a few comments upon a surface that has several very unusual properties. This surface is one-sided. A fly can walk from any point on it to any other point without crossing an edge. Unlike a table top or a wall, it does not have a top and a bottom or a front and a back. This surface is called a

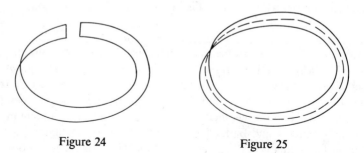

Figure 24   Figure 25

Moebius strip, and it may be very easily constructed from a rectangular piece of paper such as a strip of gummed tape. Size is theoretically unimportant, but a strip an inch or two wide and about a foot long is easy to handle. We may construct a Moebius strip by twisting the strip of gummed tape just enough to stick the gummed edge of one end to the gummed edge of the other end (Fig. 24). If we cut across this strip, we again get a single strip similar to the one we started with (Fig. 24). But if we start with a rectangular strip and cut around the center of the Moebius strip (see the dotted line in Fig. 25), we do not get two strips.

Rather, we get one strip with two twists in it. William Hazlett Upson used this peculiar property of Moebius strips in his story of "Paul Bunyan versus the Conveyer Belt" [50]. Anyone can use it with children and adults.

These one-sided surfaces have been used as place cards at a seven-year-old's birthday party. They are suitably shaped for this purpose. Then, while waiting for dessert, the youngsters were encouraged to cut the strip down the middle while guessing what the result would be. They were suitably impressed when they found only one piece, and were anxious to cut it again. Once more they were suitably impressed when they found two pieces linked together. Almost a year after such a party, one of the boys asked about the piece of paper that was in only one piece after it was cut in two. The smaller children can usually cut the strip at most twice, but older children and adults enjoy cutting the strip several times and several ways to see what will happen. Children and adults will ask questions that the teacher cannot answer and that most college mathematics professors cannot answer. This will be good for all concerned, since it will impress upon them the fact that there is more to mathematics than formal algebraic manipulations and classical geometric constructions.

All teachers of mathematics can use this and other topological properties to challenge and interest children of all ages as well as adults. These properties may be used with superior students, in mathematics clubs, and for the general enrichment of one's teaching. They will help us encourage a genuine interest in fundamental principles of mathematics.

Application and Additional Readings

We have tried to illustrate for you some of the consequences of continuity—that is, some of the properties of topology, the geometry based upon continuous transformations. We hope that you have gained a new appreciation of Euclidean geometry, in addition to recognizing that there exist other geometries. In particular, there is topology, a geometry which has Euclidean geometry as a special case and which may be used, even in elementary schools, to interest and challenge the students and to emphasize the importance of one of the fundamental concepts of mathematics—continuity.

This chapter has been devoted to an informal presentation of topology.

In its previous form [33], it has been used successfully by many teachers with mathematics clubs and in classes on special days when students find it particularly difficult to concentrate on ordinary lessons. The following references are suggested in addition to those already mentioned in the chapter: [23], [15], [43], and [10].

Answers for Exercises

16–1 *Transformations*

1.   **2.**

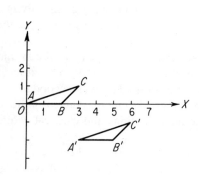

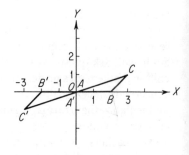

3.   **4.**

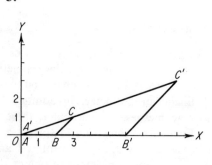

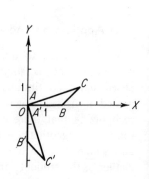

5.   **6.**

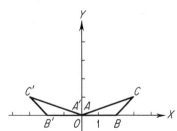 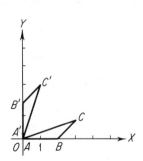

7. In Ex. 1, the transformation is a translation three units to the right and two down; in Ex. 2, a rotation of 180° about the origin; in Ex. 3, a dilation moving each point three times as far from the origin as it had been; in Ex. 4, a rotation of 90° clockwise about the origin. [Notice also that in Ex. 5 the transformation is a reflection in the *y*-axis; in Ex. 6, a reflection in the line $y = x$.]

16–3 *Topologically Equivalent Curves*

Note: There are many correct answers for each exercise. Here is a sample.

1.      Also any curve in Fig. 6.

2.      Also any curve in Fig. 7.

3.

4.

16–7 *Traversable Networks*

1. Traversable; start anywhere.

2. Traversable; start at *B* or *D*.

3. Not traversable, since *A*, *B*, *C*, and *D* are all odd vertices.

4. Traversable; start at *A* or *B*.

REFERENCES

1. Abbott, Edwin A., *Flatland.* New York: Dover, 1952.

2. Adler, Irving, *The New Mathematics.* New York: The John Day Company, 1958.

3. Aiken, D. J., and C. A. Beseman, *Modern Mathematics, Topics and Problems.* New York: McGraw-Hill Book Company, Inc., 1959.

4. Allendoerfer, C. B., and C. O. Oakley, *Principles of Mathematics.* New York: McGraw-Hill Book Company, Inc., 1955.

5. Anderson, Richard B., *Concepts of Informal Geometry.* Vol. V of *Studies in Mathematics.* School Mathematics Study Group.

6. Andree, Richard V., *Selections from Modern Abstract Algebra.* New York: Holt, Rinehart and Winston, Inc., 1958.

7. Beberman, Max, and Bruce E. Meserve, "The Concept of a Literal Number System," *The Mathematics Teacher*, April, 1955, pp. 198–202.

8. ———, "An Exploratory Approach to Solving Equations," *The Mathematics Teacher*, January, 1956, pp. 15–18.

9. ———, "Graphing in Elementary Algebra," *The Mathematics Teacher*, April, 1956, pp. 260–266.

10. Bing, R. H., "Point Set Topology," *Insights into Modern Mathematics*, The Twenty-Third Yearbook of the National Council of Teachers of Mathematics.

11. Breuer, Joseph, translated by Howard F. Fehr, *Introduction to the Theory of Sets*. Englewood Cliffs, N.J.: Prentice-Hall, Inc., 1958.

12. Commission on Mathematics of the College Entrance Examination Board, *Introductory Probability and Statistical Inference for Secondary Schools, an Experimental Course*. New York: College Entrance Examination Board, 1957.

13. ———, *Program for College Preparatory Mathematics*, Report of the Commission on Mathematics. New York: College Entrance Examination Board, 1959.

14. ———, *Appendices*, Report of the Commission on Mathematics. New York: College Entrance Examination Board, 1959.

15. Courant, R., and H. E. Robbins, *What is Mathematics: an Elementary Approach to Ideas and Methods*. New York: Oxford University Press, 1941.

16. Exner, Robert M., and Myron F. Rosskopf, *Logic in Elementary Mathematics*. New York: McGraw-Hill Book Company, Inc., 1959.

17. Freund, John E., *A Modern Introduction to Mathematics*. Englewood Cliffs, N.J.: Prentice-Hall, Inc., 1956.

18. Haag, Vincent, *Structure of Elementary Algebra*. Vol. III of *Studies in Mathematics*. School Mathematics Study Group.

19. Huff, Darrell, *How to Lie with Statistics*. New York: W. W. Norton and Company, Inc., 1954.

20. ———, *How to Take a Chance*. New York: W. W. Norton and Company, Inc., 1959.

21. Johnson, Donovan A., *Paper Folding for the Mathematics Class*. Pamphlet, National Council of Teachers of Mathematics, 1957.

22. Johnson, Donovan A., and W. H. Glenn, *Sets, Sentences, and Operations*. St. Louis: Webster Publishing Company, 1960.

23. ———, *Topology, the Rubber Sheet Geometry*. St. Louis: Webster Publishing Company, 1960.

24. Jones, Burton W., *Elementary Concepts of Mathematics*. New York: The Macmillan Company, 1947.

25. Kasner, E., and J. R. Newman, *Mathematics and the Imagination*. New York: Simon and Schuster, Inc., 1940.

26. Kelley, John L., *Introduction to Modern Algebra*. Princeton, N. J.: D. Van Nostrand Co., Inc., 1960.

27. Kemeny, J. G., J. L. Snell, and G. L. Thompson, *Introduction to Finite Mathematics*. Englewood Cliffs, N.J.: Prentice-Hall, Inc., 1957.

28. Lieber, L. R., and H. G. Lieber, *Non-Euclidean Geometry*. New York: Galois Institute, 1940.

29. Mallory, V. S., B. E. Meserve, and K. C. Skeen, *A First Course in Geometry*, Syracuse, N.Y.: L. W. Singer, 1959.

30. McCoy, Neal H., *Introduction to Modern Algebra*. Boston: Allyn and Bacon, Inc., 1960.

31. Meserve, Bruce E., *Fundamental Concepts of Algebra*. Cambridge, Mass.: Addison-Wesley Publishing Co., Inc., 1953.

32. ————, *Fundamental Concepts of Geometry*. Cambridge, Mass.: Addison-Wesley Publishing Co., Inc., 1955.

33. ————, "Topology for Secondary Schools," *The Mathematics Teacher*, November, 1953, pp. 465–474.

34. Meserve, B. E., and R. E. Pingry, "Some Notes on the Prismoidal Formula," *The Mathematics Teacher*, April, 1952, pp. 257–263.

35. Mosteller, F., R. E. Rourke, and G. B. Thomas, Jr., *Probability and Statistics*. Cambridge, Mass.: Addison-Wesley Publishing Co., Inc., 1961.

36. National Council of Teachers of Mathematics, *The Growth of Mathematical Ideas, Grades K-12. Twenty-Fourth Yearbook*. Washington, D.C.: National Council of Teachers of Mathematics, 1959.

37. ————, "The Secondary Mathematics Curriculum," *The Mathematics Teacher*, May, 1959, pp. 389–417.

38. New York State Education Department, *Mathematics 7-8-9, An Integrated Sequence for the Junior High School Grades*. Albany, N. Y.: The State Education Department, 1954.

39. ————, *Mathematics 10-11-12, An Integrated Sequence for the Senior High School Grades*. Albany, N. Y.: The State Education Department, 1957.

40. Richardson, M., *Fundamentals of Mathematics*. New York: The Macmillan Company, 1958.

41. Sawyer, W. W., *A Concrete Approach to Abstract Algebra*. San Francisco: Freeman, 1959.

42. School Mathematics Study Group. For all publications of this organization, write to address given at end of Chapter 1 of this text.

43. Steinhaus, Hugo, *Mathematical Snapshots*. New York: Oxford University Press, 1950.

44. Suppes, Patrick, *Sets and Numbers*, Books 1 and 2. Stanford, California: Stanford University, Patrick Suppes, 1960.

45. Swain, Robert L., *Understanding Arithmetic*. New York: Holt, Rinehart, and Winston, Inc., 1957.

46. Tucker, A. W., and H. S. Bailey, Jr., "Topology," *The Scientific American*, Vol. CLXXXII (1950), pp. 18–24.

47. University of Illinois, *Mathematical Needs of Prospective Students in the College of Engineering of the University of Illinois*, a University of Illinois Bulletin, Vol. 49, No. 9.

48. University of Illinois Committee on School Mathematics. For all publications of this organization, write to address given at end of Chapter 1 of this text.

49. University of Maryland Mathematics Project. For all publications of this organization, write to address given at end of Chapter 1 of this text.

50. Upson, W. H., "Paul Bunyan versus the Conveyer Belt," *Ford Times*, Vol. XLI (1949), pp. 14–17.

51. Wallis, W. A., and H. V. Roberts, *Statistics: A New Approach*. Glencoe, Ill.: The Free Press, 1956.

52. Western, Donald, and Vincent Haag, *An Introduction to Mathematics*, New York: Holt, Rinehart, and Winston, Inc., 1959.

53. Woodward, E. J., and R. C. McLennan, *Elementary Concepts of Sets*. New York: Holt, Rinehart, and Winston, Inc., 1959.

INDEX

A

Abelian group, 50
Abscissa, 242
Absolute value, 92
Abstract algebra, 155
Addition:
  of complex numbers, 165
  of integers, 132
  of natural numbers, 127
  of rational numbers, 135
Affine geometry, 294, 335
  line, 293
  plane, 305
Algebra, 76
Angle, 181
  dihedral, 181
  exterior of, 181
  interior of, 181
  standard position of, 262
Application and Additional Readings,
  25, 41, 53, 71, 86, 110, 138,
  168, 190, 212, 238, 266, 306,
  335, 353
Aristotle's laws of logic, 195, 203
Arithmetic, 10
  around the clock, 32
  modular, 32
Associative law, 49, 51
  for addition, 37, 127
  for multiplication, 38, 158
Axes:
  of ellipse, 256
  of hyperbola, 258
  rotation of, 260
  translation of, 260, 340

B

Bases:
  change of, 17
  of five, 12
    computation in, 14

Bases (*Continued*)
  N, 20
  number, 11
  of ten, 11
  of two, 23
Beberman, Dr. Max, 3
Begle, Prof. E. G., 5
Betweenness, 243
Binary notation, 23
  recreational items in, 24
Binary operation, 37, 48, 51, 128
Binomial distribution, 60, 68

C

Caliph's problem, 347
Cardinality of sets, 78
Carnegie Corporation of New York,
  3, 5
Cartesian product, 102
CEEB, 3
Center:
  of circle, 256
  of ellipse, 257
  of hyperbola, 258
Circle, 256
  center of, 256
  paper folding to obtain a, 261
Circular functions, 262
Classification of equations, 100
  conditional, 100
  identity, 100
  impossible, 100
Closure, 48, 51
  under addition, 37, 127, 132, 136,
    156
  under multiplication, 38, 158
College Entrance Examination Board,
  3, 8
  changes in examinations, 4
Commission on Mathematics of the
  College Entrance Examination
  Board, 3, 8, 196, 222